# Sign Up Online

# STAAR Redesign

## Grade 7 ELA Practice

# Texas State Test Prep: Grade 7 English Language Arts Literacy (ELA) Practice Workbook and Full-length Online Assessments: STAAR Study Guide

| | |
|---|---|
| Contributing Editor | - Stacy Zeiger |
| Contributing Editor | - Mechelle Craig |
| Contributing Editor | - George Smith |
| Executive Producer | - Mukunda Krishnaswamy |
| Designer and Illustrator | - Sowmya R. |

ISBN-13: 978-1949855364

Printed in the United States of America

Last updated - October 2022

## For permissions and additional information contact us

Lumos Information Services, LLC
PO Box 1575, Piscataway, NJ 08855-1575
http://www.LumosLearning.com

Email: support@lumoslearning.com
Tel: (732) 384-0146
Fax: (866) 283-6471

This book is specifically designed to improve student achievement on the State of Texas Assessment of Academic Readiness (STAAR). With over a decade of expertise in developing practice resources for standardized tests, Lumos Learning has designed the most efficient methodology to help students succeed on state assessments (See Figure 1).

Lumos Smart Test Prep provides students with STAAR Redesign assessment rehearsal and an efficient pathway to overcome standards proficiency gaps. Students perform at their best on standardized tests when they feel comfortable with the test content and format. Lumos online practice tests are meticulously designed to mirror the STAAR Redesign assessment. It adheres to the guidelines provided for the number of questions, standards, difficulty level, sessions, question types, and duration.

The process starts with students taking the online diagnostic assessment. This online diagnostic test helps to assess the student's proficiency levels in various standards.

After completion of the diagnostic test, students can take note of the standards where improvement is needed. This step helps parents and educators in developing a targeted remedial study plan based on the student's proficiency gaps.

Once the targeted remedial study plan is in place, students can start practicing the lessons in this workbook that are focused on specific standards.

On completing the targeted remedial practice, the student should attempt the second online STAAR Redesign practice test. Record the proficiency levels in the second practice test to measure the student's progress and identify any additional learning gaps. Further targeted practice can be planned to help students gain comprehensive skills mastery needed to ensure success in the state assessment.

## Lumos Smart Test Prep Methodology

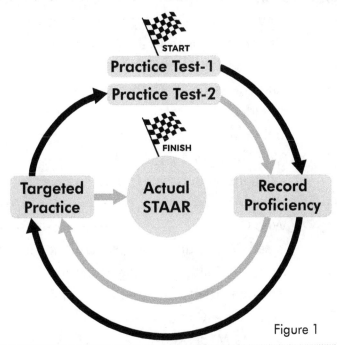

Figure 1

# Table of Contents

Introduction ···················································································· 1

Chapter 1 Lumos Smart Test Prep Methodology ······························· 4

Chapter 2 Developing and Sustaining Foundational Language Skills ······· 9
Lesson 1   ELAR 7.1          Speaking & Listening ···························· 10
Lesson 2   ELAR 7.2          Learning And Using Academic Vocabulary ······ 11
Lesson 3   ELAR 7.2.A        Consulting Sources ···························· 15
Lesson 4   ELAR 7.2.B        Figuring It Out With Context Clues ········· 18
Lesson 5   ELAR 7.2.B        Which Fits? Multiple Meaning Words ········· 22
Lesson 6   ELAR 7.2.C        Review - Roots And Affixes ················· 25
Lesson 7   ELAR 7.6          Precise And Concise Language ··············· 28
Lesson 8   ELAR 7.9.D        Give It A Shot - Figures Of Speech ········· 31
Lesson 9   ELAR 7.9.D        We're Related - Word Relationships ········· 34
Lesson 10  ELAR 7.10.D.i     Good Sentences Are Built On Agreement ······ 37
Lesson 11  ELAR 7.10.D.vii   Phrases And Clauses Are Coming To Town ····· 39
Lesson 12  ELAR 7.10.D.vii   Using Coordinate Adjectives ················ 42
Lesson 13  ELAR 7.10.D.viii  Managing Modifiers ·························· 44
Lesson 14  ELAR 7.10.D.ix    Spellcheck! ································· 47
Lesson 15  N/A               Would You Rather Own A Boat Or A Yacht? Denotation And Connotation ···· 49
                             **Answer Key & Detailed Explanations** ···· 52

Chapter 3 Comprehension Skills ················································ 69
Lesson 1   ELAR 7.5.F        Prove It! (with Evidence From The Text) ···· 70
Lesson 2   ELAR 7.5.F        Use Those Clues - Make An Inference ········ 77
Lesson 3   ELAR 7.5.G        What Is It All About? ······················ 88
Lesson 4   ELAR 7.5.G        And The Point Of This Is...? ··············· 97
Lesson 5   ELAR 7.5.G        Key Ideas And Details ······················ 108
Lesson 6   ELAR 7.5.G        Get Right To The Point ····················· 113
Lesson 7   ELAR 7.5.H        One Thing Leads To Another ················· 120
Lesson 8   ELAR 7.6.A        Relationship Between People And Events ····· 129
Lesson 9   ELAR 7.7.D        When And Where? ···························· 131
Lesson 10  ELAR 7.7.D        Who Or What? ······························· 141
Lesson 11  ELAR 7.8.A        Based On A True Story - History And Fiction ···· 149
Lesson 12  ELAR 7.8.D        How Is It Built? Analyzing Structure ······· 155
Lesson 13  ELAR 7.8.D.iii    Finding Patterns - Comparing And Contrasting ···· 167
Lesson 14  ELAR 7.8.F        Comparing Media ···························· 176
Lesson 15  ELAR 7.9.B        How It's Made And What It Means ············ 181

Lesson 16    ELAR 7.9.D      A Matter Of Attitude ·································· 189
Lesson 17    ELAR 7.9.D      Getting Technical ····································· 197
Lesson 18    ELAR 7.9.E      What's The Author's Point? ······················ 203
                             **Answer Key & Detailed Explanations** ················· 213

**Chapter 4    Author's Purpose and Craft** ···················· 240
Lesson 1    ELAR 7.7.B      What A Character! ·································· 241
Lesson 2    ELAR 7.9        Equal? Alike? Different? Comparing Authors ······ 249
Lesson 3    ELAR 7.9.A      What's The Author's Angle? ······················ 253
                            **Answer Key & Detailed Explanations** ················ 261

**Chapter 5    Composition** ········································ 266
Lesson 1     ELAR 7.10.A       Who Are You Talking To? ························ 267
Lesson 2     ELAR 7.10.B.i     A Picture Is Worth A Thousand Words ·········· 272
Lesson 3     ELAR 7.10.B.i     Getting From Here To There - Transitions ······· 278
Lesson 4     ELAR 7.10.B.i     Mixing It Up - More Interesting Sentences ········ 282
Lesson 5     ELAR 7.10.D       Taking A Closer Look - Editing ················ 286
Lesson 6     ELAR 7.10.D.vii   Say What You Mean ·························· 290
Lesson 7     ELAR 7.12.B       Measure Twice, Cut Once - The Importance Of Planning ······· 295
Lesson 8     ELAR 7.12.B       Take Another Look - Revising Your Work ········· 307
Lesson 9     ELAR 7.12.D       Building Your Foundation ···················· 312
Lesson 10    ELAR 7.12.F       Give Credit Where Credit Is Due ············· 316
Lesson 11    ELAR 7.12.H.ii    Beginnings And Endings ···················· 319
                               **Answer Key & Detailed Explanations** ·············· 322

**Chapter 6    Inquiry and Research** ···························· 337
Lesson 1    ELAR 7.12.D     Sifting Through The Nonsense - Finding Information ··········· 338
Lesson 2    ELAR 7.12.G     In Your Own Words, Or Not ······················ 342
                            **Answer Key & Detailed Explanations** ················ 348

**Additional Information** ·············································· 353
**STAAR FAQ** ·························································· 353
**Progress Chart** ····················································· 356

# Chapter 1
# Lumos Smart Test Prep Methodology

## Step 1: Access Online STAAR Practice Test

The online practice tests mirror the actual STAAR Redesign assessment in the number of questions, item types, test duration, test tools, and more.

After completing the test, the student will receive immediate feedback with detailed reports on standards mastery and a personalized study plan to overcome any learning gaps. Using this study plan, practice the next section of the workbook.

**Use the URL and access code provided below or scan the QR code to access the first STAAR Redesign practice test to get started.**

| URL | QR Code |
|---|---|
| Visit the URL below and place the book access code<br><br>**http://www.lumoslearning.com/a/tedbooks**<br><br>**Access Code: STAARG7E-20874-P** | |

# Step 2: Review the Personalized Study Plan Online

After students complete the online Practice Test 1, they can access their individualized study plan from the table of contents (Figure 2) Parents and Teachers can also review the study plan through their Lumos account (parent or teacher) portal.

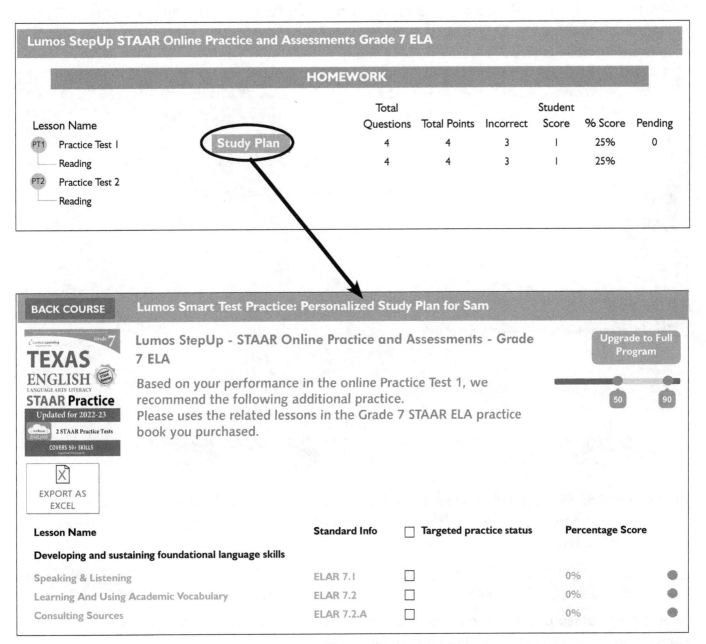

Figure 2

# Step 3: Complete Targeted Practice

Using the information provided in the study plan report, complete the targeted practice using the appropriate lessons to overcome proficiency gaps. With lesson names included in the study plan, find the appropriate topics in this workbook and answer the questions provided. Students can refer to the answer key and detailed answers provided for each lesson to gain further understanding of the learning objective. Marking the completed lessons in the study plan after each practice session is recommended.(See Figure 3)

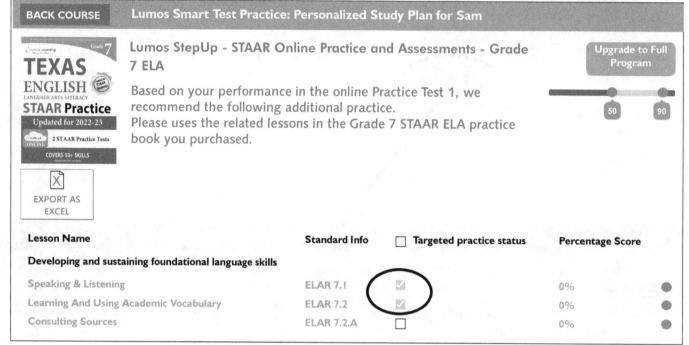

Figure 3

# Step 4: Access the Practice Test 2 Online

After completing the targeted practice in this workbook, students should attempt the second practice test online. Using the student login name and password, login to the Lumos website to complete the second practice test.

# Step 5: Repeat Targeted Practice

Repeat the targeted practice as per Step 3 using the second study plan report for Practice test 2 after completion of the second STAAR Redesign rehearsal.

Visit www.lumoslearning.com/a/lstp for more information on Lumos Smart Test Prep Methodology or Scan the QR Code

## What if I buy more than one Lumos Study Program?

**Step 1** ⟶ **Visit the URL given below and login to your account**

www.lumoslearning.com

**Step 2** ⟶ **Click on 'My Subscriptions' under the "Account" tab and goto "My tedBook"**

Place the Book Access Code and submit.

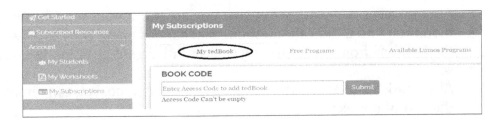

**Step 3** ⟶ **Add the new book**

To add the new book for a registered student, choose the **'Existing Student'** button, select the student and submit.

To add the new book for a new student, choose the **'Add New Student'** button and complete the student registration.

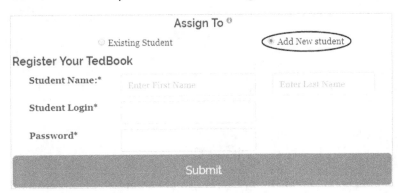

# Test Taking Tips

1) **The day before the test,** make sure you get a good night's sleep.

2) **On the day of the test,** be sure to eat a good hearty breakfast! Also, be sure to arrive at school on time.

3) **During the test:**

- **Read every question carefully.**

  - Do not spend too much time on any one question. Work steadily through all questions in the section.
  - Attempt all of the questions even if you are not sure of some answers.
  - If you run into a difficult question, eliminate as many choices as you can and then pick the best one from the remaining choices. Intelligent guessing will help you increase your score.
  - Also, mark the question so that if you have extra time, you can return to it after you reach the end of the section.
  - Some questions may refer to a graph, chart, or other kind of picture. Carefully review the graphic before answering the question.
  - Be sure to include explanations for your written responses and show all work.

- **While Answering Multiple-Choice questions.**

  - Read the question completely.
  - Go through the answer choices.
  - If you are struggling with picking out a correct answer, it is best to eliminate some of the choices. At least try to eliminate two of the choices.
  - Reread the question and find support from the passage to support one of the answers.
  - Recheck the question and your answer.

**Note: The Texas STAAR Redesign Math assessments also includes Grid In type questions in the pencil and paper version of the test.**

# Chapter 2

# Developing and Sustaining Foundational Language Skills

## Chapter 2

### Lesson 1: Speaking & Listening

**NOTE:**

This lesson is an audio-visual lesson and is available online for your practice. Please use the link or QR code given below to practice the lesson. If you don't have an account, please register.

Have lots of fun!

| Link | QR Code |
|------|---------|
| http://lumoslearning.com/a/181252 |  |

**"Bruno the Bear"**
**Excerpt from The Bond of Love**

For the next three hours, she would not leave that cage. She gave him tea, lemonade, cakes, ice cream, and whatnot. Then 'closing time' came and we had to leave. My wife cried bitterly; Bruno cried bitterly; even the hardened curator and the keepers felt depressed. As for me, I had reconciled myself to what I knew was going to happen next.

"Oh please, sir," she asked the curator, "may I have my Bruno back"? Hesitantly, he answered, "Madam, he belongs to the zoo and is Government property now. I cannot give away Government property. But if my boss, the superintendent, agrees, certainly, you may have him back."

There followed the return journey home and a visit to the superintendent's office. A tearful pleading: "Bruno and I are both fretting for each other. Will you please give him back to me?" He was a kind-hearted man and consented. Not only that, but he wrote to the curator, telling him to lend us a cage for transporting the bear back home.

Back we went to the zoo again, armed with the superintendent's letter. Bruno was driven into a small cage and hoisted on top of the car; the cage was tied securely, and a slow and careful return journey back home was accomplished.

Once home, a squad of workers were engaged for special work around our yard. An island was made for Bruno. It was twenty feet long and fifteen feet wide and was surrounded by a dry moat, six feet wide and seven feet deep. A wooden box that once housed fowls was brought and put on the island for Bruno to sleep in at night. Straw was placed inside to keep him warm, and his 'baby,' the gnarled stump, along with his 'gun,' the piece of bamboo, both of which had been sentimentally preserved since he had been sent away to the zoo, were put back for him to play with. In a few days, the workers hoisted the cage on to the island, and Bruno was released. He was delighted; standing on his hind legs, he pointed his 'gun' and cradled his 'baby.' My wife spent hours sitting on a chair there while he sat on her lap. He was fifteen months old and pretty heavy too!

1. **superintendent; curator; squad of workers**

   **Which word describes "a keeper or custodian of a collection"? Mention in the box below.**

2.  superintendent; curator; squad of workers

    Which word describes "a high-ranking official" or "someone who manages an organization"?  Mention in the box below.

    [                                                        ]

3.  superintendent; curator; squad of workers

    Which word describes "a group of people assembled to complete a task"? Mention in the box below.

    [                                                        ]

**Fall leaves**
**USDA Forest Service**

We almost always think of trees as being green, but there is one time of year when their leaves turn a myriad orange, red, yellow, and brown: the beautiful and chilly days of fall. Those living in the Eastern or Northern United States come to anticipate the change in color starting in September or October every single year. But what causes the leaves to change color, and why?

Just like many animals that hibernate for the winter, trees experience a unique change during the winter months. During summer, for instance, plants use the process of photosynthesis to transform carbon dioxide found in the air into organic compounds like sugars using energy from the sun. During the winter, however, there is less light to go around, and their ability to create food from the photosynthesis process is limited.

What does that have to do with a leaf's color? The substance that allows trees to turn carbon dioxide into food (chlorophyll) is also the cause of the leaf's green sheen. As the photosynthesis process wanes in the colder months due to the lack of sun, so does its greenish hue, allowing other elements present in the leaf to show through. Believe it or not, the yellows and oranges that appear in fall have actually been there all year in the form of nutrients like carotene (also found in carrots). The intense green color of the chlorophyll had simply overshadowed them. But what about the reds and browns? And what causes the leaves to fall away after they change color? The bright reds and purples in each leaf come from a strong antioxidant that many trees create on their own because of their protective qualities. The antioxidant helps protect the trees from the sun, lower their freezing levels, and protect them from frost. As winter comes, so does the need for the antioxidant (similar to the way a dog gets more fur during winter to stay warmer).

4. **Based on the passage, what gives carrots their orange color?**

   Ⓐ chlorophyll
   Ⓑ photosynthesis
   Ⓒ antioxidant
   Ⓓ carotene

5. **Based on the passage, what substance helps give leaves their green color?**

   Ⓐ chlorophyll
   Ⓑ photosynthesis
   Ⓒ antioxidant
   Ⓓ carotene

6. **Based on the passage, what is photosynthesis?**

   Ⓐ A process that helps get energy from sunlight and produce food
   Ⓑ A substance that helps turn carbon dioxide into food
   Ⓒ A protective chemical that helps protect trees from the sun
   Ⓓ A chemical that gives leaves their orange and yellow colors

7. **Based on the passage, what is an antioxidant?**

   Ⓐ A process that helps get energy from sunlight and produce food
   Ⓑ A substance that helps turn carbon dioxide into food
   Ⓒ A protective chemical that helps protect trees from the sun
   Ⓓ A chemical that gives leaves their orange and yellow colors

## Bushmen

With so much technology around us each day, it is hard to imagine that anyone in the world would live without television, let alone a cell phone or radio. Still, there are a few cultures that maintain an extremely primitive lifestyle, nearly untouched by the modern world. One of those is commonly known as the Bushmen of Kalahari.

The Bushmen, also known as the "Basarwa" or "San" are found throughout southern Africa in regions of the Kalahari Desert. Nomadic hunters and gatherers by nature, they roam the region living in small kinship groups and, relatively isolated from the rest of society, have developed an extremely unique culture not otherwise seen or understood by modern man.

Unlike English, which is built on a complex system of sounds and letters, the Bushmen speak an extremely difficult to communicate with non-Bush people.

In addition to language, the Bushmen have a very different way of living. Similar to Eskimos, groups of Bushmen will live in "kinship" societies. Led by their elders, they travel together, with women in the group gathering food while men hunt for it. Children, on the other hand, have no duties other than playing. In fact, leisure is an extremely important part of the Bushmen society. Dance, music, and humor are essential, with a focus on family rather than technology or development. Because of this, some people associate the Bush culture with a backward kind of living or low status.

Because of the increased speed of advancement and urban development, the Bushmen culture is in danger. Some have already been forced to switch from hunting to farming due to modernization programs in their countries. Others have been forced to move to certain areas of their countries so that modernization can continue to occur there. With so much development, it's clear that though the Bushmen culture is very rich, it is also in danger of extinction. It is unclear how long the Bush culture will continue.

https://en.wikipedia.org/wiki/Bushmen

8. **Based on the passage, what is the best meaning of primitive?**

   Ⓐ New and modern
   Ⓑ Not sophisticated or developed
   Ⓒ Cultural traits or traditions
   Ⓓ Languages unlike English

9. **The passage describes kinship societies. If the word "kin" means "family or relations," then kinship societies are most likely...**

   Ⓐ Groups of individuals who came together from different tribes
   Ⓑ Groups of individuals from the same family
   Ⓒ Groups of individuals who are married
   Ⓓ Groups of individuals who follow one leader

10. **Based on the passage, what is the meaning of the word modernization?**

   Ⓐ Keeping traditional practices and traditions
   Ⓑ Bringing computers and other cutting-edge technology
   Ⓒ Incorporating new practices and ideas
   Ⓓ Speaking a new language, such as English

## Chapter 2

### Lesson 3: Consulting Sources

While reading his science textbook, Jorge comes across the following sentence:
Animals are part of different ecosystems around the world.

1.  **If he wanted to find the meaning of "ecosystems," where would be the best place to look so he can find the definition quickly?**

    Ⓐ  In a dictionary
    Ⓑ  In the glossary
    Ⓒ  In a thesaurus
    Ⓓ  In another chapter

2.  **If Jorge wanted to find words similar to the word "ecosystems" where would be the best place to look- in a dictionary; glossary or a thesaurus? Mention in the box below.**

3.  **Jorge decides to look up the word "ecosystem" in a dictionary. Where will he find the word?**

    Ⓐ  Before ecology
    Ⓑ  After edifice
    Ⓒ  Between ecology and edifice
    Ⓓ  Between ebb and ecology

While reading his science textbook, Jorge comes across the following sentence:
Animals are part of different ecosystems around the world.

When Jorge finds the word "ecosystem" in the dictionary he sees the following:

Ecosystem n. (ek-o-sys-tem)
1. a community of interacting organisms
2. a general term to describe a complex system

4.  **What do the letters in parentheses represent?**

    Ⓐ The word's part of speech
    Ⓑ How to pronounce the word
    Ⓒ The main meaning of the word
    Ⓓ The secondary meaning of the word

5.  **Based on the dictionary entry, what part of speech is the word "ecosystem"?**

    Ⓐ Adjective
    Ⓑ Noun
    Ⓒ Pronoun
    Ⓓ Verb

6.  **Which two definitions fit the word "ecosystem" based on what Jorge read?**

    Ⓐ A community of interacting organisms
    Ⓑ A general term used to describe a complex system
    Ⓒ Neither of the two
    Ⓓ The meanings vary according to the place one is in

Lynn is looking for a synonym to use in her essay, so she opens the thesaurus. She looks up the following entry.

delay v. 1. *Storms delayed the construction process.* curb, detain, hamper, hinder, hold.
2. *He delayed his admission until he got back from Europe.* postpone, hold, put off, shelve.
3. *Don't delay, the sale is almost over.* hedge, hang back, hesitate, pause, stall.

7.  **Why does the thesaurus include the sentences in italics?**

    Ⓐ To help the reader get ideas about what to write
    Ⓑ To help the reader distinguish between the meanings of the word by providing examples
    Ⓒ To help the reader find the perfect word
    Ⓓ To help the reader see the different parts of speech of the word

8.  **Lynn is writing a news article for the school paper. She wants a synonym for "delay" that says the lack of the principal's signature is delaying the arrival of the new vending machines. Which are the two best synonyms for her to use?**

    Ⓐ Hesitate
    Ⓑ Put off
    Ⓒ Postpone
    Ⓓ Shelve

Lynn is looking for a synonym to use in her essay, so she opens the thesaurus. She looks up the following entry.

delay v. 1. Storms delayed the construction process. curb, detain, hamper, hinder, hold. 2. He delayed his admission until he got back from Europe. postpone, hold, put off, shelve. 3. Don't delay, the sale is almost over. hedge, hang back, hesitate, pause, stall.

9. **Lynn wants to write a piece that encourages students to express their concerns to the principal without causing her to delay. What would be the BEST synonym that explains the situation above?**

   Ⓐ Hesitate
   Ⓑ Put off
   Ⓒ Hinder
   Ⓓ Shelve

10. **Lynn writes the following sentence: "The delay caused the vendors to take back their deal." She wants to find a synonym for "delay," but this particular thesaurus entry won't help. Which choice best explains why?**

   Ⓐ The thesaurus entry focuses on delay as a verb, not a noun.
   Ⓑ The thesaurus entry only contains three forms of the verb delay.
   Ⓒ The thesaurus entry covers the word "delay."
   Ⓓ The thesaurus entry is not the best place to find a word, the dictionary is.

## Chapter 2

## Lesson 4: Figuring It Out With Context Clues

Still, there was something that was bothering Sam. The tryouts for the tennis team were on the same day as his mom's birthday, and he knew his family was planning a huge surprise party for her. He didn't want to hurt his mom's feelings by missing the party, but he also didn't want to miss his one shot at being a champion tennis player just because the tryouts were on his mom's birthday. He was in a quandary; he didn't know what to do.

1.  **What is the meaning of the word "quandary" in the above passage? Select two options.**

    Ⓐ  a state of elation
    Ⓑ  a state of certainty
    Ⓒ  a state of perplexity
    Ⓓ  a state of uncertainty


Hold him, everybody! In goes the hypodermic—Bruno squeals — 10 c.c. of the antidote enters his system without a drop being wasted. Ten minutes later: condition unchanged! Another 10 c.c. Injected! Ten minutes later: breathing less torturous— Bruno can move his arms and legs a little although he cannot stand yet. Thirty minutes later: Bruno gets up and has a great feed! He looks at us disdainfully, as much as to say, 'What's barium carbonate to a big black bear like me?' Bruno was still eating. I was really happy to see him recover.

2.  **What is the meaning of the word "hypodermic"?**

    Ⓐ  aortic
    Ⓑ  skin
    Ⓒ  orally administered drugs
    Ⓓ  injection


Of all the life forms on earth, those living in the rivers, lakes, and oceans seem to be most interesting to people. We are extremely curious about these aquatic creatures. Countless movies, television shows, books and magazines focus on animals living in the water.

3.  **What is the meaning of the underlined word in this passage?**

    Ⓐ  fish
    Ⓑ  blue-colored
    Ⓒ  exciting
    Ⓓ  living in water

What will you do with me if my father, the king, does not pay the $5 million ransom for my return?" asked the lovely princess as the kidnapper pushed her into his carriage.

"Well, my dear," the kidnapper replied with a <u>sinister</u> smile, "your father has two choices. He can either give me the money or he can say goodbye to his daughter...forever!"

**4. What is the meaning of sinister as it is used in this passage? Select two options.**

Ⓐ helpful
**Ⓑ evil**
**Ⓒ disturbing**
Ⓓ kind

The committee worked for weeks to write a set of rules for the new rock climbing club at our middle school. The students, parents, and teachers in the group wanted to make sure that the rules would be easy to follow and easy to read. To help the club members better understand the rules, they wrote a <u>preamble</u> explaining how they came up with these rules to put at the front of the set of rules.

**5. What is the meaning of the underlined word in this passage?**

**Ⓐ introduction**
Ⓑ cover
Ⓒ rule
Ⓓ page

### From "Bruno the Bear"
### From <u>A Bond of Love</u>

The bear became very attached to our two dogs and all the children living in and around our farm. He was left quite free in his younger days and spent his time playing, running into the kitchen, and going to sleep in our beds.

One day an accident befell him. I put down poison (barium carbonate) to kill the rats and mice that had got into my library. Bruno entered the library as he often did and ate some of the poison. **Paralysis** set into the extent that he could not stand on his feet. But he dragged himself on his stumps to my wife, who called me. I guessed what had happened. Off I rushed him in the car to the vet's residence. A case of poisoning! Tame Bear—barium carbonate—what to do? Out came his medical books, and a feverish reference to index began: "What poison did you say, sir?" he asked, "Barium carbonate," I said.

"Ah yes—B—Ba—Barium Salts—Ah! Barium carbonate! Symptoms— paralysis—treatment—injections of . .. Just a minute, sir. I'll bring my syringe and the medicine." Said the doc.

I dashed back to the car. Bruno was still floundering about on his stumps, but clearly, he was weakening rapidly; there was some vomiting, he was breathing heavily, with heaving flanks and gaping mouth. I was really scared and did not know what to do. I was feeling very guilty and was running in and out of the vet's house doing everything the doc asked me.

"Hold him, everybody!" In goes the hypodermic—Bruno squeals — 10 c.c. of the antidote enters his system without a drop being wasted. Ten minutes later: condition unchanged! Another 10 c.c. Injected! Ten minutes later: breathing less torturous— Bruno can move his arms and legs a little although he cannot stand yet. Thirty minutes later: Bruno gets up and has a great feed! He looks at us disdainfully, as much as to say, 'What's barium carbonate to a big black bear like me?' Bruno was still eating. I was really happy to see him recover.

6.  **Based on its use in this selection, what can you infer the meaning of the bold word is?**

    Ⓐ  Inability to eat
    Ⓑ  Inability to move
    Ⓒ  Poisoning
    Ⓓ  Confusion

As Sade was about to bungee jump off the bridge, she had a <u>fleeting</u> thought of death. Luckily, the thought was gone as quickly as it came.

7.  **What is the meaning of the underlined word? Select two options.**

    Ⓐ  passing rapidly
    Ⓑ  remaining only for a brief period of time
    Ⓒ  clear
    Ⓓ  frightening

The baseball players and the owner of the team could not come to a contract agreement. The two parties had been arguing for months. Finally, an <u>arbitrator</u> was brought in to help come up with an agreement that both parties could agree on.

8.  **What is the meaning of the underlined word?**

    Ⓐ  Person who bets on the odds of winning
    Ⓑ  Person who argues for one side of a disagreement
    Ⓒ  Person who settles disagreements

Even though the snake only <u>grazed</u> the leg of my pants, I was still extremely frightened and upset.

**9. What is the meaning of the underlined word?**

    Ⓐ  Ate a small amount
    Ⓑ  Circled around
    ●  Lightly touched
    Ⓓ  Looked at

Although the other children were <u>regaled</u> by the musician, Terry found him dull.

**10. What is the meaning of regaled?**

    Ⓐ  Entertained
    Ⓑ  Bored
    Ⓒ  Afraid
    Ⓓ  Interested

## Chapter 2

## Lesson 5: Which fits? Multiple meaning words

Amelia worked very hard on her Social Studies project, but there were many mistakes in the essay part of the project. Her teacher didn't want to discount the effort Amelia put into the project, so she raised her grade from a C to a B.

1. **Which two definitions of the word, discount, best fits its use in this paragraph?**

   Ⓐ take an amount of money off of a bill or a price
   Ⓑ paying interest on a loan before the payment is due
   Ⓒ disregard
   Ⓓ leave out or not pay attention to

Even though the seventh grade class had never taken an overnight field trip before, the principal decided to approve Mr. Juarez's request to take his students to the beach for two days to study whales.

2. **Which meaning of the word approve is used in this sentence?**

   Ⓐ talk about in a positive way
   Ⓑ officially agree to
   Ⓒ agree to informally
   Ⓓ show

Because the assistant manager was the manager's subordinate, he had to work on Christmas Day while the manager had the day off to spend with her family.

3. **Which definition of the word subordinate best fits its use in this sentence?**

   Ⓐ someone in a lower position
   Ⓑ not as important
   Ⓒ junior
   Ⓓ not as good

This morning I was awoken at 5:00AM by a **racket**! My next door neighbor was mowing his lawn with his noisy, old lawn mower. This was not a great way to start the day!

### 4. What is the definition of the bold word in this sentence?

Ⓐ piece of sports equipment used to play tennis
Ⓑ dishonest business deal
Ⓒ loud noise
Ⓓ illegal activity

### Baseball Card Collecting

Looking for a new hobby? Do you like baseball? If you answered "yes" to these two questions, then baseball card collecting might be a fun pastime for you to begin! Ever since candy and gum manufacturers started putting cards with pictures of popular baseball players into the packages in the 1800's to encourage young people to buy their sweets, kids have been collecting baseball cards. Now, more than 200 years later, baseball card collecting has become a popular hobby for children and adults alike.

### 5. Based on this paragraph, what can you infer "sweets" are?

Ⓐ Cookies
Ⓑ Candy
Ⓒ Baseball cards
Ⓓ Apple Pie

The workers from the power company told us to beware of downed power-lines after the storm because many of the wires were **live**.

### 6. Which definition of live is used in this sentence?

Ⓐ to have life
Ⓑ at the time the event is occurring
Ⓒ emitting electrical power
Ⓓ to dwell in

I was so happy when I discovered the local news channel was broadcasting the award show **live** instead of on a ten minute delay.

7.  **Which definition of live is used in this sentence?**

    Ⓐ to have life
    Ⓑ at the time the event is occurring
    Ⓒ emitting electrical power
    Ⓓ to dwell in

I felt lightheaded from the chemicals I used to **strip** the paint from the patio furniture.

8.  **Which definition of strip is used in this sentence?**

    Ⓐ to remove
    Ⓑ long, narrow piece of cloth
    Ⓒ to remove clothes
    Ⓓ to clear out

The chess club decided to **bar** Igor from joining because he talked too much during chess matches.

9.  **Which definition of bar is used in this sentence?**

    Ⓐ A square of material
    Ⓑ A place where people eat and drink
    Ⓒ To prevent
    Ⓓ To equip

10. **Which of these are meanings that the word track can have?**

    Ⓐ Footprint left by an animal
    Ⓑ Transparent
    Ⓒ A sports event
    Ⓓ Monitor

## Lesson 6: Review - Roots And Affixes

1. **Determine the meaning of the word autonomous based on the following affixes.**

   Auto-=self
   Nom=order
   -ous=having the quality of

   Ⓐ ordering something for yourself
   Ⓑ being different than other people
   Ⓒ having the qualities of self and order
   Ⓓ being able to do something by yourself

2. **The affix path means "to feel". What is the meaning of empathetic in the following sentence? Select two options.**

   Because Mrs. Anderson is an empathetic person, she tries to help everyone in her church who is suffering.

   Ⓐ unbothered
   Ⓑ caring
   Ⓒ kind hearted
   Ⓓ cruel

3. **If Juan is aquaphobic, what would be true about him?**

   Aqua-=water
   Phobos=fear

   Ⓐ He would love to go to the swimming pool.
   Ⓑ He would wash the dishes after dinner each night.
   Ⓒ He would avoid taking baths and showers.
   Ⓓ He would want a fish as a pet.

4. **Which of these would a person who is antisocial enjoy? Select those that apply.**

   Ⓐ going to a big party.
   Ⓑ spending time alone in his or her room.
   Ⓒ playing video games.
   Ⓓ hiking by him or herself.

5. **Determine the meaning of the word digress based on the following affixes.**

di-= to the opposite
gress=to go

Ⓐ the opposite of going
Ⓑ move away from the main topic
Ⓒ go on vacation
Ⓓ opposed to something

6. **Based on your understanding of prefixes, when can you infer that something that is postmortem occurs?**

The word postmortem is made up of two affixes:
post- + mortem
mortem means "life"

Ⓐ Before someone is born
Ⓑ During someone's life
Ⓒ After someone is dead
Ⓓ When someone is living

7. **The suffix -an means "from".**

**What can you assume is true about the person in the following sentence?**

Lars was proud to be a Norwegian.

Ⓐ Lars is from nowhere in particular.
Ⓑ Lars is from Norwalk, Connecticut.
Ⓒ Lars is from Norway.
Ⓓ Lars is from Norfolk, Virginia.

8. **Based on the prefix, octogenarian most likely means?**

Ⓐ A kind of sea creature
Ⓑ A person who is in his or her eighties
Ⓒ A kind of book
Ⓓ The next generation

9. Based on the suffix, brimful most likely means?

   Ⓐ Capable
   Ⓑ Full of
   Ⓒ Smaller
   Ⓓ Few

10. Based on the prefix, unacceptable means which of the following two options?

   Ⓐ doable
   Ⓑ objectionable
   Ⓒ understandable
   Ⓓ undesirable

## Chapter 2

## Lesson 7: Precise And Concise Language

1. **Which choice best rewrites the following sentence with precise, concise language?**

   I am having a good day.

   Ⓐ  I am having a great day.
   Ⓑ  I am having a really good day.
   Ⓒ  I am having an extremely productive day.
   Ⓓ  I am having a really, really good day.

2. **Which choice uses the most precise and concise language?**

   Ⓐ  Hunting animals, like those who are endangered, is very wrong and not okay to do.
   Ⓑ  Hunting animals, like those who are endangered, is very wrong.
   Ⓒ  Hunting endangered animals is very wrong.
   Ⓓ  Hunting endangered animals is illegal.

In the first line of her book report, Maria writes:
The novel I read is about a pig whose name is Wilbur and he lives on a farm.

3. **How can Maria make her sentence more precise? Select three options.**

   Ⓐ  Include the title of the book instead of "the novel I read."
   Ⓑ  Change "whose name is" to "named"
   Ⓒ  Say "who lives on a farm" instead of "and he lives on a farm."
   Ⓓ  Add more details about Wilbur.

4. **Which choice represents the MOST precise opening line Maria could write?**

   Ⓐ  *Charlotte's Web* is about a pig named Wilbur who lives on a farm.
   Ⓑ  The novel I read is about a pig named Wilbur and he lives on a farm.
   Ⓒ  The novel I read is about a pig whose name is Wilbur who lives on a farm.
   Ⓓ  *Charlotte's Web* is about a pig named Wilbur and he lives on a farm.

Alfonso is writing a restaurant review. He writes the following:
The baked goods were delicious.

**5.  How can Alfonso be more precise with his review?**

Ⓐ  Change "baked goods" to a specific baked good he tried.
Ⓑ  Change "delicious" to "good".
Ⓒ  Change "baked goods" to "bakery items"
Ⓓ  Change "The" to the name of the restaurant.

**6.  Which sentences below are the most precise? Select three options.**

Ⓐ  The baked goods were incredibly yummy and delicious.
Ⓑ  The cakes and cookies were the best I've ever had.
Ⓒ  The donuts were soft and warm.
Ⓓ  The chocolate chip cookies were ooey and gooey.

After seeing a play, Yuri writes the following sentence:
The actresses wore dresses.

**7.  What two things can Yuri do to make the sentence more precise?**

Ⓐ  Describe the kinds of dresses
Ⓑ  Talk a little about the play
Ⓒ  Include what the actors wore too
Ⓓ  Describe the color of the dresses

**8.  Which sentence makes Yuri's sentence more precise while still being concise?**

Ⓐ  The actresses wore frilly dresses from the Victorian era.
Ⓑ  The actresses wore red, frilly, beautiful dresses.
Ⓒ  The lead actress, Mona Kent, and the others wore a frilly Victorian dress.
Ⓓ  All of the actresses wore frilly Victorian dresses.

While spending a week at camp, George writes the following letter home to his parents:

I love camp. I love it because we play sports. I also love it because we go canoeing. And I love it because we get to sing songs by the campfire.

9. **How can George make the sentence "I love it because we play sports" more precise?**

    Ⓐ Combine it with some of the other sentences
    Ⓑ Tell the time of day he plays sports
    Ⓒ Say why he loves playing sports
    Ⓓ Include a few specific sports

10. **Which choice makes George's letter most precise and concise?**

    Ⓐ I love camp. I love it because we play sports, go canoeing, and sing songs by the campfire.
    Ⓑ I love camp. I love it because we play basketball and football, go canoeing, and sing songs by the campfire.
    Ⓒ I love camp because we play basketball and football, go canoeing, and sing songs by the campfire.
    Ⓓ I love camp because we play sports, go canoeing, and sing songs by the campfire.

## Chapter 2

### Lesson 8: Give It A Shot - Figures Of Speech

As soon as Hector ate the fifteenth hotdog, he knew he had made a mistake entering the hot dog eating contest. His stomach felt <u>like a ton of bricks</u> with all that meat and bread in it!

1. **What are two of the meanings of the underlined figure of speech?**

   Ⓐ light
   Ⓑ empty
   Ⓒ heavy
   Ⓓ full

Kim had spent the last three days writing the speech she was going to give the students during the assembly. She wanted more than anything to be elected as the president of the student council. When she looked down at the paper in her hand, she realized she was holding her math homework, not a copy of the speech. Kim looked up to see hundreds of pairs of eyes looking at her. Not wanting to give up on her dream of being elected and not wanting to appear unprepared, <u>Kim gave her speech off the cuff.</u>

2. **What is the meaning of the underlined figure of speech?**

   Ⓐ quickly
   Ⓑ quietly
   Ⓒ embarrassedly
   Ⓓ freely

3. **What does the author mean by "hundreds of pairs of eyes"?**

   Ⓐ Many people were watching Kim carefully.
   Ⓑ Many people were laughing at Kim.
   Ⓒ Many people were watching Kim angrily.
   Ⓓ Many people were smiling at Kim.

The unit on quadratic equations that we are studying in Math right now is so confusing. <u>I may die trying to learn this information!</u>

**4. What is the author trying to convey to the reader through the underlined phrase?**

Ⓐ How exhausting quadratic equations are
Ⓑ How physically ill Math class makes her
Ⓒ How much effort she is having to put into learning quadratic equations
Ⓓ How math is deadly

Brittany had never met anyone quite like Brian. When the two spent time together, she felt <u>as if no one else in the world existed</u> other than she and Brian.

**5. What are NOT the meanings of the underlined phrase?**

Ⓐ Their love took them to another planet in the solar system,
Ⓑ Nothing else mattered when the two were together.
Ⓒ Everyone tends to leave a couple in love alone.
Ⓓ He was the only man she'd met.

Nikki came home after her curfew three nights in a row. Her father didn't want this to become a problem, so he decided to <u>nip it in the bud</u> by grounding her for a week.

**6. What are two of the meanings of the underlined figure of speech?**

Ⓐ stop immediately
Ⓑ not encourage
Ⓒ punish
Ⓓ stop gradually

After Cece's mother watched her spend the first week of summer vacation sitting on the couch watching television, she signed her daughter up to volunteer at the local retirement home.
When Cece complained, her mother told her, "Idle hands are the devil's handiwork."

**7. What does Cece's mother mean by this statement?**

Ⓐ Laziness causes nothing but trouble.
Ⓑ Watching too much television is sinful.
Ⓒ Cece's hands are looking like the Devil's.
Ⓓ Wasting time is not a good idea.

Sammy's English teacher last year was extremely strict and gave her students hours of homework each night. So far, his new English teacher, Mr. Tucker, seemed very nice and had only given one short homework assignment. Sammy thought this year's English class was going to be <u>a walk in the park</u>.

**8. What is the meaning of the underlined figure of speech?**

   Ⓐ difficult
   Ⓑ easy
   Ⓒ confusing
   Ⓓ fun

After working in the yard mowing and planting shrubs for eight hours in the hot sun, Doreen decided to <u>call it a day</u>.

**9. What is the meaning of the underlined figure of speech?**

   Ⓐ go to bed
   Ⓑ stop working
   Ⓒ talk to a friend on the phone
   Ⓓ watch the sun set

My older brother never does the jobs my mother asks him to do around the house. I always end up having to do his chores. He's always <u>passing the buck</u> to me.

**10. What is the meaning of the underlined figure of speech?**

   Ⓐ paying for jobs
   Ⓑ ignoring
   Ⓒ forcing to do work
   Ⓓ putting the responsibility on

## Chapter 2

### Lesson 9: We're Related - Word Relationships

1. **What is the relationship between the words serial and cereal?**

   (A) They are synonyms.
   (B) They are antonyms.
   (C) They are homonyms.
   (D) They are opposites.

2. **What is the relationship between the words annoying and unpleasant?**

   (A) They are synonyms.
   (B) They are antonyms.
   (C) They are homonyms.
   (D) They are homographs.

3. **Which two of the following words are antonyms of the underlined word in the sentence?**

   Augustus enjoys <u>helping</u> others, so he volunteers at the local food bank.

   (A) aiding
   (B) entertaining
   (C) burdening
   (D) harming

4. **Which of the following words is a synonym of the underlined word in the sentence?**

   Now that I have enough money, I can <u>purchase</u> the video game I have been wanting for months.

   (A) sell
   (B) look for
   (C) buy
   (D) win

5.  **Which of the following words is an antonym of the underlined word in the sentence?**

My cousin and I used to enjoy spending weekends together at her house, but after she started hanging out with people I don't like, I have nothing but <u>animosity</u> for her.

Ⓐ love
Ⓑ dislike
Ⓒ anger
Ⓓ sadness

6.  **What are two synonyms of the underlined word?**

Books in the library are <u>classified</u> according to subject.

Ⓐ organized
Ⓑ catalogued
Ⓒ ordered
Ⓓ disorganized

7.  **What are three antonyms for the word in bold?**

Lewis was **patient** as he waited for his appointment.

Ⓐ Tolerant
Ⓑ Complaining
Ⓒ Impatient
Ⓓ Fed up

8.  **What is a synonym for the word in bold?**

"Ouch! That **smarts**!" exclaimed Julia when she stepped on a tack.

Ⓐ Stings
Ⓑ Is intelligent
Ⓒ Is confusing
Ⓓ Sounds loud

9.  **The words in bold in this sentence are**

It took an **hour** for **our** parade to pass.

Ⓐ Homophones
Ⓑ Synonyms
Ⓒ Antonyms
Ⓓ None of the above.

## 10. What is an antonym for the word in bold?

I couldn't cut anything with that **dull** knife.

Ⓐ Sharp
Ⓑ Boring
Ⓒ Interesting
Ⓓ Comfortable

## Chapter 2

## Lesson 10: Good Sentences Are Built On Agreement

1. **Which of the following verb forms correctly fills in the blank in the following sentence?**

   Almost everybody _____ glad we do not have school next Monday.

   (A) is
   (B) are
   (C) were
   (D) am

2. **Which of the following sentences has correct subject-verb agreement?**

   (A) Each of my sisters have their rooms.
   (B) Marco's car needs a new transmission and a new clutch.
   (C) My cat don't fit through the kitty door because its stomach is so fat.
   (D) Drinking water help you lose weight.

3. **Which of the following verb forms correctly fills in the blank in the following sentence?**

   Even though Randy _____ tomatoes, he loves spaghetti sauce.

   (A) hate
   (B) hates
   (C) hated
   (D) like

4. **Which of the following sentences has correct subject-verb agreement?**

   (A) Every one of us have a purpose in life.
   (B) Angela and her best friend goes out for pizza every Friday night.
   (C) I hope my favorite football team play well this weekend.
   (D) Why do my neighbors always get louder at night?

5. **Which of the following verb forms correctly fills in the blank in the following sentence?**

   Neither of my parents _____ going on vacation.

   (A) enjoy
   (B) enjoys
   (C) enjoying
   (D) are enjoying

6. **Which of the following versions of the sentence has correct subject-verb agreement?**

   Ⓐ A positive attitude and motivation make school easier.
   Ⓑ A positive attitude and motivation makes school easier.
   Ⓒ A positive attitude and motivation is making school easier.
   Ⓓ A positive attitude and motivation maked school easier.

7. **Which sentence has correct subject-verb agreement?**

   Ⓐ Both my cat and my dogs enjoy eating "people" food.
   Ⓑ Both my cat and my dogs enjoys eating "people" food.
   Ⓒ Both my cat and my dogs enjoying eating "people" food.
   Ⓓ Both my cat and my dogs eats "people" food.

8. **Which of the verb forms correctly fills in the blank in the following sentence- is or are?**

   Lindsay, my favorite of all my cousins, _____ coming to visit me in October.

9. **Which of the following verb forms correctly fills in the blank in the following sentence?**

   Some people _____ watching golf tournaments. Others find the tournaments very boring.

   Ⓐ enjoy
   Ⓑ enjoys
   Ⓒ enjoying
   Ⓓ enjoyed

10. **Which version of this sentence has correct subject-verb agreement?**

    Ⓐ An ant which climbs on a picnic table risk being squashed.
    Ⓑ An ant which climb on a picnic table risk being squashed.
    Ⓒ An ant which climbs on a picnic table risks being squashed.
    Ⓓ An ant which climbing on a picnic table risking being squashed.

## Chapter 2

## Lesson 11: Phrases And Clauses Are Coming To Town

1. **What type of word group is the following?**

   Walking down the street

   Ⓐ Phrase
   Ⓑ Dependent Clause
   Ⓒ Independent Clause
   Ⓓ Dependent Phrase

2. **What type of word group is the underlined portion of the following sentence?**

   After leaving school, <u>I realized I left my science textbook in my locker.</u>

   Ⓐ Phrase
   Ⓑ Dependent Clause
   Ⓒ Independent Clause
   Ⓓ Complete Phrase

3. **What type of word group is the underlined portion of the following sentence?**

   <u>Next Saturday</u>, my family is going to the beach.

   Ⓐ Phrase
   Ⓑ Dependent Clause
   Ⓒ Independent Clause
   Ⓓ Complete Clause

4. **What type of word group is the underlined portion of the following sentence?**

   I need a new cell phone because my old phone <u>fell in the toilet</u>.

   Ⓐ Phrase
   Ⓑ Dependent clause
   Ⓒ Independent clause
   Ⓓ Prepositional clause

5. **What type of word group is the underlined portion of the following sentence?**

I need a new cell phone <u>because my old phone fell in the toilet</u>.

Ⓐ Phrase
Ⓑ Dependent Clause
Ⓒ Independent Clause
Ⓓ Complete Clause

6. **What type of word group is the underlined portion of the following sentence?**

The actor <u>who starred in the movie version of one of my favorite books</u> did a horrible job playing the main character.

Ⓐ Phrase
Ⓑ Dependent Clause
Ⓒ Independent Clause
Ⓓ Interrupter phrase

7. **What type of word group is the underlined portion of the following sentence?**

<u>I decided to hope for the best</u>, but to expect the worst.

Ⓐ Phrase
Ⓑ Dependent clause
Ⓒ Independent clause
Ⓓ Dependent phrase

8. **What type of word group is the underlined portion of the following sentence?**

Fireworks are <u>amazing and beautiful</u> to me.

Ⓐ Phrase
Ⓑ Dependent clause
Ⓒ Independent clause
Ⓓ Adverbial clause

9. **What type of word group is the underlined portion of the following sentence?**

Good things tend to happen to you <u>when you least expect them</u>.

Ⓐ Phrase
Ⓑ Dependent clause
Ⓒ Independent clause
Ⓓ Dependent phrase

**10. What type of word group is the underlined portion of the following sentence?**

<u>Carley and Lori both bought their prom dresses from the same boutique</u> and their shoes from the same shoe store.

 Ⓐ Phrase
 Ⓑ Dependent Clause
 Ⓒ Independent Clause
 Ⓓ Prepositional phrase

## Chapter 2

## Lesson 12: Using Coordinate Adjectives

1. **Where should a comma be placed in the following sentence? Rewrite the sentence with the comma in the box below.**

   The fascinating intelligent old man told us all about his experiences during the war.

   ┌─────────────────────────────────────────────────────────────┐
   │                                                               │
   │                                                               │
   │                                                               │
   └─────────────────────────────────────────────────────────────┘

2. **Which choice best combines the following sentences with coordinate adjectives?**

   Slippery roads are common during the winter.
   Slippery roads are also dangerous roads.

   Ⓐ Slippery and dangerous roads are common during the winter.
   Ⓑ Slippery, dangerous roads are common during the winter.
   Ⓒ Slippery, and also dangerous, roads are common during the winter.
   Ⓓ Slippery roads are common during the winter and are dangerous.

3. **Which sentence contains coordinate adjectives?**

   Ⓐ The loud African parrot squawked at me.
   Ⓑ Angry, frustrated customers stormed the store.
   Ⓒ The sleepy little baby rubbed his eyes.
   Ⓓ Adorable baby jaguars ran around at the zoo.

4. **Which sentence uses coordinate adjectives correctly?**

   Ⓐ He was wearing running, black and striped shoes.
   Ⓑ He was wearing black striped running shoes.
   Ⓒ He was wearing black, striped running shoes.
   Ⓓ He was wearing black, running striped shoes.

5. **Which sentence uses coordinate adjectives incorrectly?**

   Ⓐ She was wearing an angora, red sweater.
   Ⓑ She was wearing a comfy, fluffy angora sweater.
   Ⓒ She was wearing a yellow, fluffy angora sweater.
   Ⓓ She was wearing a soft, fluffy angora sweater.

6. **Which sentence uses coordinate adjectives correctly?**

   Ⓐ He was wearing purple, rubber boots.
   Ⓑ He travelled along a curvy, slippery highway.
   Ⓒ He visited his aging, maternal grandmother.
   Ⓓ He needs a cold, diet soda.

7. **Which sentence uses coordinate adjectives correctly?**

   Ⓐ Mr. Crank was an angry, bitter old man.
   Ⓑ Mr. Crank was an angry old man.
   Ⓒ Mr. Crank was a bitter old man.
   Ⓓ Mr. Crank was an old, bitter angry man.

8. **How could the following sentence be changed to use coordinate adjectives correctly?**

   Alisha wanted to go to a tropical, warm, sunny island for Christmas.

   Ⓐ Remove tropical from the sentence.
   Ⓑ Move tropical after sunny and separate them with a comma.
   Ⓒ Move tropical after sunny and do not add a comma.
   Ⓓ Move warm before tropical.

9. **How could the following sentence be changed to use coordinate adjectives correctly?**

   Mom wanted a cashmere, red sweater for her birthday.

   Ⓐ Switch cashmere and red and remove the comma.
   Ⓑ Remove the comma between cashmere and red.
   Ⓒ Switch cashmere and red, remove the comma, and add another adjective with a comma before red.
   Ⓓ Add another adjective before cashmere, separating it from the others with a comma.

10. **Which choice correctly combines the two sentences using coordinate adjectives?**

    My dog lived a long life.
    My dog lived a happy life.

    Ⓐ My dog lived a long, happy life.
    Ⓑ My dog lived a long happy life.
    Ⓒ My dog lived a long life and it was happy.
    Ⓓ My dog lived a long life and a happy life.

## Chapter 2

## Lesson 13: Managing Modifiers

1.  **Which of the following adverbs fits best in the blank in this sentence?**

    My uncle's computer which was made in 1987 connects _____ to the Internet.

    Ⓐ angrily
    Ⓑ slowly
    Ⓒ quickly
    Ⓓ fast

2.  **What piece of punctuation should always appear between two coordinate adjectives?**

    Ⓐ A semi-colon
    Ⓑ A comma
    Ⓒ A period
    Ⓓ A colon

3.  **What part of speech is the underlined word in the following sentence?**

    After a long, drawn out argument, the girl and her mother hugged for a long time and decided the girl's curfew was <u>hardly</u> worth fighting about.

    Ⓐ Adverb
    Ⓑ Adjective
    Ⓒ Noun
    Ⓓ Verb

4.  **In which of the following two sentences, is the underlined word an adjective?**

    Ⓐ Marta hardly knew where to find her <u>orange</u> sweater.
    Ⓑ The large, angry dog <u>rushed</u> towards the mailman.
    Ⓒ Everyone knows that <u>kind</u> words get a person better results than insults do.
    Ⓓ I wanted to go to the movies this weekend, but I can't <u>afford</u> to because I don't get paid until next Thursday.

5. **Select the sentences with the adjective underlined.**

   Ⓐ Because my alarm <u>clock</u> didn't go off this morning and there was traffic due to an accident on the highway, I was very late for my appointment with Dr. Huang.
   Ⓑ Because my alarm clock didn't go off this morning and there was traffic due to an accident on the highway, I was very <u>late</u> for my appointment with Dr. Huang.
   Ⓒ Because my alarm clock didn't go off this morning and there was traffic due to an accident on the highway, I was very late for my appointment with <u>Dr. Huang</u>.
   Ⓓ Because my alarm clock didn't go off this morning and there was <u>heavy</u> traffic due to an accident on the highway, I was very late for my appointment with Dr. Huang.

6. **Select the version of the sentence with the adverb underlined.**

   Ⓐ When Megan's <u>best</u> friend told her she no longer wanted to be friends, Megan angrily slammed down the phone smashing it to pieces.
   Ⓑ When Megan's best friend told her she no longer <u>wanted</u> to be friends, Megan angrily slammed down the phone smashing it to pieces.
   Ⓒ When Megan's best friend told her she no longer wanted to be friends, Megan <u>angrily</u> slammed down the phone smashing it to pieces.
   Ⓓ When Megan's best friend told her she no longer wanted to be friends, Megan angrily slammed down the phone <u>smashing</u> it to pieces.

7. **Which of the following adjectives best completes this sentence?**

   The huge, _____ fire destroyed seven out of the twelve businesses in the downtown area.

   Ⓐ large
   Ⓑ violent
   Ⓒ contained
   Ⓓ temporary

8. **Select the sentence with the adverb underlined.**

   Ⓐ Teenagers <u>rarely</u> think their parents know very much.
   Ⓑ Our <u>ugly</u>, overgrown garden looks more like a weed patch than a vegetable garden.
   Ⓒ Alesandro caught a ten-foot long <u>wide-mouthed</u> bass from the lake.
   Ⓓ I can't figure out why it takes me longer to shower than it does to do my <u>homework.</u>

9. **Which of the following sentences shows coordinate adjectives correctly punctuated and written precisely?**

   Ⓐ The bride's flowing, long, wedding, dress drew everyone's attention.
   Ⓑ The rich, dark chocolate cake, my grandmother makes is my favorite dessert.
   Ⓒ Rarely, can you find a short, interesting book to read when you have to write a book report.
   Ⓓ Last nights dinner was a healthy.

## 10. What part of speech is the underlined word in the following sentence?

After a <u>long, drawn</u> out argument, the girl and her mother hugged for a long time and decided the girl's curfew was hardly worth fighting about.

Ⓐ large
Ⓑ violent
Ⓒ contained
Ⓓ temporary

## Chapter 2

## Lesson 14: Spellcheck!

**1. Which word in the following sentence is misspelled? Write in the box below.**

We all go threw difficult times in our lives when we feel sad and lonely.

**2. Which of the following words are misspelled?**

Ⓐ Fierce
Ⓑ Sliegh
Ⓒ Experement
Ⓓ Weird

**3. Which word is misspelled in the following sentence?**

My favorite meal at the restaraunt is pasta with mushrooms and broccoli.

Ⓐ favorite
Ⓑ restaraunt
Ⓒ mushrooms
Ⓓ broccoli

**4. Which word is misspelled in the following sentence?**

I was recognised as the top spelunker at least week's cave exploration

Ⓐ recognised
Ⓑ spelunker
Ⓒ exploration
Ⓓ tournament

5. **Which of the following two words contain spelling mistakes?**

   Ⓐ Apendix
   Ⓑ Rupture
   Ⓒ Paniked
   Ⓓ Arguing

6. **Which of the following words is misspelled?**

   Ⓐ Accessory
   Ⓑ Harass
   Ⓒ Neccessary
   Ⓓ Possession

7. **Which word completes the following sentence?**

   Make sure you have _____ umbrella with you because it is supposed to rain today.

   Ⓐ you're
   Ⓑ your

8. **Which word completes the following sentence?**

   Every young girl grows up and becomes a _____.

   Ⓐ woman
   Ⓑ women

9. **What is the correct spelling of the word that completes this sentence?**

   It is better to give than to _____.

   Ⓐ receive
   Ⓑ recieve
   Ⓒ recive
   Ⓓ reacieve

10. **Which word completes the following sentence?**

    We arrived at the play _____ late to be seated. We had to stand in the back of the theater to watch the play.

    Ⓐ to
    Ⓑ too
    Ⓒ two

## Chapter 2

## Lesson 15: Would You Rather Own A Boat Or A Yacht? Denotation And Connotation

Omar is always making jokes and trying to get others to laugh. Even when a situation is serious, he tries to make light of it by joking. When Omar told his friends that his grandmother was very sick and might die, everyone thought he was just joking around. Omar was trying to share something very sad, but his friends thought he was being <u>facetious</u>.

1. **The denotation of facetious is "amusing or funny". Based on the context of its use in this paragraph, what is the connotation of the word?**

   Ⓐ positive
   Ⓑ negative

Selma is often late to work, and when she does arrive there, she is lazy and rude to the customers. Selma's boss, Nick, met with her to talk with her about her job performance. Nick said Selma has many good qualities, but he needs to <u>boot</u> her from her job immediately.

The word boot means "to end someone's employment."

2. **Based on this paragraph, the connotation of this word is...**

   Ⓐ negative
   Ⓑ positive
   Ⓒ neutral

The manager of the sandwich shop takes home the leftover rolls and bread each night to feed his children and his wife. He does this because his family is <u>needy.</u>

3. **If the underlined word was changed to greedy, how would the connotation of the sentence change?**

   Ⓐ The reader would think of the manager as someone who wants, but does not need the leftovers.
   Ⓑ The reader would think of the manager as someone who needs, but does not want the leftovers.
   Ⓒ The reader's view of the manager will not change because the connotation of both words is the same.

Noah's mother grounded him for a week because his room was so <u>filthy.</u>

4.  **If the underlined word was changed to untidy, how would the connotation of the sentence change?**

    Ⓐ The reader would think that Noah's room was disorganized, but not extremely dirty.
    Ⓑ The reader would think that Noah's room was extremely dirty instead of being just disorganized.
    Ⓒ The reader's view of Noah's room would not change because the connotation of both words is the same.

Billy lives for football season. He is a <u>devoted</u> fan of the Chicago Bears.
Billy lives for football season. He is an <u>obsessed</u> fan of the Chicago Bears.

*Devoted* and *obsessed* are considered synonyms. However, each has a different connotation.

5.  **How does the connotation of the sentence change when *devoted* is changed to obsessed?**

    Ⓐ Devoted has a more positive connotation than obsessed does
    Ⓑ Devoted has a more negative connotation than obsessed does
    Ⓒ There is no change in connotation when the words are exchanged.

When the Water-Shed Commission said that it must move or be destroyed, the <u>residents</u> of Katonah gathered together, and decided that rather than be wiped off the face of the map, it would pick up its houses and move itself.

6.  **How would the connotation of this sentence change if the underlined word was changed to *taxpayers*?**

    Ⓐ Residents focuses on the people being pushy. Taxpayers focuses on the people doing what they are supposed to do.
    Ⓑ Taxpayers focuses on the people living in houses with their families. Residents focuses on the money they pay to the government.
    Ⓒ Residents focuses on the people living in houses with their families. Taxpayers focuses on the money they pay to the government.
    Ⓓ Residents focuses on the people pulling together. Taxpayers makes the people sound divided.

The idea is to make it impossible for England to <u>interfere</u> if we wish to make a treaty with another country.

7.  **How does the connotation of this sentence change if the underlined word is changed to** *help*?

   Ⓐ  Interfere has a positive connotation, but help has a negative connotation.
   Ⓑ  Help has a positive connotation, but interfere has a negative connotation.
   Ⓒ  The connotation will not change because both words have the same meaning.

Carley has <u>a large</u> amount of homework to do this weekend.

8.  **What two options could replace the underlined words to emphasize the size of the work Carley has?**

   Ⓐ  a big
   Ⓑ  a huge
   Ⓒ  an enormous
   Ⓓ  a moderate

Lori had a <u>bad</u> fear of snakes and spiders.

9.  **What two options could replace the underlined word to show that Lori's fear is very strong?**

   Ⓐ  a dreadful
   Ⓑ  a small
   Ⓒ  a strong
   Ⓓ  an intense

Julius is a <u>very good</u> student. He has had all A's on his report cards since kindergarten.

10. **What two options could replace the underlined words to emphasize Julius' skills?**

   Ⓐ  an exceptional
   Ⓑ  a mediocre
   Ⓒ  an unexceptional
   Ⓓ  a bright

# Answer Key and Detailed Explanations

## Chapter 2: Developing and Sustaining Foundational Language Skills

## Lesson 1: Speaking & Listening

**NOTE:**

This lesson is an audio-visual lesson and is available online for your practice. Please use the link or QR code given below to practice the lesson. If you don't have an account, please register.

Have lots of fun!

| Link | QR Code |
|---|---|
| http://lumoslearning.com/a/181252 | |

# Lesson 2: Learning and Using Academic Vocabulary

| Question No. | Answer | Detailed Explanations |
|---|---|---|
| 1 | curator | "A keeper or custodian of a collection" is a curator. |
| 2 | superin-tendent | "A high-ranking official" or "someone who manages an organization" is a superintendent. |
| 3 | squad of workers | "A group of people assembled to complete a task" is a squad of workers. |
| 4 | D | Answer choice four is correct. The passage says carotene is present in yellow and orange leaves, so it can be inferred it also gives carrots their orange color. |
| 5 | A | Answer choice one is correct. The passage says chlorophyll helps gives leaves their green color. |
| 6 | A | Answer choice one is correct. The passage describes photosynthesis as a process. |
| 7 | C | Answer choice three is correct. The passage describes an antioxidant as a protective substance/coating. |
| 8 | B | Answer choice two is correct. Primitive describes something not sophisticated or developed. For example, early man is often considered primitive. |
| 9 | B | Answer choice two is correct. A kinship society is most likely formed with groups of individuals from the same families. |
| 10 | C | Answer choice three is correct. Modernization does not just involve technology (choice two), but bringing in new ideas and practices. |

# Lesson 3: Consulting Sources

| Question No. | Answer | Detailed Explanations |
|---|---|---|
| 1 | B | Answer choice two is correct. To find the answer quickly, Jorge should look up the meaning in the glossary of the textbook. |
| 2 | thesaurus | A thesaurus contains synonyms which would help Jorge. |
| 3 | C | Answer choice three is correct. Words in dictionaries are in alphabetical order so he will find it between ecology and edifice. |
| 4 | B | Answer choice two is correct. The words in parentheses will help Jorge know how to pronounce the word "ecosystem." |
| 5 | B | Answer choice two is correct. The n. shows that the word "ecosystem" is a noun. |
| 6 | A and B | Based on what Jorge read, ecosystem is a community of interacting organisms or a general term used to describe a complex system. |
| 7 | B | Answer choice two is correct. The sentences in italics help the reader distinguish between the different meanings of the word by providing examples of usage. |
| 8 | B and C | Put off and postpone are the best synonyms for Lynn to use. |
| 9 | A | Answer choice one is correct. The synonym she needs is most related to the third definition of delay, so hesitate is a good choice. |
| 10 | A | Answer choice one is correct. The thesaurus entry covers delay as a verb, not as a noun. Students should look closely at the part of speech before choosing a synonym. |

# Lesson 4: Figuring It Out With Context Clues

| Question No. | Answer | Detailed Explanations |
|---|---|---|
| 1 | C and D | Quandary means a state of perplexity or a state of uncertainty. |
| 2 | D | Bruno receives medicine through a shot injection. The answer choice is D. Also it is used as a noun in the story. |
| 3 | D | Answer choice four is the correct answer. The sentences discuss animals living in rivers and lakes. Also the second sentence mentions animals living in water. |
| 4 | B and C | Sinister here is used to mean evil or disturbing. |
| 5 | A | Answer choice one is the correct answer. Based on the passage, it states "to help the club better understand the rules" is a hint that something before the rules must be read. |
| 6 | B | Answer choice two is correct. The sentence continues to explain that Bruno could not stand or move. This tells the reader that paralysis must mean inability to move. |
| 7 | A and B | The meaning of the underlined word, fleeting is, passing rapidly and remaining only for a brief period of time. |
| 8 | C | Answer choice three is correct. The sentence(s) mention a disagreement. Then, "an arbitrator was brought in to help" is stated. This tells the reader that an arbitrator can help with a dispute, and that they must be a person who helps settle arguments. |
| 9 | C | Answer choice three is correct. "Only grazed my pants...I was still upset" tells the reader that only grazed means barely. |
| 10 | A | Answer choice one is correct. The words "even though" coupled with "found dull" tell the reader that something different than dull is intended. They should understand the opposite of dull could be entertained. |

# Lesson 5: Which Fits? Multiple Meaning Words

| Question No. | Answer | Detailed Explanations |
|---|---|---|
| 1 | C and D | The word discount is used here to mean disregard or leave out/not pay attention to. |
| 2 | B | Answer choice two is correct. Approve means to give approval, or say okay. |
| 3 | A and C | The word subordinate is used here to mean someone in a lower position or a junior. |
| 4 | C | Answer choice three is correct. A racket that awakes someone is a noise. This is slang for noisy activity. |
| 5 | B | Answer choice two is correct. It is typical to refer to candy and dessert type foods as "sweets." The reader knows the word sweets in this passage means candy because the passage states that candy companies put the cards in the packages to encourage the kids to buy the candy. |
| 6 | C | Answer choice three is correct. Sometimes after a storm electrical lines are down. If the power company warns someone from wire, one that is "live," then the consumer should assume it is dangerous. And dangerous to a power company means electricity. |
| 7 | B | Answer choice two is correct. If they were going to broadcast "without a delay," then the reader understands that "live" means as it is happening. |
| 8 | A | Answer choice one is correct. Strip, when used as a verb, means to take off. So, to strip paint means to remove it. |
| 9 | C | Answer choice three is correct. The sentence discusses how someone had misbehaved, and then had a consequence. So, to the reader, bar should mean prohibit, or keep from. |
| 10 | A and D | The word track can mean footprints left by an animal or to monitor. |

# Lesson 6: Review - Roots And Affixes

| Question No. | Answer | Detailed Explanations |
|---|---|---|
| 1 | C | Answer choice three is correct. Autonomous means to be in control of self. |
| 2 | B and C | Empathetic can mean both caring and kind hearted. |
| 3 | C | If he is phobic of aqua, he is afraid of water. Being afraid of water would make it difficult to get in to water. The other answer choices are about someone who LIKES water. |
| 4 | B, C and D | An antisocial person might enjoy spending time alone in his or her room, playing video games and hiking by him or herself. |
| 5 | B | Answer choice two is the correct answer. To digress means to get away from, or to stray from focus. |
| 6 | C | Answer choice three is correct. A postmortem is something studied or done after death. |
| 7 | C | Answer choice three is correct. The suffix added to many country names indicates a person from that country. |
| 8 | B | Answer choice two. Octo (like octagon in a stop sign) means 8. And octogenarian is a person in their 80's. |
| 9 | B | Answer choice two is correct. Full to the brim; brimful. |
| 10 | B and D | Unacceptable means objectionable and undesirable. |

# Lesson 7: Precise And Concise Language

| Question No. | Answer | Detailed Explanations |
|---|---|---|
| 1 | C | Answer choice three is correct. All of the other choices are general. Choice three is more specific and precise. |
| 2 | D | Answer choice four is correct. Answer choices one and two are longer and more redundant. Answer choice three is better, but can still be cleaned up. |
| 3 | A, B and C | To make her sentence more precise, Maria can Include the title of the book instead of "the novel I read."Change "whose name is" to "named"Say "who lives on a farm" instead of "and he lives on a farm." |
| 4 | A | Answer choice one is correct. The first choice is specific and condenses the line without losing information. |
| 5 | A | Answer choice one is correct. The first choice will give Alfonso the opportunity to give specific details. |
| 6 | A, C and D | Options A, C and D describe the baked goods and are hence most precise. |
| 7 | B and C | Two things Yuri can do to make the sentence more precise are describing the kinds and colors of the dresses. |
| 8 | D | Answer choice four is correct. It references that all of the actresses were involved, but condenses the description of the dresses, keeping it precise but concise. |
| 9 | D | Answer choice four is correct. I love it because we go canoeing and we get to sing songs by the campfire. Being precise means being specific. Canoeing and singing songs by the campfire are specific activities. |
| 10 | C | Answer choice three is correct. Even though choice four is shorter, choice three is concise and specific (precise). |

# Lesson 8: Give It A Shot - Figures Of Speech

| Question No. | Answer | Detailed Explanations |
|---|---|---|
| 1 | C and D | Heavy and full are the two meanings of "like a ton of bricks". |
| 2 | D | Answer choice four is the correct answer. Off the cuff usually means with no notes or talking points. The person just "does it." |
| 3 | A | Answer choice one is the correct answer. There probably were hundreds of pairs of eyes, since there were likely several hundred people in the auditorium, but this is an expression that illustrates to the reader how nervous Kim was. |
| 4 | C | Answer choice three is the best answer. This is a hyperbole, an exaggeration, to make a point of how difficult the work is. |
| 5 | A, C and D | Options A, C and D are not the meanings of the underlined phrase. |
| 6 | A and B | To nip it in the bud means to stop immediately and not encourage. |
| 7 | A | Answer choice one is correct. This is an idiom that was used many years ago. It means that if a person doesn't stay busy, she could find herself somewhere she does not belong. |
| 8 | B | Answer choice two is correct. A walk in the park would be an easy and enjoyable stroll. So, this saying indicates something will be easy to accomplish. |
| 9 | B | Answer choice two is correct. This is a common idiom that means to decide the work day is complete. |
| 10 | D | Answer choice four is correct. This means to not do work, or make decisions. It is meant to indicate someone is avoiding what they are to do. |

# Lesson 9: We're Related - Word Relationships

| Question No. | Answer | Detailed Explanations |
|---|---|---|
| 1 | C | Homonyms are words that sound the same when they are pronounced, but that are spelled differently and usually have different meanings. |
| 2 | A | Synonyms are words that have similar meanings. They can usually replace each other in a sentence and the sentence will hold the same meaning. |
| 3 | C and D | Burdening and harming are close opposites of "helping". |
| 4 | C | Synonyms are words that have the same meaning as each other. |
| 5 | A | Antonyms are words that have opposite meanings. |
| 6 | A and B | Synonyms of classified are organized and catalogued. |
| 7 | B, C and D | The antonyms for patient are these-<br>Complaining<br>Impatient<br>Fed up |
| 8 | A | Answer choice one is a synonym of "smarts" as it is used. |
| 9 | A | Answer choice one is correct. They sound the same, but have different spellings and meanings. |
| 10 | A | Answer choice one is correct. In the case of the knife, the opposite would mean sharp, as in easy to cut. |

# Lesson 10: Good Sentences Are Built On Agreement

| Question No. | Answer | Detailed Explanations |
|---|---|---|
| 1 | A | Answer choice one is correct. Everybody is a singular subject, so it requires a verb that ends in is. |
| 2 | B | Answer choice two is correct. Subjects and verbs must match in number (number of items in the subject) and person (1st, 2nd or 3rd). In this sentence the subject, "car", is singular and third person. The verb "needs" is also singular, third person. |
| 3 | B | Randy is a singular subject. Therefore, the verb related to this subject must end in -s. |
| 4 | D | Answer choice four is correct. The verb do is singular because the subject my is also singular. |
| 5 | B | Answer choice two is correct. Neither is the subject of this sentence. Neither is a singular subject. Therefore, the verb related to it must end in -s. |
| 6 | A | Answer choice one is correct. The subject is plural, so the verb must be plural as well (no -s) |
| 7 | A | Answer choice one is correct. The subject of this sentence is plural, so the verb must also be plural. |
| 8 | is | The answer is "is" since Lindsay is one person. |
| 9 | A | Answer choice one is correct. People is a plural form of person. The verb must be plural (no -s). Answer choice four cannot be used, although it "sounds right" because the next sentence's tense does not agree with this verb tense. |
| 10 | C | Answer choice three is correct. One ant needs the singular verb forms (ending in -s). |

# Lesson 11: Phrases And Clauses Are Coming To Town

| Question No. | Answer | Detailed Explanations |
|---|---|---|
| 1 | A | Answer choice one is correct. There is no subject but there is a verb, so this is a phrase. A phrase is a meaningful group of words which may appear to contain either a subject OR a verb--but NOT both. A phrase can NOT stand alone as a sentence.<br>A clause is a meaningful group of words which contains a subject and a verb. There are two types of clauses: 1) independent and 2) dependent. |
| 2 | C | Answer choice three is correct. An independent clause contains all of the parts of a complete sentence: a subject, verb and a complete thought. |
| 3 | A | Answer choice one is correct. A phrase contains only a subject or a verb. This phrase has only a subject (Saturday). A phrase is a meaningful group of words which may appear to contain either a subject OR a verb--but NOT both. A phrase can NOT stand alone as a sentence.<br>A clause is a meaningful group of words which contains a subject and a verb. There are two types of clauses: 1) independent and 2) dependent. |
| 4 | A | Answer choice one is correct. The part of the sentence contains a verb.<br>A phrase is a meaningful group of words which may appear to contain either a subject OR a verb--but NOT both. A phrase can NOT stand alone as a sentence.<br>A clause is a meaningful group of words which contains a subject and a verb. There are two types of clauses: 1) independent and 2) dependent. |
| 5 | B | Answer choice two is correct. A dependent clause contains a subject and a verb, but cannot be a sentence by itself because it begins with a dependent word such as "because".<br>A phrase is a meaningful group of words which may appear to contain either a subject OR a verb--but NOT both. A phrase can NOT stand alone as a sentence.<br>A clause is a meaningful group of words which contains a subject and a verb. There are two types of clauses: 1) independent and 2) dependent. |

| Question No. | Answer | Detailed Explanations |
|---|---|---|
| 6 | A | Answer choice one is correct.<br>A phrase is a meaningful group of words which may appear to contain either a subject OR a verb--but NOT both. A phrase can NOT stand alone as a sentence.<br>A clause is a meaningful group of words which contains a subject and a verb. There are two types of clauses: 1) independent and 2) dependent. |
| 7 | C | Answer choice three is correct. This clause contains a subject, verb and it completes a thought.<br>A phrase is a meaningful group of words which may appear to contain either a subject OR a verb--but NOT both. A phrase can NOT stand alone as a sentence.<br>A clause is a meaningful group of words which contains a subject and a verb. There are two types of clauses: 1) independent and 2) dependent. |
| 8 | A | A phrase is a meaningful group of words which may appear to contain either a subject OR a verb--but NOT both. A phrase can NOT stand alone as a sentence.<br><br>A clause is a meaningful group of words which contains a subject and a verb. There are two types of clauses: 1) independent and 2) dependent.<br><br>The underlined portion is a phrase. |
| 9 | B | A phrase is a meaningful group of words which may appear to contain either a subject OR a verb--but NOT both. A phrase can NOT stand alone as a sentence.<br>A clause is a meaningful group of words which contains a subject and a verb. There are two types of clauses: 1) independent and 2) dependent.<br><br>The underlined portion is a clause. |
| 10 | C | A clause is a meaningful group of words which contains a subject and a verb. There are two types of clauses: 1) independent and 2) dependent.<br>An independent clause is a clause that can stand alone as a sentence. A dependent clause (or subordinate clause) is one that cannot stand alone as a complete sentence (i.e., it does not express a complete thought).<br>The underlined portion is an independent clause. |

# Lesson 12: Using Coordinate Adjectives

| Question No. | Answer | Detailed Explanations |
|---|---|---|
| 1 | - | The fascinating, intelligent old man told us all about his experiences during the war. |
| 2 | B | Answer choice two is correct. Commas go between coordinate adjectives. Since you can place an "and" between slippery and dangerous, they are coordinate adjectives. |
| 3 | B | Answer choice two is correct. Commas go between coordinate adjectives. Since you can place an "and" between angry and frustrated, they are coordinate adjectives. |
| 4 | C | Answer choice three is correct. Commas go between coordinate adjectives and coordinate adjectives are interchangeable. Running is not interchangeable, but black and striped are and should be separated with a comma. |
| 5 | A | Answer choice one is correct. Commas go between coordinate adjectives and coordinate adjectives are interchangeable. Angora is not interchangeable as it's a specific type of sweater. |
| 6 | B | Answer choice two is correct. Commas go between interchangeable coordinate adjectives. Only the adjectives in choice two are interchangeable. |
| 7 | A | Answer choice one is correct. Commas go between coordinate adjectives and coordinate adjectives are interchangeable. Only angry and bitter are interchangeable in this sentence. |
| 8 | C | Answer choice three is correct. Coordinate adjectives are separated by a comma and are interchangeable. In this sentence, tropical is not interchangeable so it needs to go before island. |
| 9 | C | Answer choice three is correct. Coordinate adjectives are separated by a comma and are interchangeable. In this sentence, red and cashmere aren't coordinate adjectives, so you need to add another adjective. Cashmere is also not interchangeable so it needs to be placed right before sweater. |
| 10 | A | Answer choice one is correct. Coordinate adjectives are separated by a comma. |

# Lesson 13: Managing Modifiers

| Question No. | Answer | Detailed Explanations |
|---|---|---|
| 1 | B | Answer choice two is the correct answer. An adverb ends in -ly. The fact that the computer is older tells the reader that it is probably not very fast or effective. So, it cannot be quickly. Fast is not appropriate due to the meaning and form of the word. Angrily does not apply to the computer's connection. It might apply to the computer operator, but not the actual machine. |
| 2 | B | Answer choice two is the correct answer. When two adjectives appear next to one another, they should be separated by a comma. It is similar to the listing rule of comma usage. |
| 3 | A | Answer choice one is correct. Adverbs modify (affect) verbs. |
| 4 | A and C | Options A and C- with orange and kind, are adjective containing sentences. |
| 5 | B and D | Options B and D contain the adjectives late and heavy. |
| 6 | C | Answer choice three is the correct answer. Adverbs modify (explain/affect) verbs. Adverbs usually end in -ly. Because angrily (adverb) explains how Megan slammed (verb) the phone, it is the correct answer. |
| 7 | B | Answer choice two is the best answer. The fire is temporary, it was or will be contained (eventually), and large is a synonym of huge, so these answers are not correct. Violent describes how serious and intense the fire was. |
| 8 | A | Answer choice one is the correct answer. Often adverbs appear after the verb, but they do not have to. Rarely (adverb) describes how teenagers think (verb). |
| 9 | C | Answer choice three is correct. The other choices have more than comma issues or do not apply. Short and interesting are adjectives to describe a book. They need to be separated by a comma. Dark chocolate is confusing because dark does describe the chocolate, but it is also a type of chocolate. Flowing and long are awkward. Usually it would be written long, flowing. Also, others aren't precise. |
| 10 | C | Answer choice three is correct. Two adjectives together (long and drawn out) describe the noun argument. |

# Lesson 14: Spellcheck!

| Question No. | Answer | Detailed Explanations |
|---|---|---|
| 1 | threw | Threw is misspelled. It should be through. |
| 2 | B and C | Options B and C. Sleigh and Experiment are misspelled as sliegh and experement. |
| 3 | B | The correct spelling of this word is "restaurant." |
| 4 | A | The correct spelling of this word is "recognized." The British spelling of the word is "recognised." |
| 5 | A and C | Apendix and paniked are misspelled. |
| 6 | C | The correct spelling of the word is "necessary." |
| 7 | B | The correct answer is two. You're is the contraction for you are, so your is correct. |
| 8 | A | Answer choice one is the correct tense, singular. |
| 9 | A | Answer choice one is correct. i before e except after c, and in cases where it says long a or long e. |
| 10 | B | Answer choice two is correct. Too, indicates an extent of something. Too much money, time etc. Also in addition. |

# Lesson 15: Would You Rather Own A Boat Or A Yacht? Denotation And Connotation

| Question No. | Answer | Detailed Explanations |
|---|---|---|
| 1 | B | Facetious is not generally used in a positive way. |
| 2 | A | Boot has negative connotations. It is not used in positive situations. |
| 3 | A | Needy has positive connotation because it focuses on needing something, but not being able to provide it for yourself. Greedy has negative connotations because it means someone is taking more than he or she needs simply because he or she wants it. |
| 4 | A | The word untidy, is not an extremely positive word, but it doesn't imply something is extremely dirty. The word filthy means that something is not only messy, but also dirty. |
| 5 | A | Answer choice one is the correct answer. Devoted generally means loving, and obsessed conjures images of someone who is excessively preoccupied or focused. |
| 6 | C | Answer choice three is correct. This word switch changes the focus of the sentence and its feelings slightly. Taxpayer is not a warm word. |
| 7 | B | Answer choice two is the best answer. Help is something people ask for and want. Interfering is something that is considered intrusive and unwanted. So, the second answer is the best way to make the sentence positive. |
| 8 | B and C | The words that could replace "a large" are "a huge" and "an enormous". |
| 9 | C and D | Options C and D- a strong, and an intense, could replace "a bad" in the sentence. |
| 10 | A and D | The two options that could replace the underlined words to emphasize Julius' skills are-<br><br>a bright, and<br>an exceptional |

# Chapter 3

# Comprehension Skills

## Chapter 3

## Lesson 1: Prove It! (With Evidence From The Text)

### From Scouting for Boys

"Hi! Stop Thief!" shouted old Blenkinsopp as he rushed out of his little store near the village. "He's stolen my sugar. Stop him."

Stop whom? There was nobody in sight running away, "Who stole it?" asked the policeman.

"I don't know, but a whole bag of sugar is missing. It was there only a few minutes ago." The policeman tried to track the thief, but it looked a pretty impossible job for him to single out the tracks of the thief from among dozens of other footprints about the store. However, he presently started off hopefully, at a jog-trot, away out into the bush. In some places, he went over the hard stony ground, but he never checked his pace, although no footmarks could be seen. People wondered how he could possibly find the trail. Still, he trotted on. Old Blenkinsopp was feeling the heat and the pace.

At length, he suddenly stopped and cast around, having evidently lost the trail. Then a grin came on his face as he pointed with his thumb over his shoulder up the tree near which he was standing. There, concealed among the branches, they saw a young man with the missing bag of sugar.

How had the policeman spotted him? His sharp eyes had detected some grains of sugar sparkling in the dust. The bag leaked, leaving a slight trail of these grains. He followed that trail, and when it came to an end in the bush, he noticed a string of ants going up a tree. They were after the sugar, and so was he, and between them, they brought about the capture of the thief.

Old Blenkinsopp was so pleased that he promptly opened the bag and spilled a lot of the sugar on the ground as a reward to the ants.

He also appreciated the policeman for his cleverness in using his eyes to see the grains of sugar and the ants, and in using his wits to know why the ants were climbing the tree.

1.  **Why could the policeman not find the footprints from among the others in the shop?**

    Ⓐ because they were clearly marked
    Ⓑ there were dozens of footprints
    Ⓒ there were no footprints to be found
    Ⓓ the footprints had been cleaned

**Tryouts**

For years, Sam had dreamed of being the best tennis player in the world. He went to tennis practice every single morning and every single night. He spent every summer at tennis camp, and he gave up long weekends at the beach to work on his game. Now, it seemed his hard work was finally paying off. He was invited to try out for the state tennis team!

Still, there was something that was bothering Sam. The tryouts for the tennis team were on the same day as his mom's birthday, and he knew his family was planning a huge surprise party for her. He didn't want to hurt his mom's feelings by missing the party, but he also didn't want to miss his one shot at being a champion tennis player. He was in a quandary; he didn't know what to do.

For days, Sam went to bed, worrying about the decision. If he went to the tryout, he worried he would seem selfish. If he stayed home, he would miss his one big shot at making the state team. In fact, despite the honor of being invited to try out, he hadn't even told his family about the opportunity. He was so stressed about deciding whether to go or not that he couldn't even think about sharing the news.

Weeks went by, and Sam was making no progress. Every day his coach asked him if he was ready for the tryout, and Sam couldn't even respond. Finally, Sam couldn't bear the stress any longer. He decided to talk to his grandfather about his predicament.

"You know, your mom wants you to be happy," he told Sam. "It would be a great birthday present for her to know you are making your dream come true."

Sam had never thought of it that way before, and after talking to his grandfather, he knew what he had to do. He immediately went home and sat down with his parents to let them know about the opportunity to try out for the state team. When Sam apologetically told his parents what day the tryouts were, they were so busy shrieking with excitement that he thought maybe they hadn't heard.

"But Mom, that means I'm going to miss your birthday," Sam said. "I am happy you are so nice about it, but I still feel really bad."

"Are you kidding?" his mom asked. "This is the best present I could ask for!"

2. **In this passage, who helps Sam make his choice- his neighbor or his grandfather? Write your answer in the box below.**

```
┌──────────────────────────────────────────────────────────────┐
│                                                                │
│                                                                │
│                                                                │
│                                                                │
└──────────────────────────────────────────────────────────────┘
```

3. **Which of the following two options are signs that Sam's parents raised him well?**

Ⓐ He understood that family and tennis were both priorities he needed to balance in his life.
Ⓑ He sought guidance from his grandfather instead of running from the problem.
Ⓒ He didn't think or fuss much about making his decision.
Ⓓ Sam didn't care about missing the party.

### Fairy Tales by A Brothers' Grimm

A certain king once fell ill, and the doctor declared that only a sudden fright would restore him to health, but the king was not a man for anyone to play tricks on, except his fool. One day, when the fool was with him in his boat, he cleverly pushed the king into the water. Help had already been arranged, and the king was drawn ashore and put to bed. The fright, the bath, and the rest in bed cured the diseased king.

The king wanted to frighten the fool for his act, so he told him that he would be put to death. He directed the executioner privately not to use the axe but to let fall a single drop of water on the fool's neck. Amidst shouts and laughter, the fool was asked to rise and thank the king for his kindness. But the fool never moved; he was dead; killed by the master's joke.

4. **What trick did the fool plan to cure the king?**

Ⓐ a lot of medicines
Ⓑ injections
Ⓒ the sudden push into the water
Ⓓ the ride in the boat

### From "The Owl and the Pussy-Cat" by Edward Lear

The Owl and the Pussy-Cat went to sea
In a beautiful pea-green boat,
They took some honey, and plenty of money
Wrapped up in a five-pound note.
The Owl looked up to the stars above,
And sang to a small guitar,
"O lovely Pussy! O Pussy, my love,
What a beautiful Pussy you are,
You are,
You are!
What a beautiful Pussy you are!"
Pussy said to the Owl, "You elegant fowl!
How charmingly sweet you sing!
O let us be married! too long we have tarried:

But what shall we do for a ring?"
They sailed away for a year and a day,
To the land where the Bong-tree grows,
And there in a wood a Piggy-wig stood,
With a ring at the end of his nose,
His nose,
His nose,
With a ring at the end of his nose.

**5. Who provides the wedding ring for the wedding? Writer your answer in the box below.**

<br>
<br>
<br>
<br>

**"The Boys and the Frogs"**
**From *Aesop's Fables*, adapted by Marmaduke Park**

Some boys, beside a pond or lake,
Were playing once at duck and drake;
When, doubtless to their heart's content,
Volleys of stones were quickly sent.
But there were some (there will be such)
Who did not seem amused so much;
These were the frogs, to whom the game,
In point of sport was not the same.

For scarce a stone arrived, 'tis said,
But gave some frog a broken head;
And scores in less than half an hour,
Perished beneath the dreadful shower.
At last, said one, "You silly folks, I say,
Do fling your stones another way;
Though sport to you, to throw them thus,
Remember, pray, 'tis death to us!"

**6. Why does the frog scold the boys?**

Ⓐ The boys hit the frog in the head with a rock.
Ⓑ The boys are polluting the pond that the frog lives in.
Ⓒ The boys refuse to let the frog play with them.
Ⓓ The boys are trying to catch the frog to keep as a pet.

7. **According to this poem what are the boys doing at the pond?**

   Ⓐ Trying to catch fish
   Ⓑ Trying to catch frogs
   Ⓒ Killing frogs
   Ⓓ Throwing stones into the pond

### From "The Dog and the Wolf" by Marmaduke Park

A wolf there was, whose scanty fare
Had made his person lean and spare;
A dog there was, so amply fed,
His sides were plump and sleek; 'tis said
The wolf once met this prosp'rous cur,
And thus began: "Your servant, sir;
I'm pleased to see you look so well,
Though how it is I cannot tell;
I have not broke my fast to-day;
Nor have I, I'm concern'd to say,
One bone in store or expectation,
And that I call a great vexation."

8. **Who is speaking in the dialogue of this selection?**

   Ⓐ The wolf
   Ⓑ The dog
   Ⓒ The dog's owner
   Ⓓ The narrator

### The Use of Transitions

(1)The wind was blowing with the gale force of over 55 miles an hour. (2) The windows of the house began to shake as we silently waited for the worst of all possible storms. (3) Kitchen plates crashed to the floor, and we trembled with fear.

(4)My trusty dog was by my side, and my little brother huddled under the table. (5) Our parents had gone to a neighbor's house for a community meeting. (6) This storm was not predicted by the weatherman earlier on TV. (7) We knew nothing of the impending danger.

(8)Within moments, the tornado warning sounded from the fire station downtown. (9) I grabbed my brother, Danny, and headed straight for the hallway. (10) On the way, I remembered to pull the mattress off of his bed. (11) We fell to the floor, pulled the mattress on top of us, and the faint sound of a train whistle began. (12) Suddenly it was as loud as if we were crossing the tracks. (13) Yes, my greatest fear was realized. (14) We were on the path of a pop-up tornado!

(15)Then as quickly as it began, silence. (16) No more wind, I thought to myself. (17) Boy, was I wrong! (18) Extremely loud crashing and banging of pane glass windows surrounded us. (19)The tornado was on top of us!

(20)Moments later, a gentle breeze came down the hall. (21) The calm after the storm, yes, that phrase fit. (22) I quickly checked Danny, who was underneath me. (23) He was as white as a sheet but grunted that he was ok. (24)Sapphire was fine, as well. (25) Not so for our living room, kitchen, and bedrooms. (26) The wind force had blown out all windows and lifted our roof to the street

(27)We just sat there in the hallway after checking the house and began to cry.

(28)Within moments the fire trucks were coming down our street. (29) Their megaphone was on and announcing an all clear. (30)They wanted everyone who could come outside.

(31)My brother and I went out slowly and carefully to avoid the glass fragments. (32) Our dog followed yelping all the way. (33) Our parents were running down the street, fearing for what had happened. (34) Ours was the only house touched by the tornado! (35) Debris was everywhere. (36) Praises to the man up above, we were safe.

(37)Family and life are more important than personal belongings. (38) That I can say.

9.  **Given the information in the selection, a substantiated critique of this selection would best read as follows.**

    Ⓐ  The author notes that tornados are frightening and can cause damage.
    Ⓑ  The author makes valid statements to back up his/her account of a damaging tornado that destroyed property but not lives.
    Ⓒ  The author fabricates the information and does not give supportive evidence to back up the selection.
    Ⓓ  The author gave limited information in regards to the tornado damage and its impact on his/her family's survival.

## Lines Written In A Young Lady's Album
## By George W. Sands

'Tis not in youth, when life is new, when but to live is sweet,
When Pleasure strews her starlike flow'rs beneath our careless feet,
When Hope, that has not been deferred, first waves its golden wings,
And crowds the distant future with a thousand lovely things; -

When if a transient grief  the spirit for a while,
The momentary tear that falls is followed by a smile;
Or if a pensive mood, at times, across the bosom steals,
It scarcely sighs, so gentle is the pensiveness it feels

It is not then the, restless soul will seek for one with whom
To share whatever lot it bears, its gladness or its gloom, -
Some trusting, tried, and gentle heart, some true and faithful breast,
Whereon its pinions it may fold, and claim a place of rest.

But oh! when comes the icy chill that freezes o'er the heart,
When, one by one, the joys we shared, the hopes we held, depart;
When friends, like autumn's withered leaves, have fallen by our side,
And life, so pleasant once, becomes a desert wild and wide; -

As for her olive branch the dove swept o'er the sullen wave,
That rolled above the olden world - its death-robe and its grave! -
So will the spirit search the earth for some kind, gentle one,
With it to share her destiny, and make it all her own!

**10. What do you think the poet is writing about in this poem? Write your answer in the box below.**

## Chapter 3

## Lesson 2: Use Those Clues - Make An Inference

### "The Lament"
### by Sravani

It is twilight. Thick wet snow is slowly twirling around the newly lighted street lamps and lying in soft thin layers on roofs, on horses' backs, on people's shoulders and hats. The cab driver, Iona Potapov, is quite white and looks like a phantom: he is bent double as far as a human body can bend double; he is seated on his box; he never makes a move. If a whole snowdrift fell on him, it seems as if he would not find it necessary to shake it off. His little horse is also quite white, and remains motionless; its immobility, its angularity, and its straight wooden-looking legs, even close by, give it the appearance of a gingerbread horse worth a kopek. It is, no doubt, plunged in deep thought. If you were snatched from the plough, from your usual gray surroundings, and were thrown into this slough full of monstrous lights, unceasing noise and hurrying people, you too would find it difficult not to think.

Iona and his little horse have not moved from their place for a long while. They left their yard before dinner and, up to now, not a fare. The evening mist is descending over the town, the white lights of the lamps are replacing brighter rays, and the hubbub of the street is getting louder.

'Cabby for Viborg Way!' suddenly hears Iona. 'Cabby!'

Iona jumps and, through his snow-covered eyelashes, sees an officer in a greatcoat, with his hood over his head.

'Viborg way!' the officer repeats. 'Are you asleep, eh? Viborg way!'

With a nod of assent, Iona picks up the reins, in consequence of which layers of snow slip off the horse's back and neck. The officer seats himself in the sleigh, the cab driver smacks his lips to encourage his horse, stretches out his neck like a swan, sits up and, more from habit than necessity, brandishes his whip. The little horse also stretches its neck, bends its wooden-looking legs, and makes a move undecidedly.

'What are you doing, werewolf!' is the exclamation Iona hears from the dark mass moving to and fro, as soon as they have started.

'Where the devil are you going? To the r-r-right!'

'You do not know how to drive. Keep to the right!' calls the officer angrily. A coachman from a private carriage swears at him; a passerby, who has run across the road and rubbed his shoulder against the horse's nose, looks at him furiously as he sweeps the snow from his sleeve. Iona shifts about on his seat as if he was on needles, moves his elbows as if he were trying to keep his equilibrium, and gasps about like someone suffocating, who does not understand why and wherefore he is there.

'What scoundrels they all are!' jokes the officer; 'one would think they had all entered into an agreement to jostle you or fall under your horse.'

Iona looks around at the officer and moves his lips. He evidently wants to say something but the only sound that issues is a snuffle.

'What?' asks the officer.

Iona twists his mouth into a smile and, with an effort, says hoarsely:
'My son, Barin, died this week.'
'Hm! What did he die of?'
Iona turns with his whole body towards his fare and says: 'And who knows! They say high fever. He was three days in the hospital and then died… God's will be done.'

"Turn round! The devil!' sounds from the darkness. 'Have you popped off, old doggie, eh? Use your eyes!'

'Go on, go on,' says the officer, 'otherwise we shall not get there by tomorrow. Hurry up a bit!'

"If you were snatched from the plough, from your usual gray surroundings, and were thrown into this slough full of monstrous lights, unceasing noise and hurrying people, you too would find it difficult not to think."

1. **What can be inferred from the first two paragraphs of the passage?**

    Ⓐ that the cab driver was very sad
    Ⓑ that the cabby was from a village or a very small town
    Ⓒ that the cab driver did not want to think
    Ⓓ that the cab driver was not thinking

### "Bruno the Bear"
### Excerpt from The Bond of Love

I will begin with Bruno, my wife's pet sloth bear. I got him for her by accident. Two years ago, we were passing through the cornfields near a small town in Iowa. People were driving away the wild pigs from the fields by shooting at them. Some were shot, and some escaped. We thought that everything was over when suddenly a black sloth bear came out panting in the hot sun.

Now I will not shoot a sloth bear wantonly, but unfortunately for the poor beast, one of my companions did not feel the same way about it and promptly shot the bear on the spot.

As we watched the fallen animal, we were surprised to see that the black fur on its back moved and left the prostrate body. Then we saw it was a baby bear that had been riding on its mother's back when the sudden shot had killed her. The little creature ran around its prostrate parent, making a pitiful noise. I ran up to it to attempt a capture. It scooted into the sugarcane field. Following it with my companions, I was at last able to grab it by the scruff of its neck while it snapped and tried to scratch me with its long, hooked claws.

We put it in one of the large jute-bags we had brought, and when I got back home, I duly presented it to my wife. She was delighted! She at once put a blue colored ribbon around its neck, and after discovering the cub was a 'boy,' she christened it Bruno.

Bruno soon took to drinking milk from a bottle. It was but a step further, and within a very few days, he started eating and drinking everything else. And everything is the right word, for he ate porridge made from any ingredients, vegetables, fruit, nuts, meat (especially pork), curry and rice regardless of condiments and chilies, bread, eggs, chocolates, sweets, pudding, ice-cream, etc., As for drink: milk, tea, coffee, lime juice, aerated water, buttermilk, beer, alcoholic liquor, and, in fact, anything liquid. It all went down with relish.

The bear became very attached to our two dogs and all the children living in and around our farm. He was left quite free in his younger days and spent his time playing, running into the kitchen, and going to sleep in our beds.

One day an accident befell him. I put down poison (barium carbonate) to kill the rats and mice that had got into my library. Bruno entered the library as he often did and ate some of the poison. Paralysis set into the extent that he could not stand on his feet. But he dragged himself on his stumps to my wife, who called me. I guessed what had happened.

Off I rushed him in the car to the vet's residence. A case of poisoning! Tame Bear—barium carbonate— what to do? Out came his medical books, and a feverish reference to index began: "What poison did you say, sir?" he asked, "Barium carbonate," I said.

"Ah yes—B—Ba—Barium Salts—Ah! Barium carbonate! Symptoms— paralysis—treatment—injections of . ... Just a minute, sir. I'll bring my syringe and the medicine." Said the doc. I dashed back to the car. Bruno was still floundering about on his stumps, but clearly, he was weakening rapidly; there was some vomiting, he was breathing heavily, with heaving flanks and gaping mouth. I was really scared and did not know what to do. I was feeling very guilty and was running in and out of the vet's house doing everything the doc asked me.

"Hold him, everybody!" In goes the hypodermic—Bruno squeals — 10 c.c. of the antidote enters his system without a drop being wasted. Ten minutes later: condition unchanged! Another 10 c.c. Injected! Ten minutes later: breathing less torturous— Bruno can move his arms and legs a little although he cannot stand yet. Thirty minutes later: Bruno gets up and has a great feed! He looks at us disdainfully, as much as to say, 'What's barium carbonate to a big black bear like me?' Bruno was still eating. I was really happy to see him recover.

The months rolled on, and Bruno had grown many times the size he was when he came. He had equaled the big dogs in height and had even outgrown them. But was just as sweet, just as mischievous, just as playful. And he was very fond of us all. Above all, he loved my wife, and she loved him too! And he could do a few tricks, too. At the command, 'Bruno, wrestle,' or 'Bruno, box,' he vigorously tackled anyone who came forward for a rough and tumble. Give him a stick and say 'Bruno, hold the gun,' and he pointed the stick at you. Ask him, 'Bruno, where's baby?' and he immediately produced and cradled affectionately a stump of wood which he had carefully concealed in his straw bed. But because of the neighborhoods' and our renters' children, poor Bruno, had to be kept chained most of the time.

Then my son and I advised my wife and friends advised her, too, to give Bruno to the zoo. He was getting too big to keep at home. After some weeks of such advice, she at last consented. Hastily, and before she could change her mind, a letter was written to the curator of the zoo. Did he want a tame bear for his collection? He replied, "Yes." The zoo sent a cage in a truck, a distance of hundred – eighty – seven miles, and Bruno was packed off. We all missed him greatly, but in a sense, we were relieved. My wife was inconsolable. She wept and fretted. For the first few days, she would not eat a thing. Then she wrote a number of letters to the curator. How was Bruno? Back came the replies, "Well, but fretting; he refuses food too."

After that, friends visiting the zoo were begged to make a point of seeing how Bruno was getting along. They reported that he was well but looked very thin and sad. All the keepers at the zoo said he was fretting. For three months, I managed to restrain my wife from visiting the zoo. Then she said one day, "I must see Bruno. Either you take me by car, or I will go myself by bus or train myself." So I took her by car. Friends had conjectured that the bear would not recognize her. I had thought so too. But while she was yet some yards from his cage, Bruno saw her and recognized her. He howled with happiness. She ran up to him, petted him through the bars, and he stood on his head in delight.

For the next three hours, she would not leave that cage. She gave him tea, lemonade, cakes, ice cream, and whatnot. Then 'closing time' came and we had to leave. My wife cried bitterly; Bruno cried bitterly; even the hardened curator and the keepers felt depressed. As for me, I had reconciled myself to what I knew was going to happen next.

"Oh please, sir," she asked the curator, "may I have my Bruno back"? Hesitantly, he answered, "Madam, he belongs to the zoo and is Government property now. I cannot give away Government property. But if my boss, the superintendent, agrees, certainly, you may have him back."

There followed the return journey home and a visit to the superintendent's office. A tearful pleading: "Bruno and I are both fretting for each other. Will you please give him back to me?" He was a kind-hearted man and consented. Not only that, but he wrote to the curator, telling him to lend us a cage for transporting the bear back home.

Back we went to the zoo again, armed with the superintendent's letter. Bruno was driven into a small cage and hoisted on top of the car; the cage was tied securely, and a slow and careful return journey back home was accomplished.

Once home, a squad of workers were engaged for special work around our yard. An island was made for Bruno. It was twenty feet long and fifteen feet wide and was surrounded by a dry moat, six feet wide and seven feet deep. A wooden box that once housed fowls was brought and put on the island for Bruno to sleep in at night. Straw was placed inside to keep him warm, and his 'baby,' the gnarled stump, along with his 'gun,' the piece of bamboo, both of which had been sentimentally preserved since he had been sent away to the zoo, were put back for him to play with. In a few days, the workers hoisted the cage on to the island, and Bruno was released. He was delighted; standing on his hind legs, he pointed his 'gun' and cradled his 'baby.' My wife spent hours sitting on a chair there while he sat on her lap. He was fifteen months old and pretty heavy too!

The way my wife reaches the island and leaves it is interesting. I have tied a rope to the overhanging branch of a maple tree with a loop at its end. Putting one foot in the loop, she kicks off with the other, to bridge the six-foot gap that constitutes the width of the surrounding moat. The return journey back is made the same way.

But who can say now that a sloth bear has no sense of affection, no memory, and no individual characteristics?

2.  **How can the reader infer the bear was depressed?**

   Ⓐ  because both the bear and the author's wife cried bitterly while departing
   Ⓑ  because the bear did not recognize its mistress
   Ⓒ  because the author's wife was lean and depressed
   Ⓓ  because Bruno would not eat anything.

## Best Friend

Ever since they were kids, Julie and Max had been best friends. They went to kindergarten together. They went to summer camp together. They hung out together every weekend. But suddenly, things between the two had started to change.

Max had started playing on the football team and didn't have much time for Julie anymore. He was always busy, and he never seemed to make it to study hall, where the two used to swap stories about their favorite (or least favorite) teachers. In class, Julie noticed that Max never seemed to have his homework done on time anymore. She even noticed that he got a 'D' on his last paper. She knew something was going on with him – but what?

At first, Julie decided to play it cool and see how things went. She tried waiting in the hall for Max after class to see if she could ask if he was OK. But days went by, and he never had time to stop.

He'd rush right past her in the hall, only to leave her feeling even worse about what was happening between them.

Even though she wasn't sure she could handle the situation herself, Julie didn't want to talk to her parents because she was afraid they would tell her not to hang out with Max anymore. She barely saw him as it was, so she knew it would just make things worse if her parents didn't approve of him. She didn't want to tell Max's parents either because she didn't want him to get in trouble. Still, it seemed like something needed to change. Julie decided to go to one of her school counselors and let her know she was concerned.

When she walked into Mrs. Smith's room, she was surprised to see that Max was already sitting there. "I'm sorry, I'll come back," Julie said.
"No, stay," said Max. "Maybe you can help."

Julie was surprised to find that Max had visited the counselor's office for the same reason she had: He was starting to feel overwhelmed with all of the things he was supposed to be doing as a student, an athlete, and a friend. He needed some guidance on how to determine what truly mattered and how to divide his time between all of the things that were important to him. When she realized that Max was still the same old Max (just a little more stressed), Julie was relieved. She was also happy to know that he had come to a conclusion on his own, without her having to talk to someone else about it. She decided it was a sign they were both growing up.

3.  **What can you infer about the relationship between Julie and Max? Select those that apply.**

    Ⓐ  They were best of friends.
    Ⓑ  They deeply cared about each other.
    Ⓒ  They hated each other, and sought to be separate.
    Ⓓ  They were neighbors.

## From "The Dog and the Wolf" by Marmaduke Park

A wolf there was, whose scanty fare
Had made his person lean and spare;
A dog there was, so amply fed,
His sides were plump and sleek; 'tis said
The wolf once met this prosp'rous cur,
And thus began: "Your servant, sir;
I'm pleased to see you look so well,
Though how it is I cannot tell;
I have not broke my fast to-day;
Nor have I, I'm concern'd to say,
One bone in store or expectation,
And that I call a great vexation."

4.  **Which of the following can be inferred about the dog based on this poem?**

    Ⓐ  That the dog was a golden retriever
    Ⓑ  That the dog had a caring master
    Ⓒ  That the dog was tall
    Ⓓ  That the dog belonged to the king

5. **What does the wolf represent in this poem?**

Ⓐ the basic idea of dieting
Ⓑ how to fast (not eat)
Ⓒ the basic needs of living
Ⓓ being a wild animal

6. **What does the dog represent in this poem?**

Ⓐ being a tamed animal
Ⓑ the comforts of having everything needed in life
Ⓒ being greedy
Ⓓ sharing with others

### "The Boys and the Frogs" by Marmaduke Park

Some boys, beside a pond or lake,
Were playing once at duck and drake;
When, doubtless to their heart's content,
Volleys of stones were quickly sent.
But there were some (there will be such)
Who did not seem amused so much;
These were the frogs, to whom the game,
In point of sport was not the same.
For scarce a stone arrived, 'tis said,
But gave some frog a broken head;
And scores in less than half an hour,
Perished beneath the dreadful shower.
At last, said one, "You silly folks, I say,
Do fling your stones another way;
Though sport to you, to throw them thus,
Remember, pray, 'tis death to us!"

7. **What is most likely true about the boys in this poem? Select two options.**

Ⓐ They are wild and unruly.
Ⓑ They regret that the rocks would harm the frogs.
Ⓒ They don't care who gets hurt in their play.
Ⓓ They like rocks more than they like frogs.

## From <u>The Children of France</u> by Ruth Royce

Before the "Squire's" son went away to war, the neighborhood children knew him only by sight and by hearing their parents speak of him as the son of "the richest man in Titusville," who never had done a day's work in his life.

Perhaps the parents were not quite right in this, for, even if Robert Favor had not gone out in the fields to labor, he had graduated from high school and college with high honors. He never spoke to the village children nor noticed them, and was not, as a result, very popular with the young people of his home town. The neighbors said this was all on account of his bringing up.

It was therefore a surprise to them when, at the beginning of the great war, after Germany swept over Belgium, Robert Favor hurried to Europe. It was later learned that he had joined what is known as the "Foreign Legion" of the French Army. Titusville next heard that he had been made a lieutenant for heroic conduct under fire. But Titusville did not believe it; it said no Favor ever did anything but run away in such circumstances. But they believed it when, later on, they read in the newspapers how Lieutenant Favor had sprung out of the trenches and ran to the rescue of a wounded private soldier who had lain in a shell hole in No Man's Land since the night before.

The village swelled with pride and the eyes of the children grew wide with wonder as they listened to the story of the heroism of the Squire's son. But this was as nothing to what occurred later. "Bob" Favor was brought home one day to the house on the hill, pale and weak from wounds received in battle.

Spring was at hand, and as soon as he was able, Captain Favor—you see he had again been pro-moted— was taken out on the lawn where, in his wheel chair he rested in the warm sunshine. The bright red top of his gray-blue cap, and the flash of the medal on his breast excited the wonder of the children, who pressed their faces against the high iron fence and gazed in awe. It was the first real hero any of them ever had seen.

Finally, chancing to look their way, the Captain smiled and waved a friendly hand. A little girl clapped her hands, others started to cheer and a little man of ten dragged an American flag from his pocket and waved it. The Captain beckoned to the children.

"Come in, folks," he called. "I wish someone to talk to me and make me laugh. Are you coming?"

They were. The children started, at first hesitatingly, then with more confidence, led by the boy with the American flag, which he was waving bravely now.
"What's your name?" demanded the Captain.
"Joe Funk, sir."

The Captain laughed. "No boy so patriotic as you are should have a name like that," he said.
"We all are going to be great friends, I am sure, and when I get this leg, that a German shell nearly blew off, in working order again, we shall have some real sport and I'll teach you all how to be soldiers. Just now I cannot do much of anything."

"Yes, you can," interrupted Joe. "You can tell us how you rescued the soldier when the Germans were shooting at you and—"

"Master Joseph," answered the Captain gravely, "a real soldier never brags about himself; but what you say does give me an idea. How would you like to have me tell you about the brave little children of France?"

"Well, I'd rather hear about how you killed the Germans, lots of 'em; I want to hear about battles and dead men and—"

"We shall speak of the children first, and I will begin right now. Let me see. Ah! I have it. Sit down on the grass, all of you, and be comfortable. Be quiet until I finish the story, then ask what questions you wish. Now listen!"

8. **Based on the details in this story, what do you think brought the Captain back to Titusville?**

   Ⓐ He was injured during the war and could no longer fight.
   Ⓑ He wanted to tell the people of Titusville his heroic stories.
   Ⓒ He wanted to make the people of Titusville proud of him.
   Ⓓ He wanted to work on his father's farm again.

"Hi! Stop Thief!" shouted old Blenkinsopp as he rushed out of his little store near the village. "He's stolen my sugar. Stop him."

Stop whom? There was nobody in sight running away, "Who stole it?" asked the policeman.

"I don't know, but a whole bag of sugar is missing. It was there only a few minutes ago." The policeman tried to track the thief but it looked a pretty impossible job for him to single out the tracks of the thief from among dozens of other footprints about the store. However, he presently started off hopefully, at a jog-trot, away out into the bush. In some places he went over hard stony ground but he never checked his pace, although no footmarks could be seen. People wondered how he could possibly find the trail. Still he trotted on. Old Blenkinsopp was feeling the heat and the pace.

At length the tracker suddenly stopped and cast around having evidently lost the trail. Then a grin came on his face as he pointed with his thumb over his shoulder up the tree near which he was standing. There, concealed among the branches, they saw a young man with the missing bag of sugar.

How had the policeman spotted him? His sharp eyes had detected some grains of sugar sparkling in the dust. The bag leaked, leaving a slight trail of these grains. He followed that trail and when it came to an end in the bush he noticed a string of ants going up a tree. They were after the sugar, and so was he, and between them they brought about the capture of the thief.

Old Blenkinsopp was so pleased that he promptly opened the bag and spilled a lot of the sugar on the ground as a reward to the ants.

He also appreciated the policeman for his cleverness in using his eyes to see the grains of sugar and the ants, and in using his wits to see why the ants were climbing the tree.

9. **The details of this story show that no one is present at the scene. Who is likely the narrator of this selection?**

   (A) the shopkeeper
   (B) the narrator is simply unnamed
   (C) the people
   (D) the thief

## Tryouts

For years, Sam had dreamed of being the best tennis player in the world. He went to tennis practice every single morning and night. He spent every summer at tennis camp, and he gave up long week-ends at the beach to work on his game. Now, it seemed his hard work was finally paying off. He was invited to try out for the state tennis team!

Still, there was something that was bothering Sam. The tryouts for the tennis team were on the same day as his mom's birthday, and he knew his family was planning a huge surprise party for her. He didn't want to hurt his mom's feelings by missing the party, but he also didn't want to miss his one shot at being a champion tennis player just because the tryouts were on his mom's birthday. He was in a quandary; he didn't know what to do.

For days, Sam went to bed, worrying about the decision. If he went to the tryout, he worried he would seem selfish. If he stayed home, he would miss his one big shot at making the state team. In fact, despite the honor of being invited to try out, he hadn't even told his family about the opportunity. He was so stressed about making the decision of whether to go that he couldn't even think about sharing the news.

Weeks went by, and Sam was making no progress. Every day his coach asked him if he was ready for the tryout, and Sam couldn't even respond. Finally, Sam couldn't bear the stress any longer. He decided to talk to his grandfather about his predicament.

"You know, your mom wants you to be happy," he told Sam. "It would be a great birthday present for her to know you are making your dream come true."

Sam had never thought of it that way before, and after talking to his grandfather, he knew what he had to do. He immediately went home and sat down with his parents to let them know about the opportunity to try out for the state team. His parents were so excited that when he told them, apologetically, what day the tryouts were, and they were so busy shrieking with excitement that he thought maybe they hadn't heard.

"But Mom, that means I'm going to miss your birthday," Sam said. "I am happy you are so nice about it, but I still feel really bad."

"Are you kidding?" his mom asked. "This is the best present I could ask for!"

10. **Which of the following is a sign that Sam's parents raised him well? Write in the box below.**

He sought guidance from his grandfather instead of running from the problem
He didn't really care about missing the party.

## Chapter 3

## Lesson 3: What Is It All About?

### Tryouts

For years, Sam had dreamed of being the best tennis player in the world. He went to tennis practice every single morning and night. He spent every summer at tennis camp, and he gave up long weekends at the beach to work on his game. Now, it seemed his hard work was finally paying off. He was invited to try out for the state tennis team!

Still, there was something that was bothering Sam. The tryouts for the tennis team were on the same day as his mom's birthday, and he knew his family was planning a huge surprise party for her. He didn't want to hurt his mom's feelings by missing the party, but he also didn't want to miss his one shot at being a champion tennis player just because the tryouts were on his mom's birthday. He was in a quandary; he didn't know what to do.

For days, Sam went to bed, worrying about the decision. If he went to the tryout, he worried he would seem selfish. If he stayed home, he would miss his one big shot at making the state team. In fact, despite the honor of being invited to try out, he hadn't even told his family about the opportunity. He was so stressed about making the decision of whether to go that he couldn't even think about sharing the news.

Weeks went by, and Sam was making no progress. Every day his coach asked him if he was ready for the tryout, and Sam couldn't even respond. Finally, Sam couldn't bear the stress any longer. He decided to talk to his grandfather about his predicament.

"You know, your mom wants you to be happy," he told Sam. "It would be a great birthday present for her to know you are making your dream come true."

Sam had never thought of it that way before, and after talking to his grandfather, he knew what he had to do. He immediately went home and sat down with his parents to let them know about the opportunity to try out for the state team. His parents were so excited that when he told them, apologetically, what day the tryouts were, and they were so busy shrieking with excitement that he thought maybe they hadn't heard.

"But Mom, that means I'm going to miss your birthday," Sam said. "I am happy you are so nice about it, but I still feel really bad."

"Are you kidding?" his mom asked. "This is the best present I could ask for!"

1.  **Which of these are not the themes of the story? Select those that apply.**

    Ⓐ  family values and priorities
    Ⓑ  pleasing everybody in your family
    Ⓒ  doing what is very important to you no matter how others feel
    Ⓓ  sports above all else

2.  **What two messages about relationship is this story trying to pass on to readers?**

    Ⓐ  Friends come and go in and out of lives.
    Ⓑ  You should always ask friends to help you with your life choices.
    Ⓒ  Open communication helps resolve seemingly difficult problems.
    Ⓓ  Family always comes to one's aid in difficulties.

### Moral of "The Dog and the Wolf" by Marmaduke Park

Our neighbors sometimes seem to be
A vast deal better off than we;
Yet seldom 'tis they really are,
Since they have troubles too to bear,
Which, if the truth were really known,
Are quite as grievous as our own.

3.  **What is the best summary of the moral of this poem?**

    Ⓐ  It's best to ignore those who complain.
    Ⓑ  Dogs and wolves will never get along.
    Ⓒ  Everyone else has problems too, that are likely to be grievous as yours.
    Ⓓ  Avoid those who look down on you.

### "The Origin of the Robin"
### From A Guide to Mythology by Cornelius Mathews

An old man had an only son, named Iadilla, who had come to that age which is thought to be most proper to make the long and final fast which is to secure through life a guardian genius or spirit. The father was ambitious that his son should surpass all others in whatever was deemed wisest and greatest among his people. To accomplish his wish, he thought it is necessary that the young Iadilla should fast a much longer time than any of those renowned for their power or wisdom, whose fame he coveted.

He, therefore, directed his son to prepare with great ceremony for the important event. After he had been several times in the sweating-lodge and bath, which were to prepare and purify him for communion with his good spirit, he ordered him to lie down upon a clean mat in a little lodge expressly provided for him. He enjoined upon him at the same time to endure his fast like a man, and promised that at the expiration of twelve days he should receive food and the blessing of his father.

The lad carefully observed the command, and lay with his face covered, calmly awaiting the approach of the spirit which was to decide his good or evil fortune for all the days of his life.

Every morning his father came to the door of the little lodge and encouraged him to persevere, dwelling at length on the vast honor and renown that must ever attend him, should he accomplish the full term of trial allotted to him.

To these glowing words of promise and glory the boy never replied, but he lay without the least sign of discontent or murmuring until the ninth day, when he addressed his father as follows:

"My father, my dreams forbode evil. May I break my fast now, and at a more favorable time make a new fast?"

The father answered:
"My son, you know not what you ask. If you get up now, all your glory will depart. Wait patiently a little longer. You have but three days more, and your term will be completed. You know it is for your own good, and I encourage you to persevere. Shall not your aged father live to see you a star among the chieftains and the beloved of battle?"

The son assented; and covering himself more closely, that he might shut out the light which prompted him to complain, he lay till the eleventh day, when he repeated his request.

The father addressed Iadilla as he had the day before, and promised that he would himself prepare his first meal, and bring it to him by the dawn of the morning.

The son moaned, and the father added:
"Will you bring shame upon your father when his sun is falling in the West?"
"I will not shame you, my father," replied Iadilla; and he lay so still and motionless that you could only know that he was living by the gentle heaving of his breast.

At the spring of day, the next morning, the father, delighted at having gained his end, prepared a repast for his son, and hastened to set it before him. On coming to the door of the little lodge, he was surprised to hear his son talking to himself. He stooped his ear to listen, and, looking through a small opening, he was yet more astonished when he beheld his son painted with vermilion over all his breast, and in the act of finishing his work by laying on the paint as far back on his shoulders as he could reach with his hands, saying at the same time, to himself:
"My father has destroyed my fortune as a man. He would not listen to my requests. He has urged me beyond my tender strength. He will be the loser. I shall be forever happy in my new state, for I have been obedient to my parent. He alone will be the sufferer, for my guardian spirit is a just one. Though not propitious to me in the manner I desired, he has shown me pity in another way—he has given me another shape; and now I must go."

At this moment the old man broke in, exclaiming:
"My son! my son! I pray you leave me not!"

But the young man, with the quickness of a bird, had flown to the top of the lodge and perched himself on the highest pole, having been changed into a beautiful robin red-breast. He looked down upon his father with pity beaming in his eyes, and addressed him as follows:
"Regret not, my father, the change you behold. I shall be happier in my present state than I could have been as a man. I shall always be the friend of men, and keep near their dwellings. I shall ever be happy and contented; and although I could not gratify your wishes as a warrior, it will be my daily aim to make you amends for it as a harbinger of peace and joy. I will cheer you by my songs, and strive to inspire in others the joy and lightsomeness of heart I feel in my present state. This will be some compensation to you for the loss of glory you expected. I am now free from the cares and pains of human life. My food is spontaneously furnished by the mountains and fields, and my pathway of life is in the bright air."

Then stretching himself on his toes, as if delighted with the gift of wings, ladilla caroled one of his sweetest songs, and flew away into a neighboring wood.

4.  **What is the theme of this story?**

    (A) Disobedient children will be punished.
    (B) Children lead their parents to Heaven.
    (C) Being obedient does not always have the intended result.
    (D) Dying is honorable.

5.  **What message about parents is the author trying to send through this story?**

    (A) Parents should listen to their children.
    (B) Effective parents are strict with their children.
    (C) Parents always know best.
    (D) Children take their parents for granted.

### Aesop in Rhyme "The Philosopher and the Acorn"
### by Marmaduke Park

A philosopher, proud of his wit and his reason,
Sat him under an oak in a hot summer season.
On the oak grew an acorn or two, it is said:
On the ground grew a pumpkin as big as his head.
Thought the sage, "What's the reason this oak is so strong
A few acorns to bear that are scarce an inch long;
While this poor feeble plant has a weight to sustain,
Which had much better hang on the tree, it is plain?"
But just at the time the philosopher spoke
An acorn dropp'd down on his head from the oak;
Then, said he, who just now thought his plan was so clever,
"I am glad that this was not a pumpkin, however."

6.  **What is the theme of this poem?**

Ⓐ  Watch out for falling objects.
Ⓑ  Just because something is small doesn't mean it isn't mighty.
Ⓒ  Don't question the way Mother Nature works.
Ⓓ  Every seed becomes a beautiful plant.

### "The Old Man and the Devils"- A Gaelic Folk Tale (Ed. Kate Douglas Wiggin)

A long time ago there was an old man who had a big lump on the right side of his face. One day he went into the mountain to cut wood when the rain began to pour and the wind to blow so very hard that, finding it impossible to return home, and filled with fear, he took refuge in the hollow of an old tree. While sitting there doubled up and unable to sleep, he heard the confused sound of many voices in the distance gradually approaching to where he was. He said to himself: "How strange! I thought I was all alone in the mountain, but I hear the voices of many people." So, taking courage, he peeped out and saw a great crowd of strange-looking beings. Some were red, and dressed in green clothes; others were black, and dressed in red clothes; some had only one eye; others had no mouth; indeed, it is quite impossible to describe their varied and strange looks. They kindled a fire so that it became as light as day. They sat down in two cross-rows, and began to drink wine and make merry just like human beings. They passed the wine cup around so often that many of them soon drank too much. One of the young devils got up and began to sing a merry song and to dance; so also many others; some danced well, others badly. One said: "We have had uncommon fun tonight, but I would like to see something new."

Then the old man, losing all fear, thought he would like to dance, and saying, "Let come what will, if I die for it, I will have a dance, too," crept out of the hollow tree and, with his cap slipped over his nose and his ax sticking in his belt, began to dance. The devils in great surprise jumped up, saying, "Who is this?" but the old man advancing and receding, swaying to and fro, and posturing this way and that way, the whole crowd laughed and enjoyed the fun, saying: "How well the old man dances! You must always come and join us in our sport; but, for fear you might not come, you must give us a pledge that you will." So the devils consulted together, and, agreeing that the lump on his face, which was a token of wealth, was what he valued most highly, demanded that it should be taken. The old man replied: "I have had this lump many years, and would not without good reason part with it; but you may have it, or an eye, or my nose either if you wish." So the devils laid hold of it, twisting and pulling, and took it off without giving him any pain, and put it away as a pledge that he would come back. Just then the day began to dawn, and the birds to sing, so the devils hurried away.

The old man felt his face and found it quite smooth, and not a trace of the lump left. He forgot all about cutting wood and hastened home. His wife, seeing him, exclaimed in great surprise, "What has happened to you?" So he told her all that had befallen him.

Now, among the neighbors, there was another old man who had a big lump on the left side of his face. Hearing all about how the first old man had got rid of his misfortune, he determined that he would also try the same plan. So he went and crept into the hollow tree, and waited for the devils to come. Sure enough, they came just as he was told, and they sat down, drank wine, and made merry just as they did before. The second old man, afraid and trembling, crept out of the hollow tree. The devils welcomed him, saying: "The old man has come; now let us see him dance." This old fellow was awkward, and did not dance as well as the other, so the devils cried out: "You dance badly, and are getting worse and worse; we will give you back the lump which we took from you as a pledge." Upon this, one of the devils brought the lump, and stuck it on the other side of his face; so the poor old fellow returned home with a lump on each side.

7. **Which of these are NOT the themes of this selection?**

   Ⓐ Dance as if no one is watching.
   Ⓑ To be healed, you have to make a deal with the Devil.
   Ⓒ Blessings come to people who don't expect them.
   Ⓓ Changing your appearance will only bring you misery.

### "The Land of Nod"
### by Robert Louis Stevenson

From breakfast on through all the day
At home among my friends I stay,
But every night I go abroad
Afar into the Land of Nod.

All by myself I have to go,
With none to tell me what to do—
All alone beside the streams
And up the mountain-sides of dreams.

The strangest things are there for me,
Both things to eat and things to see,
And many frightening sights abroad
Till morning in the Land of Nod.

Try as I like to find the way,
I never can get back by day,
Nor can remember plain and clear
The curious music that I hear.

**8. What is the theme of this selection?**

Ⓐ When we nod our heads, we get to see new places.
Ⓑ Dreams let you travel to new and magical places.
Ⓒ Traveling to the Land of Nod is exciting.
Ⓓ People can travel anywhere they want to go.

## "The Lad and the Diel"
### by Sir George Webbe Dasent

Once upon a time, there was a lad who was walking along a road cracking nuts, so he found one that was worm-eaten, and just at that very moment, he met the Deil (Devil).

"Is it true, now," said the lad, "what they say, that the Deil can make himself as small as he chooses, and thrust himself on through a pinhole?"

"Yes, it is," said the Deil. "Oh! it is, is it? then let me see you do it, and just creep into this nut," said the lad.

So the Deil did it. Now, when he had crept well into it through the worm's hole, the lad stopped it up with a pin.

"Now, I've got you safe," he said, and put the nut into his pocket.

So when he had walked on a bit, he came to a smith, and he turned in and asked the smith if he'd be good enough to crack that nut for him.

"Ay, that'll be an easy job," said the smith, and took his smallest hammer, laid the nut on the anvil, and gave it a blow, but it wouldn't break.

So he took another hammer a little bigger, but that wasn't heavy enough either. Then he took one bigger still, but it was still the same story, and so the smith got wroth and grasped his great sledge-hammer.

"Now, I'll crack you to bits," he said, and let drive at the nut with all his might and main.

And so the nut flew to pieces with a bang that blew off half the roof of the smithy, and the whole house creaked and groaned as though it were ready to fall. "Why! if I don't think the Deil must have been in that nut," said the smith.

"So he was; you're quite right," said the lad, as he went away laughing.

9. **What is the theme of this selection?**

Ⓐ Violence causes the Devil to come out.
Ⓑ It's not kind to play tricks on unsuspecting people.
Ⓒ Sometimes the Devil is in the smallest, least expected places.
Ⓓ It is important to ask for help.

### "The Wonderful Hair"
### by A. H. Wraitslaw

There was a man who was very poor, but so well supplied with children that he was utterly unable to maintain them, and one morning more than once prepared to kill them, in order not to see their misery in dying of hunger, but his wife prevented him. One night a child came to him in his sleep, and said to him: "Man! I see that you are making up your mind to destroy and to kill your poor little children, and I know that you are distressed thereat; but in the morning you will find under your pillow a mirror, a red kerchief, and an embroidered pocket-handkerchief; take all three secretly and tell nobody; then go to such a hill; by it, you will find a stream; go along it till you come to its fountain-head; there you will find a damsel as bright as the sun, with her hair hanging down over her back. Be on your guard, that the ferocious she-dragon do not coil around you; do not converse with her if she speaks; for if you converse with her, she will poison you, and turn you into a fish or something else, and will then devour you but if she bids you examine her head, examine it, and as you turn over her hair, look, and you will find one hair as red as blood; pull it out and run back again; then, if she suspects and begins to run after you, throw her first the embroidered pocket-handkerchief, then the kerchief, and, lastly, the mirror; then she will find occupation for herself. And sell that hair to some rich man, but don't let them cheat you, for that hair is worth countless wealth; and you will thus enrich yourself and maintain your children."

When the poor man awoke, he found everything under his pillow, just as the child had told him in his sleep; and then he went to the hill. When there, he found the stream, went on and on alongside of it, till he came to the fountain-head. Having looked about him to see where the damsel was, he espied her above a piece of water, like sunbeams threaded on a needle, and she was embroidering at a frame on stuff, the threads of which were young men's hair. As soon as he saw her, he made a reverence to her, and she stood on her feet and questioned him: "Whence are you, unknown young man?" But he held his tongue. She questioned him again: "Who are you? Why have you come?" and much else of all sorts, but he was as mute as a stone, making signs with his hands as if he were deaf and wanted help. Then she told him to sit down on her skirt. He did not wait for any more orders but sat down, and she bent down her head to him, that he might examine it. Turning over the hair of her head, as if to examine it, he was not long in finding that red hair, and separated it from the other hair, pulled it out, jumped off her skirt, and ran away back as he best could. She noticed it and ran at his heels full speed after him. He looked around, and seeing that she was about to overtake him, threw, as he was told, the embroidered pocket-handkerchief on the way, and when she saw the pocket-handkerchief, she stooped and began to overhaul it in every direction, admiring the embroidery, till he had got a good way off. Then the damsel placed the pocket-handkerchief in her bosom and ran after him again.

When he saw that she was about to overtake him, he threw the red kerchief, and she again occupied herself, admiring and gazing, till the poor man had again got a good way off. Then the damsel became exasperated, and threw both the pocket-handkerchief and the kerchief on the way, and ran after him in pursuit. Again, when he saw that she was about to overtake him, he threw the mirror. When the damsel came to the mirror, the like of which she had never seen before, she lifted it up, and when she saw herself in it, not knowing that it was herself, but thinking that it was somebody else, she, as it were, fell in love with herself in the mirror, and the man got so far off that she was no longer able to overtake him. When she saw that she could not catch him, she turned back, and the man reached his home safe and sound. After arriving at his home, he showed his wife the hair and told her all that had happened to him, but she began to jeer and laugh at him. But he paid no attention to her and went to a town to sell the hair. A crowd of all sorts of people and merchants collected round him; one offered a sequin, another two, and so on, higher and higher, till they came to a hundred gold sequins. Just then, the emperor heard of the hair, summoned the man into his presence, and said to him that he would give him a thousand sequins for it, and he sold it to him. What was the hair? The emperor split it in two from top to bottom and found registered in it in writing many remarkable things, which happened in the olden time since the beginning of the world. Thus the man became rich and lived on with his wife and children. And that child, that came to him in his sleep was an angel sent by the Lord God, whose will it was to aid the poor man and to reveal secrets which had not been revealed till then.

## 10. What is the theme of this story?

Ⓐ It is wrong for a parent to want to hurt his children.
Ⓑ The things we do for family can bring about great wealth for many.
Ⓒ God rewards those who protect their children.
Ⓓ His character does not have any influence on the plot.

## Chapter 3

## Lesson 4: And The Point Of This Is...?

**"Bruno the Bear"**
**Excerpt from The Bond of Love**

I will begin with Bruno, my wife's pet sloth bear. I got him for her by accident. Two years ago, we were passing through the cornfields near a small town in Iowa. People were driving away the wild pigs from the fields by shooting at them. Some were shot, and some escaped. We thought that everything was over when suddenly a black sloth bear came out panting in the hot sun.

Now I will not shoot a sloth bear wantedly, but unfortunately for the poor beast, one of my companions did not feel the same way about it and promptly shot the bear on the spot.

As we watched the fallen animal, we were surprised to see that the black fur on its back moved and left the prostrate body. Then we saw it was a baby bear that had been riding on its mother's back when the sudden shot had killed her. The little creature ran around its prostrate parent, making a pitiful noise. I ran up to it to attempt a capture. It scooted into the sugarcane field. Following it with my companions, I was at last able to grab it by the scruff of its neck while it snapped and tried to scratch me with its long, hooked claws.

We put it in one of the large jute-bags we had brought, and when I got back home, I duly presented it to my wife. She was delighted! She at once put a blue colored ribbon around its neck, and after discovering the cub was a 'boy,' she christened it Bruno.

Bruno soon took to drinking milk from a bottle. It was but a step further, and within a very few days, he started eating and drinking everything else. And everything is the right word, for he ate porridge made from any ingredients, vegetables, fruit, nuts, meat (especially pork), curry and rice regardless of condiments and chilies, bread, eggs, chocolates, sweets, pudding, ice-cream, etc., As for drink: milk, tea, coffee, lime juice, aerated water, buttermilk, beer, alcoholic liquor, and, in fact, anything liquid. It all went down with relish.

The bear became very attached to our two dogs and all the children living in and around our farm. He was left quite free in his younger days and spent his time playing, running into the kitchen, and going to sleep in our beds.

One day an accident befell him. I put down poison (barium carbonate) to kill the rats and mice that had got into my library. Bruno entered the library as he often did and ate some of the poison. Paralysis set into the extent that he could not stand on his feet. But he dragged himself on his stumps to my wife, who called me. I guessed what had happened.

Off I rushed him in the car to the vet's residence. A case of poisoning! Tame Bear—barium carbonate— what to do? Out came his medical books, and a feverish reference to index began: "What poison did you say, sir?" he asked, "Barium carbonate," I said.

"Ah yes—B—Ba—Barium Salts—Ah! Barium carbonate! Symptoms— paralysis—treatment—injections of . .. Just a minute, sir. I'll bring my syringe and the medicine." Said the doc. I dashed back to the car. Bruno was still floundering about on his stumps, but clearly, he was weakening rapidly; there was some vomiting, he was breathing heavily, with heaving flanks and gaping mouth. I was really scared and did not know what to do. I was feeling very guilty and was running in and out of the vet's house doing everything the doc asked me.

"Hold him, everybody!" In goes the hypodermic—Bruno squeals — 10 c.c. of the antidote enters his  system without a drop being wasted. Ten minutes later: condition unchanged! Another 10 c.c. Injected! Ten minutes later: breathing less torturous— Bruno can move his arms and legs a little although he cannot stand yet. Thirty minutes later: Bruno gets up and has a great feed! He looks at us disdainfully, as much as to say, 'What's barium carbonate to a big black bear like me?' Bruno was still eating. I was really happy to see him recover.

The months rolled on, and Bruno had grown many times the size he was when he came. He had equaled the big dogs in height and had even outgrown them. But was just as sweet, just as mischievous, just as playful. And he was very fond of us all. Above all, he loved my wife, and she loved him too! And he could do a few tricks, too. At the command, 'Bruno, wrestle,' or 'Bruno, box,' he vigorously tackled anyone who came forward for a rough and tumble. Give him a stick and say 'Bruno, hold the gun,' and he pointed the stick at you. Ask him, 'Bruno, where's baby?' and he immediately produced and cradled affectionately a stump of wood which he had carefully concealed in his straw bed. But because of the neighborhoods' and our renters' children, poor Bruno, had to be kept chained most of the time.

Then my son and I advised my wife and friends advised her, too, to give Bruno to the zoo. He was getting too big to keep at home. After some weeks of such advice, she at last consented. Hastily, and before she could change her mind, a letter was written to the curator of the zoo. Did he want a tame bear for his collection? He replied, "Yes." The zoo sent a cage in a truck, a distance of hundred – eighty – seven miles, and Bruno was packed off. We all missed him greatly, but in a sense, we were relieved. My wife was inconsolable. She wept and fretted. For the first few days, she would not eat a thing. Then she wrote a number of letters to the curator. How was Bruno? Back came the replies, "Well, but fretting; he refuses food too."

After that, friends visiting the zoo were begged to make a point of seeing how Bruno was getting along. They reported that he was well but looked very thin and sad. All the keepers at the zoo said he was fretting. For three months, I managed to restrain my wife from visiting the zoo. Then she said one day, "I must see Bruno. Either you take me by car, or I will go myself by bus or train myself." So I took her by car. Friends had conjectured that the bear would not recognize her. I had thought so too. But while she was yet some yards from his cage, Bruno saw her and recognized her. He howled with happiness. She ran up to him, petted him through the bars, and he stood on his head in delight.

For the next three hours, she would not leave that cage. She gave him tea, lemonade, cakes, ice cream, and whatnot. Then 'closing time' came and we had to leave. My wife cried bitterly; Bruno cried bitterly; even the hardened curator and the keepers felt depressed. As for me, I had reconciled myself to what I knew was going to happen next.

"Oh please, sir," she asked the curator, "may I have my Bruno back"? Hesitantly, he answered, "Madam, he belongs to the zoo and is Government property now. I cannot give away Government property. But if my boss, the superintendent, agrees, certainly, you may have him back."

There followed the return journey home and a visit to the superintendent's office. A tearful pleading: "Bruno and I are both fretting for each other. Will you please give him back to me?" He was a kind-hearted man and consented. Not only that, but he wrote to the curator, telling him to lend us a cage for transporting the bear back home.

Back we went to the zoo again, armed with the superintendent's letter. Bruno was driven into a small cage and hoisted on top of the car; the cage was tied securely, and a slow and careful return journey back home was accomplished.

Once home, a squad of workers were engaged for special work around our yard. An island was made for Bruno. It was twenty feet long and fifteen feet wide and was surrounded by a dry moat, six feet wide and seven feet deep. A wooden box that once housed fowls was brought and put on the island for Bruno to sleep in at night. Straw was placed inside to keep him warm, and his 'baby,' the gnarled stump, along with his 'gun,' the piece of bamboo, both of which had been sentimentally preserved since he had been sent away to the zoo, were put back for him to play with. In a few days, the workers hoisted the cage on to the island, and Bruno was released. He was delighted; standing on his hind legs, he pointed his 'gun' and cradled his 'baby.' My wife spent hours sitting on a chair there while he sat on her lap. He was fifteen months old and pretty heavy too!

The way my wife reaches the island and leaves it is interesting. I have tied a rope to the overhanging branch of a maple tree with a loop at its end. Putting one foot in the loop, she kicks off with the other, to bridge the six-foot gap that constitutes the width of the surrounding moat. The return journey back is made the same way.

But who can say now that a sloth bear has no sense of affection, no memory, and no individual characteristics?

1.  **Which of the following would make the best alternate title for this selection?**

    Ⓐ  The Pet
    Ⓑ  Hungry for Love
    Ⓒ  The Author's Wife
    Ⓓ  The Animal in the Zoo

2.  **What is this story mostly about?**

    (A) about having a bear as a pet and how to care for it
    (B) about the bond that the bear and the author's wife shared
    (C) about rescuing a bear
    (D) about animals

3.  **What is the central idea of paragraphs 1-10?**

    (A) Bruno eats rat poison, but doesn't die.
    (B) An accident almost causes the narrator's family to lose its pet.
    (C) A vet treats a pet bear.
    (D) The narrator feels guilty about accidentally poisoning his pet bear.

### "The Old Man and the Devils"- A Gaelic Folk Tale (Ed. Kate Douglas Wiggin)

A long time ago there was an old man who had a big lump on the right side of his face. One day he went into the mountain to cut wood when the rain began to pour and the wind to blow so very hard that, finding it impossible to return home, and filled with fear, he took refuge in the hollow of an old tree. While sitting there doubled up and unable to sleep, he heard the confused sound of many voices in the distance gradually approaching to where he was. He said to himself: "How strange! I thought I was all alone in the mountain, but I hear the voices of many people." So, taking courage, he peeped out and saw a great crowd of strange-looking beings. Some were red, and dressed in green clothes; others were black, and dressed in red clothes; some had only one eye; others had no mouth; indeed, it is quite impossible to describe their varied and strange looks. They kindled a fire so that it became as light as day. They sat down in two cross-rows, and began to drink wine and make merry just like human beings. They passed the wine cup around so often that many of them soon drank too much. One of the young devils got up and began to sing a merry song and to dance; so also many others; some danced well, others badly. One said: "We have had uncommon fun tonight, but I would like to see something new."

Then the old man, losing all fear, thought he would like to dance, and saying, "Let come what will, if I die for it, I will have a dance, too," crept out of the hollow tree and, with his cap slipped over his nose and his ax sticking in his belt, began to dance. The devils in great surprise jumped up, saying, "Who is this?" but the old man advancing and receding, swaying to and fro, and posturing this way and that way, the whole crowd laughed and enjoyed the fun, saying: "How well the old man dances! You must always come and join us in our sport; but, for fear you might not come, you must give us a pledge that you will." So the devils consulted together, and, agreeing that the lump on his face, which was a token of wealth, was what he valued most highly, demanded that it should be taken. The old man replied: "I have had this lump many years, and would not without good reason part with it; but you may have it, or an eye, or my nose either if you wish." So the devils laid hold of it, twisting and pulling, and took it off without giving him any pain, and put it away as a pledge that he would come back. Just then the day began to dawn, and the birds to sing, so the devils hurried away.

The old man felt his face and found it quite smooth, and not a trace of the lump left. He forgot all about cutting wood and hastened home. His wife, seeing him, exclaimed in great surprise, "What has happened to you?" So he told her all that had befallen him.

Now, among the neighbors, there was another old man who had a big lump on the left side of his face. Hearing all about how the first old man had got rid of his misfortune, he determined that he would also try the same plan. So he went and crept into the hollow tree, and waited for the devils to come. Sure enough, they came just as he was told, and they sat down, drank wine, and made merry just as they did before. The second old man, afraid and trembling, crept out of the hollow tree. The devils welcomed him, saying: "The old man has come; now let us see him dance." This old fellow was awkward, and did not dance as well as the other, so the devils cried out: "You dance badly, and are getting worse and worse; we will give you back the lump which we took from you as a pledge." Upon this, one of the devils brought the lump, and stuck it on the other side of his face; so the poor old fellow returned home with a lump on each side.

4.  **Which is the best summary of the second paragraph of the story?**

   Ⓐ  Two men who have deformities are "cured" in different ways by a group of devils.
   Ⓑ  An old man with a lump on his face dances freely with a group of devils.
   Ⓒ  An old man dances freely and is rewarded for his talent by a group of devils who cure him of a deformity that never really bothered him.
   Ⓓ  The old man returns to his home free of the lump on his face. His wife is shocked by his trans formation.

### Tryouts

For years, Sam had dreamed of being the best tennis player in the world. He went to tennis practice every single morning and night. He spent every summer at tennis camp, and he gave up long week-ends at the beach to work on his game. Now, it seemed his hard work was finally paying off. He was invited to try out for the state tennis team!

Still, there was something that was bothering Sam. The tryouts for the tennis team were on the same day as his mom's birthday, and he knew his family was planning a huge surprise party for her. He didn't want to hurt his mom's feelings by missing the party, but he also didn't want to miss his one shot at being a champion tennis player just because the tryouts were on his mom's birthday. He was in a quandary; he didn't know what to do.

For days, Sam went to bed, worrying about the decision. If he went to the tryout, he worried he would seem selfish. If he stayed home, he would miss his one big shot at making the state team. In fact, despite the honor of being invited to try out, he hadn't even told his family about the opportunity. He was so stressed about making the decision of whether to go that he couldn't even think about sharing the news.

Weeks went by, and Sam was making no progress. Every day his coach asked him if he was ready for the tryout, and Sam couldn't even respond. Finally, Sam couldn't bear the stress any longer. He decided to talk to his grandfather about his predicament.

"You know, your mom wants you to be happy," he told Sam. "It would be a great birthday present for her to know you are making your dream come true."

Sam had never thought of it that way before, and after talking to his grandfather, he knew what he had to do. He immediately went home and sat down with his parents to let them know about the opportunity to try out for the state team. His parents were so excited that when he told them, apologetically, what day the tryouts were, and they were so busy shrieking with excitement that he thought maybe they hadn't heard.

"But Mom, that means I'm going to miss your birthday," Sam said. "I am happy you are so nice about it, but I still feel really bad."

"Are you kidding?" his mom asked. "This is the best present I could ask for!"

5. **Would "How Sam Ruined His Mother's Birthday" be an appropriate alternate title for this story? Write your answer with a reason in the box below.**

## MY SHADOW
### by Robert Louis Stevenson

I have a little shadow that goes in and out with me,
And what can be the use of him is more than I can see.

He is very, very like me, from the heels up to the head;
And I see him jump before me, when I jump into my bed.

The funniest thing about him is the way he likes to grow—
Not at all like proper children, which is always very slow;

For he sometimes shoots up taller, like an India-rubber ball,
And he sometimes gets so little that there's none of him at all.

**6.** **Which of these do not appropriately summarize the above two stanzas of the poem?**

Ⓐ A little boy who does not understand shadows delights in playing with his shadow.
Ⓑ A little boy plays with a friend.
Ⓒ A little boy is confused by the shadow that is following him around as he plays.
Ⓓ A little boy tries to control his shadow as he plays.

## THE WONDERFUL HAIR by A. H. Wraitslaw

There was a man who was very poor, but so well supplied with children that he was utterly unable to maintain them, and one morning more than once prepared to kill them, in order not to see their misery in dying of hunger, but his wife prevented him. One night a child came to him in his sleep, and said to him: "Man! I see that you are making up your mind to destroy and to kill your poor little children, and I know that you are distressed thereat; but in the morning you will find under your pillow a mirror, a red kerchief, and an embroidered pocket-handkerchief; take all three secretly and tell no-body; then go to such a hill; by it, you will find a stream; go along it till you come to its fountain-head; there you will find a damsel as bright as the sun, with her hair hanging down over her back. Be on your guard, that the ferocious she-dragon do not coil around you; do not converse with her if she speaks; for if you converse with her, she will poison you, and turn you into a fish or something else, and will then devour you but if she bids you examine her head, examine it, and as you turn over her hair, look, and you will find one hair as red as blood; pull it out and run back again; then, if she suspects and begins to run after you, throw her first the embroidered pocket-handkerchief, then the kerchief, and, lastly, the mirror; then she will find occupation for herself. And sell that hair to some rich man, but don't let them cheat you, for that hair is worth countless wealth; and you will thus enrich yourself and maintain your children."

When the poor man awoke, he found everything under his pillow, just as the child had told him in his sleep; and then he went to the hill. When there, he found the stream, went on and on alongside of it, till he came to the fountain-head. Having looked about him to see where the damsel was, he espied her above a piece of water, like sunbeams threaded on a needle, and she was embroidering at a frame on stuff, the threads of which were young men's hair. As soon as he saw her, he made a reverence to her, and she stood on her feet and questioned him: "Whence are you, unknown young man?" But he held his tongue. She questioned him again: "Who are you? Why have you come?" and much else of all sorts, but he was as mute as a stone, making signs with his hands as if he were deaf and wanted help. Then she told him to sit down on her skirt. He did not wait for any more orders but sat down, and she bent down her head to him, that he might examine it. Turning over the hair of her head, as if to examine it, he was not long in finding that red hair, and separated it from the other hair, pulled it out, jumped off her skirt, and ran away back as he best could. She noticed it and ran at his heels full speed after him. He looked around, and seeing that she was about to overtake him, threw, as he was told, the embroidered pocket-handkerchief on the way, and when she saw the pock-et- handkerchief, she stooped and began to overhaul it in every direction, admiring the embroidery, till he had got a good way off. Then the damsel placed the pocket-handkerchief in her bosom and ran after him again.

When he saw that she was about to overtake him, he threw the red kerchief, and she again occupied herself, admiring and gazing, till the poor man had again got a good way off. Then the damsel be-came exasperated, and threw both the pocket-handkerchief and the kerchief on the way, and ran af-ter him in pursuit. Again, when he saw that she was about to overtake him, he threw the mirror. When the damsel came to the mirror, the like of which she had never seen before, she lifted it up, and when she saw herself in it, not knowing that it was herself, but thinking that it was somebody else, she, as it were, fell in love with herself in the mirror, and the man got so far off that she was no longer able to overtake him. When she saw that she could not catch him, she turned back, and the man reached his home safe and sound. After arriving at his home, he showed his wife the hair and told her all that had happened to him, but she began to jeer and laugh at him. But he paid no attention to her and went to a town to sell the hair. A crowd of all sorts of people and merchants collected round him; one of-fered a sequin, another two, and so on, higher and higher, till they came to a hundred gold sequins. Just then, the emperor heard of the hair, summoned the man into his presence, and said to him that he would give him a thousand sequins for it, and he sold it to him. What was the hair? The emperor split it in two from top to bottom and found registered in it in writing many remarkable things, which happened in the olden time since the beginning of the world. Thus the man became rich and lived on with his wife and children. And that child, that came to him in his sleep was an angel sent by the Lord God, whose will it was to aid the poor man and to reveal secrets which had not been revealed till then.

7. **Which best summarizes the directions the child gives the poor man while he is sleeping?**

   Ⓐ  Go to the stream and find a damsel who will give you a great deal of money.
   Ⓑ  You should not kill your children because there is a damsel at the stream who will help you by giving you a lock of her hair.
   Ⓒ  You will find a hair masked as blood that will cause you great trouble.
   Ⓓ  At the stream, there is a damsel who can help you make money for your family. You must not speak to her and may need to trick her to get a piece of her hair that you can sell for a great deal of money.

## "The Smith and the Fairies": A Gaelic Folk Tale (Ed. Kate Douglas Wiggin)

Years ago, there lived in Crossbrig, a smith of the name of MacEachern. This man had an only child, a boy of about thirteen or fourteen years of age, cheerful, strong, and healthy. All of a sudden, he fell ill, took to his bed, and moped whole days away. No one could tell what was the matter with him, and the boy himself could not, or would not, tell how he felt. He was wasting away fast; getting thin, old, and yellow; and his father and all his friends were afraid that he would die.

At last one day, after the boy had been lying in this condition for a long time, getting neither better nor worse, always confined to bed, but with an extraordinary appetite—one day, while sadly revolving these things, and standing idly at his forge, with no heart to work, the smith was agreeably surprised to see an old man, well known for his sagacity and knowledge of out-of-the-way things, walk into his workshop. Forthwith he told him the occurrence which had clouded his life.

The old man looked grave as he listened, and after sitting a long time pondering over all he had heard, gave his opinion thus: "It is not your son you have got. The boy has been carried away by the 'Daione Sith,' and they have left a Sibhreach in his place." "Alas! and what then am I to do?" said the smith. "How am I ever to see my own son again?" "I will tell you how," answered the old man. "But, first, to make sure that it is not your own son you have got, take as many empty egg-shells as you can get, go into his room, spread them out carefully before his sight, then proceed to draw water with them, carrying them two and two in your hands as if they were a great weight, and arrange them when full, with every sort of earnestness around the fire." The smith accordingly gathered as many broken egg-shells as he could get, went into the room, and proceeded to carry out all his instructions.

He had not been long at work before there arose from the bed a shout of laughter, and the voice of the seeming sick boy exclaimed, "I am eight hundred years of age, and I have never seen the like of that before."

The smith returned and told the old man. "Well, now," said the sage to him, "did I not tell you that it was not your son you had: your son is in Borracheill in a digh there (that is, a round green hill frequented by fairies). Get rid as soon as possible of this intruder, and I think I may promise you your son.

You must light a very large and bright fire before the bed on which this stranger is lying. He will ask you, 'What is the use of such a fire as that?' Answer him at once, 'You will see that presently!' and then seize him and throw him into the middle of it. If it is your own son you have got, he will call out to you to save him; but if not, the thing will fly through the roof."

The smith again followed the old man's advice: kindled a large fire, answered the question put to him as he had been directed to do, and seizing the child flung him in without hesitation. The Sibhreach gave an awful yell and sprang through the roof, where a hole had been left to let the smoke out.

On a certain night, the old man told him the green round hill, where the fairies kept the boy, would be open, and on that date the smith, having provided himself with a Bible, a dirk, and a crowing cock, was to proceed to the hill. He would hear singing and dancing, and much merriment going on, he had been told, but he was to advance boldly; the Bible he carried would be a certain safeguard to him against any danger from the fairies. On entering the hill he was to stick the dirk in the threshold, to prevent the hill from closing upon him; "and then," continued the old man, "on entering you will see a spacious apartment before you, beautifully clean, and there, standing far within, working at a forge, you will also see your own son. When you are questioned, say you come to seek him, and will not go without him."

Not long after this, the time came round, and the smith sallied forth, prepared as instructed. Sure enough, as he approached the hill, there was a light where the light was seldom seen before. Soon after, a sound of piping, dancing, and joyous merriment reached the anxious father on the night wind.

Overcoming every impulse to fear, the smith approached the threshold steadily, stuck the dirk into it as directed, and entered. Protected by the Bible he carried on his breast, the fairies could not touch him; but they asked him, with a good deal of displeasure, what he wanted there. He answered, "I want my son, whom I see down there, and I will not go without him."

Upon hearing this, the whole company before him gave a loud laugh, which wakened up the cock he carried dozing in his arms, who at once leaped upon his shoulders, clapped his wings lustily, and crowed loud and long.

The fairies, incensed, seized the smith and his son and throwing them out of the hill, flung the dirk after them, and in an instant, all was dark.

For a year and a day the boy never did a turn of work, and hardly ever spoke a word; but at last one day, sitting by his father and watching him finishing a sword he was making for some chief, and which he was very particular about, he suddenly exclaimed, "That is not the way to do it;" and taking the tools from his father's hands he set to work himself in his place, and soon fashioned a sword, the like of which was never seen in the country before.

From that day the young man wrought constantly with his father and became the inventor of a peculiarly fine and well-tempered weapon, the making of which kept the two Smiths, father and son, in constant employment, spread their fame far and wide, and gave them the means in abundance, as they before had the disposition, to live content with all the world and very happy with each other.

8. **Which sentence best summarizes the second to last paragraph in this story?**

   Ⓐ The smith's son returns to his father and does not speak for a year and a day.
   Ⓑ The smith's son criticizes his father's work.
   Ⓒ When the smith's son finally speaks after a year and one day of silence, he offers valuable advice to his father on how to make a sword.
   Ⓓ The smith's son has nothing to say until he sees his father not doing his best work.

## HOW WISDOM BECAME THE PROPERTY OF THE HUMAN RACE
### (West African Folktale)

THERE once lived, in Fanti-land, a man named Father Anansi. He possessed all the wisdom in the world. People came to him daily for advice and help.

One day the men of the country were unfortunate enough to offend Father Anansi, who immediately resolved to punish them. After much thought, he decided that the severest penalty he could inflict would be to hide all his wisdom from them. He set to work at once to gather again all that he had already given. When he had succeeded, as he thought, in collecting it, he placed all in one great pot. This he carefully sealed and determined to put it in a spot where no human being could reach it.

Now, Father Anansi had a son, whose name was Kweku Tsin. This boy began to suspect his father of some secret design, so he made up his mind to watch carefully. The next day he saw his father quietly slip out of the house, with his precious pot hung around his neck. Kweku Tsin followed. Father Anansi went through the forest until he had left the village far behind. Then, selecting the highest and most inaccessible-looking tree, he began to climb. The heavy pot, hanging in front of him, made his ascent almost impossible. Again and again, he tried to reach the top of the tree, where he intended to hang the pot. There, he thought, Wisdom would indeed be beyond the reach of everyone but himself. He was unable, however, to carry out his desire. At each trial, the pot swung in his way.

For some time, Kweku Tsin watched his father's vain attempts. At last, unable to contain himself any longer, he cried out: "Father, why do you not hang the pot on your back? Then you could easily climb the tree."

Father Anansi turned and said: "I thought I had all the world's wisdom in this pot. But I find you possess more than I do. All my wisdom was insufficient to show me what to do, yet you have been able to tell me." In his anger he threw the pot down. It struck on a great rock and broke. The wisdom contained in it escaped and spread throughout the world.

**9.  Which sentence best summarizes the first two paragraphs?**

Ⓐ  Father Anansi wanted to teach the men a lesson.
Ⓑ  The men wanted Father Anansi to provide them with wisdom and he refused.
Ⓒ  To punish the men for offending him, Father Anansi hid all of his wisdom where they could not find it.
Ⓓ  Father Anansi hid away all of his wisdom until the men apologized.

**10. What was the name of Father Anansi's son? Write in the box below.**

## Chapter 3

## Lesson 5: Key Ideas And Details

### From Guiseppi Verdi by Thomas Trapper

Whenever the organ man came into the village of Roncole, in Italy (where Verdi was born, October 10, 1813), Verdi could not be kept indoors. But he followed the wonderful organ and the wonderful man who played it, all day long, as happy as he could be.

When Giuseppe was seven years old, his father, though only a poor innkeeper, bought him a spinet, a sort of small piano. So faithfully did the little boy practice that the spinet was soon quite worn out and new jacks, or hammers, had to be made for it. This was done by Stephen Cavaletti, who wrote a message on one of the jacks telling that he made them anew and covered them with leather, and fixed the pedal, doing all for nothing, because the little boy, Giuseppe Verdi, showed such willingness to practice and to learn. Thus the good Stephen thought this was pay enough.

1. **What can you deduce about Verdi's feelings about his first spinet from the sentence below? Select those options that apply.**

   **"So faithfully did the little boy practice that the spinet was soon quite worn out and new jacks, or hammers, had to be made for it."**

   Ⓐ He loved his spinet
   Ⓑ He did not think it was too fancy
   Ⓒ He was embarrassed by how worn out it was
   Ⓓ He practiced it diligently

### Skunk Chow

Skunks are omnivores. They can be found eating nuts, berries, roots, leaves, grasses, and even some types of fungi (mushroom-like plants). For animals, they enjoy dining on rodents such as mice and rats, insects, earthworms, frogs, lizards, toads, and birds. Sometimes when they are unable to find live animals to eat, they become scavengers eating dead animals left behind. When they live close to people's homes, skunks sometimes will even get into trash cans, eating garbage.

When skunks eat, they do not limit themselves to small meals. They like to "pig out" on whatever food they can find. When there is a large amount of food available, skunks get very fat very quickly. http://en.wikipedia.org/wiki/Skunk

2. **If you had to answer the question "Can skunks control their appetites?" which sentence would you use to support your answer?**

Ⓐ "They can be found eating nuts, berries, roots, leaves, grasses, and even some types of fungi (mushroom-like plants)."

Ⓑ "For animals, they enjoy dining on rodents such as mice and rats, insects, earth worms, frogs, lizards, toads, and birds."

Ⓒ "When they live close to people's homes, skunks sometimes will even get into trash cans, eating garbage."

Ⓓ "They like to 'pig out' on whatever food they can find. When there is a large amount of food, skunks get fat very quickly."

3. **If the author removed the sentence telling you skunks were omnivores, could you still infer that skunks are omnivores?**

Ⓐ No, because the author does not tell me what an omnivore is or what it eats.

Ⓑ No, because the author does not provide enough information about the types of food a skunk eats.

Ⓒ Yes, because the author shows that a skunk eats both plants and animals.

Ⓓ Yes, because the author says that skunks are also scavengers.

Scientists in South Korea have developed a type of artificial skin that will allow robots to feel slight vibrations. This skin, developed by weaving together extremely small nano hairs made of polymer or plastic, is more sensitive than human skin. When vibration is applied to this artificial skin, the nano hairs bend against each other to generate an electrical current. Sensors within the skin evaluate the current and using that information determine the source of the vibration.

Researchers are excited about the potential for this new development. The artificial skin could be used to cover prosthetic limbs to help those who have lost a limb experience more realistic sensations and function more naturally.

http://en.wikipedia.org/wiki/Neuroplasticity

4. **Which sentence best explains why scientists are developing the artificial skin?**

Ⓐ "The artificial skin could be used to cover prosthetic limbs to help those who have lost a limb experience more realistic sensations and function more naturally."

Ⓑ "Sensors within the skin evaluate the current and using that information determine the source of the vibration."

Ⓒ "This skin, developed by weaving together extremely small nano hairs made of polymer or plastic is more sensitive than human skin."

Ⓓ "Scientists in South Korea have developed a type of skin that will allow robots to feel slight vibrations."

# Diabetic Help

Researchers at pharmaceutical company Eli Lilly and an association that places assistance dogs in Indianapolis, IN, are working together on an exciting new project that will study how dogs are able to detect low blood sugar in their diabetic owners. Diabetics suffer from a condition by which the pancreas does not produce enough insulin to maintain a healthy level of blood glucose. If a diabetic person's blood glucose level drops too low, he or she may become unconscious or even go into a coma.

One dog who has had a lot of success in identifying low blood sugar is a two-year-old named Pete. Pete, like all dogs, has a sense of smell 10,000 times more sensitive than that of humans. Pete's owner is a scientist with Eli Lilly, and she is trying to figure out what is inside a dog's nose that makes it possible to smell low blood sugar. If the researcher can figure out how to reproduce that kind of sensitivity, more diabetic people can be protected from the consequences of low blood sugar.

Until the researchers isolate what is inside Pete's nose, the Indiana Canine Assistance Network will continue to train dogs like Pete. It's a slow and expensive process, though. In the last ten years, the organization has trained 100 dogs, and the training has cost $25,000 or more for each dog. http://www.diabetesadvocacy.com/diabetes_news.htm

5.  **Which sentence from this article best explains how dogs can help diabetic owners?**

    Ⓐ "In the last ten years, the organization has trained 100 dogs, and the training has cost $25,000 or more for each dog."
    Ⓑ "If the researcher can figure out how to reproduce that kind of sensitivity, more diabetic people can be protected from the consequences of low blood sugar."
    Ⓒ "Pete's owner is a scientist with Eli Lilly, and she is trying to figure out what is inside a dog's nose that makes it possible to smell low blood sugar."
    Ⓓ "If a diabetic person's glucose drops too low he or she may become unconscious or even drop into a coma."

6.  **Based on the sentence, "if the researcher can figure out how to reproduce that sensitivity, more diabetic people can be protected from the consequences of low blood sugar," you can infer that...**

    Ⓐ The researcher wants to come up with technology that can help detect low blood sugar similar to how dogs can detect low blood sugar.
    Ⓑ The researcher wants to breed more dogs with the same sensitivity to low blood sugar as Pete.
    Ⓒ The researcher wants to train more dogs to detect low blood sugar levels in diabetic patients.
    Ⓓ The researcher wants to reproduce the same sensitivity in herself so she can detect low blood sugar levels in diabetic patients.

7. **Which sentence from the passage best explains why scientists want to reproduce the sensitivity rather than simply training dogs to recognize the sensitivity?**

  Ⓐ "It's a slow and expensive process though."
  Ⓑ "Until the researchers isolate what is inside Pete's nose, the Indiana Canine Assistance Net work will continue to train dogs like Pete."
  Ⓒ "If the researcher can figure out how to reproduce that kind of sensitivity, more diabetic people can be protected from the consequences of low blood sugar."
  Ⓓ "One dog who has had a lot of success in identifying low blood sugar is a two year old named Pete."

**Class Rules and Expectations
7th Grade-Reading**

1. NO HUNTING! Be nice.
2. No gum allowed.
3. You must be in your seat when the bell rings. If you are not, you are tardy and appropriate consequences will be enforced.
4. Students start the class...not the bell.
5. Make-up work is the student's responsibility.
6. No rude gestures or comments. If you cannot say something nice, do not say anything at all.
7. Have all of your materials with you and ready at the beginning of class.
8. There are no dumb questions...ask if you do not understand.
9. Respect others. This includes teachers as well as students.
10. Keep your hands and feet to yourself.
11. Every student will learn and have fun.

8. **Which rule explains what happens if a student is late to class? Write in the box below.**

# The Assassination of President Lincoln
## April 14, 1865

Shortly after 10 p.m. on April 14, 1865, actor, John Wilkes Booth entered the presidential box at Ford's Theatre in Washington D.C. and fatally shot President Abraham Lincoln. As Lincoln slumped forward in his seat, Booth leapt onto the stage and escaped through the back door. A doctor in the audience rushed over to examine the paralyzed president. Lincoln was then carried across the street to Petersen's Boarding House, where he died early the next morning.

Lincoln was the first president assassinated in U.S. history. Why did Booth do it? He thought it would aid the South, which had just surrendered to Federal forces. It had nearly the opposite effect, ending Lincoln's plans for a rather generous peace. Booth did not act alone. This "wanted" poster appeared everywhere, offering a reward for the arrest of Booth and his accomplices. The conspirators were all captured, and Booth was shot while trying to escape from Union soldiers.

The whole country grieved the death of President Lincoln. As the nine-car funeral train carried President Lincoln home for burial in Springfield, Illinois, people showed up at train stations all along the way to pay their respects.

"The Assassination of President Lincoln." The Assassination of President Lincoln. N.p., n.d. Web. 15 July 2013.

9. **Which sentence best explains why Booth shot Lincoln?**

   Ⓐ "He thought it would aid the South, which had just surrendered to Federal forces."
   Ⓑ "It had nearly the opposite effect, ending Lincoln's plans for a rather generous peace."
   Ⓒ "This "wanted" poster appeared everywhere, offering a reward for the arrest of Booth and his accomplices."
   Ⓓ "The conspirators were all captured, and Booth was shot while trying to escape from Union soldiers."

10. **Which detail in the first sentence helps you infer how Booth was able to get access to the theater?**

   Ⓐ It was 10 p.m.
   Ⓑ He was an actor.
   Ⓒ He was going to the presidential box.
   Ⓓ It was on April 14.

## Chapter 3

## Lesson 6: Get Right To The Point

**Fall Leaves**
**USDA Forest Service**

We almost always think of trees as being green, but there is one time of year when their leaves turn a myriad orange, red, yellow, and brown: the beautiful and chilly days of fall. Those living in the Eastern or Northern United States come to anticipate the change in color starting in September or October every single year. But what causes the leaves to change color, and why?

Just like many animals that hibernate for the winter, trees experience a unique change during the winter months. During summer, for instance, plants use the process of photosynthesis to transform carbon dioxide found in the air into organic compounds like sugars using energy from the sun. During the winter, however, there is less light to go around, and their ability to create food from the photosynthesis process is limited.

What does that have to do with a leaf's color? The substance that allows trees to turn carbon dioxide into food (chlorophyll) is also the cause of the leaf's green sheen. As the photosynthesis process wanes in the colder months due to the lack of sun, so does its greenish hue, allowing other elements present in the leaf to show through. Believe it or not, the yellows and oranges that appear in fall have actually been there all year in the form of nutrients like carotene (also found in carrots). The intense green color of the chlorophyll had simply overshadowed them. But what about the reds and browns? And what causes the leaves to fall away after they change color?

The bright reds and purples in each leaf come from a strong antioxidant that many trees create on their own because of their protective qualities. The antioxidant helps protect the trees from the sun, lower their freezing levels, and protect them from frost. As winter comes, so does the need for the antioxidant (similar to the way a dog gets more fur during winter to stay warmer).

As for the leaves falling, that is another story. At the base of each leaf, there is a layer of cells that carry food and water from the leaf to the tree during the summer months to keep it fed. In the fall, that layer actually starts to harden, preventing the passage of nutrients. Because of this, the nutrients and waste that previously passed from the leaf into the tree become trapped in the leaf with no fresh water to clean it. Not only does this cause the leaf to turn brown, eventually it causes the cells within it to harden so much that the leaf tears and blows away. Thus the pile of leaves you enjoyed jumping in as a child.

Because each tree, and each leaf, contains a unique amount of nutrients depending on how well-nourished it was over the spring and summer, the way each leaf breaks down during the winter months is also quite different. The result is the unique and complex facet of colors we see in each neighborhood or forest each fall.
http://www.sciencemadesimple.com/leaves.htm

1. **What is the main theme of the above passage?**

    Ⓐ Fall weather
    Ⓑ What happens to the leaves during fall
    Ⓒ The life cycle of a tree during fall
    Ⓓ Weather during fall

2. **Which of these are NOT the purposes of this excerpt?**

    Ⓐ to explain why leaves change colors and drop from trees.
    Ⓑ to describe the colors of leaves in the fall
    Ⓒ to tell the reader about the North East part of the country
    Ⓓ to define chlorophyll

## History of Olympics
### From *Ancient Olympics* Guide

Even though the modern Olympic Games are held every four years, they bear little resemblance to the athletic contests held at Olympia in Greece in ancient times.

The games were open to competitors from all over Greece, and the contests included chariot racing, horse racing, running, wrestling, boxing, and the pentathlon, a contest involving jumping, quoit-throwing, javelin throwing, running, and wrestling.

Scholars date the earliest contests at 776 B.C., more than two and a half thousand years ago. The first trophies that were won consisted not of gold medals and cups but of simple crowns of olive leaves. Women and slaves were admitted neither as contestants nor as spectators. The classical games ceased to be held probably about A.D.393.

Much of the credit for the revival of the Games held at Athens in 1896 goes to Baron Pierre de Coubertin, a French classical scholar, who greatly admired the sporting ideals of the ancient Greeks. As an educationist and lover of amateurism, he looked upon physical exercise as an essential feature of balanced education. Forty-two events were contested and new disciplines such as cycling, hurdling, the high jump, shooting, and gymnastics were introduced.

One of the most popular events of the modern Olympics is the marathon. This very tiring twenty-six mile foot race over an open course is the supreme test of the runners' endurance. The marathon was not a part of the ancient Olympics although it originated in Greece.

And, finally, a more recent development in the Olympics is the introduction of the winter games, which were started in 1924. They are held separately from the summer games but in the same year. The Winter Olympics provide competition in skiing, speed and figure skating, ice hockey, and rifle shooting. Such cold weather sports could never have developed in the warm climate of Greece.

LumosLearning.com

3. **Which is a more suitable alternate title for this passage between "Popular Sports" and "How the Olympics Evolved". Write in the box below.**

## Egyptian Pyramids

Today, we have high-tech cranes and other machines to help us create massive skyscrapers and other modern works of architecture. Still, some of the most breathtaking architecture in the world, such as the ancient pyramids of Egypt, were created before those high-tech machines even existed. So how did those ancient civilizations create them?

Believe it or not, though they are one of the most studied and admired relics in history, there is no evidence to tell historians exactly how the Ancient Egyptians built the pyramids. Thus, they have been left to create their own theories as to how Egyptians created such amazing and awe-inspiring works of art.

According to one theory, the Egyptians placed logs under the large stone blocks in order to roll or transport them to the pyramid building location. Large groups of men would work to push or pull them into place (although historians also disagree on whether these men were slaves or skilled artisans).

Still more, once the men moved the blocks to the pyramid location, they needed to lift them to ever-increasing heights to reach the top levels of the pyramid as it grew. Without modern cranes, many scientists have been baffled as to how they were able to do it. Some believe they used a ramp system that would allow them to roll the blocks upward around or through the pyramids; others believe they must have used a combination of pulleys and lifts. Still, most agree that once they did, they used a mixture of gravel and limestone to help fill any crevices and hold the mound together.

With such a primitive yet impressive building process, it's obvious that the pyramids must have taken a great deal of time to build. With an estimated 2 million blocks weighing an average of 2.5 million tons each, the Great Pyramid of Giza, for instance, is estimated to have taken some 20 years to build. At 481 feet tall, it held the record of tallest building for 3,800 years – not bad for a building created almost entirely by hand.

Even though scientists don't know exactly how the Egyptians did it, they do know that the method the Egyptians used to build pyramids changed over time. In the early days, the pyramids were made completely of stone, with limestone used to create the main body and higher quality limestone being used for the smooth outer casing. Later on, the pyramids were made mostly of mud brick with a limestone casing. Though they were likely much easier to build, they didn't stand up nearly as well over time, leaving archaeologists with even fewer clues about their creation.
http://en.wikipedia.org/wiki/Egyptian_pyramid_construction_techniques

4. **What is the main idea of this selection?**

   Ⓐ The Egyptians had a very advanced way of building the pyramids.
   Ⓑ The Ancient Egyptians built the pyramids by hand.
   Ⓒ To this day, historians are not entirely sure how the Egyptians built the pyramids.

5. **What is the theme of this excerpt?**

   Ⓐ how the Egyptian army was used to build the pyramids
   Ⓑ several theories about how the Egyptian pyramids were built
   Ⓒ how the boulders were carved for the Egyptian pyramids
   Ⓓ how the Egyptians used architecture to build the pyramids

### From <u>Guiseppi Verdi</u>
### by Thomas Trapper

Whenever the organ man came into the village of Roncole, in Italy (where Verdi was born, October 10, 1813), Verdi could not be kept indoors. But he followed the wonderful organ and the wonderful man who played it, all day long, as happy as he could be.

When Guiseppi was seven years old, his father, though only a poor innkeeper, bought him a spinet, a sort of small piano. So faithfully did the little boy practice that the spinet was soon quite worn out and new jacks, or hammers, had to be made for it. This was done by Stephen Cavaletti, who wrote a message on one of the jacks telling that he made them anew and covered them with leather, and fixed the pedal, doing all for nothing, because the little boy, Guiseppi Verdi, showed such willingness to practice and to learn. Thus the good Stephen thought this was pay enough.

6. **What is the main idea the writer wants the reader to draw from these paragraphs?**

   Ⓐ Verdi was drawn and committed to music from an early age.
   Ⓑ Verdi was hard on his spinet because he played it every day.
   Ⓒ Verdi practiced the spinet for too many hours each day.
   Ⓓ Verdi lived in Italy when he was a child.

### Gettysburg Address

Four score and seven years ago, our fathers brought forth on this continent, a new nation, conceived in liberty and dedicated to the proposition that all men are created equal.

Now we are engaged in a great civil war, testing whether that nation or any nation so conceived and so dedicated, can long endure. We are met on a great battlefield of that war. We have come to dedicate a portion of that field as a final resting place for those who here gave their lives that that nation might live. It is altogether fitting and proper that we should do this.

But in a larger sense, we cannot dedicate - we cannot consecrate - we cannot hallow - this ground. The brave men, living and dead, who struggled here, have consecrated it, far above our poor power to add or detract. The world will little note, nor long remember, what we say here, but it can never forget what they did here. It is for us the living, rather, to be dedicated here to the unfinished work which they who fought here have thus far so nobly advanced. It is rather for us to be here dedicated to the great task remaining before us - that from these honored dead we take increased devotion to that cause for which they gave the last full measure of devotion - that we here highly resolve that these dead shall not have died in vain - that this nation, under God, shall have a new birth of freedom - and that government of the people, by the people, for the people, shall not perish from the earth.

President Abraham Lincoln - November 19, 1863

**7.  What is Lincoln's purpose in delivering this speech?**

Ⓐ  To encourage people to not give up on the country being united as one country
Ⓑ  To encourage people to end the war and honor the dead
Ⓒ  To convince the south to surrender so that it would end more quickly
Ⓓ  To build a new cemetery at this location


The bread-and-butter of the film industry is the action movie. Each summer, audiences can expect to see car chases, gunfights, and explosions, and studios can expect to see millions and millions of dollars in return. Though most viewers and critics see these movies as "fluff" entertainment, there is one director who puts as much heart and soul into his "fluff" as any number of talented directors put into their "serious" movies. His name is John Woo. Even though you may not have heard about him, he is widely considered to be the best contemporary director of action films working anywhere.

John Woo, after many years of hard work, has become known as the world's best action film director. His action sequences have become the stuff of legend and are now the basis from which all other action movies are judged. More importantly, along with the bloodshed, Woo has proven that he can create real characters with real emotions that the audience can sympathize with.

He's a bold visual stylist who stages a kinetic scene of over-the-top gunplay with fluid camera movements, extremely long takes, and perfectly timed choreography of movement. Woo's on the spot improvising that also delivered one of the most amazing gun-blazing sequences when in the middle of the movie, a full-blooded gunfight erupts but is played out in balletic slow-motion to "Somewhere Over The Rainbow," heard through child's headphones. The song was put in to represent the child's innocence, and also to show how that innocence is being corrupted by the violence around him. Woo gets upset when he hears about violence, and when he is angry and directing, he thinks, "let's hit the villain with more bullets, let's beat him up just a little bit more."

Woo considers himself to be an artist, as he does once in a while get emotional while filming one of his movies. This goes to show that he relates his movies well to real life, and has an understanding of what it takes to become a great director.
http://www.hollywoodauditions.com/news/celebrities/directors.htm

8. **What is an appropriate title for this article?**

Ⓐ John Woo Puts the Action in Action!
Ⓑ A History of Action Movies
Ⓒ The Director who Hates Violence
Ⓓ Somewhere over the Rainbow

## The Great Round World and What's Going On In It
### magazine article -- Anonymous author

Did you ever see a house move?
If you have not, you have missed a very funny sight.
Imagine driving along a country road, and meeting a three-story house making a journey along the highway to new quarters.
There is a good deal of this to be seen just now at Katonah, New York.
A year or so ago the Croton water-shed water, which is in use in New York City, was found to be impure.

A commission was appointed to go and examine the Croton Water-Shed. This meant that they were to examine the little streams, and brooks, and rivers, and lakes, which supplied the water to our aqueduct, and see what the trouble was.

They found that along the banks of these streams and lakes, in villages and out in the country, a great many dwelling-houses and shanties had been built, the occupants of which were in the habit of throwing all sorts of rubbish into the water, making it unfit for drinking.

In consequence of this, all of the houses were ordered to be torn down or moved away, and one small village of shanties was destroyed. Among others, the inhabitants of Katonah were ordered to move, that the banks of the stream might be cleared of dwellings.

Katonah has a railroad depot, and a post office, and thinks a good deal of itself. When the Water-Shed Commission said that it must move or be destroyed, the residents of Katonah gathered together, and decided that rather than be wiped off the face of the map, it would pick up its houses and move itself.

So a new Katonah was established, about a quarter of a mile away from the old one, and just outside the Water-Shed on which it was forbidden to build, for fear of spoiling the water for New York. For several months past there has been a procession of houses moving from old Katonah to new.
http://www.gutenberg.org/files/15326/15326.txt

9. **What is the main idea of this article?**

Ⓐ The water in Kantonah is polluted.
Ⓑ Many people are moving their homes because the water in Kantonah is polluted.
Ⓒ Everyone should have the experience of seeing a house being moved.
Ⓓ The people of Kantonah are angry because of the quality of their drinking water.

## The Great Round World and What's Going On In It
### magazine article -- Anonymous author

The news comes from Hamburg that the strike of the dock laborers is over.

The strikers have been beaten because of their lack of money.

In No. 7 of The Great Round World, you will find an account of the strike, and if you will also refer to No. 10, you will see that it was thought that the strikers could not hold out very much longer.

The money the strikers expected to receive from other labor unions to help them was so slow in coming that the men and their families were in want, and no man is likely to stand out for the benefit of others when his own children are suffering from cold and hunger.

The men have gone back to their old employers and asked for work. The pity of it all is, however, that during the strike, others have been taken on in their places, and the employers have now no work to give them.

After holding out since the end of October, and refusing the masters' offer to give them $1.10 a day, and let all future troubles be settled by arbitration, the strikers have had to give in without gaining a single point. It is very sad.

### 10. What is this short article mostly about?

Ⓐ  Where to find more information about the Hamburg workers' strike
Ⓑ  The end result of the Hamburg workers' strike
Ⓒ  The causes of the Hamburg workers' strike
Ⓓ  The Hamburg unions

## Chapter 3

## Lesson 7: One Thing Leads To Another

### "The Lament"
### by Svern

It is twilight. Thick wet snow is slowly twirling around the newly lighted street lamps and lying in soft thin layers on roofs, on horses' backs, on people's shoulders and hats. The cab driver, Iona Potapov, is quite white and looks like a phantom: he is bent double as far as a human body can bend double; he is seated on his box; he never makes a move. If a whole snowdrift fell on him, it seems as if he would not find it necessary to shake it off. His little horse is also quite white, and remains motionless; its immobility, its angularity, and its straight wooden-looking legs, even close by, give it the appearance of a gingerbread horse worth a kopek. It is, no doubt, plunged in deep thought. If you were snatched from the plough, from your usual gray surroundings, and were thrown into this slough full of monstrous lights, unceasing noise and hurrying people, you too would find it difficult not to think.

Iona and his little horse have not moved from their place for a long while. They left their yard before dinner and, up to now, not a fare. The evening mist is descending over the town, the white lights of the lamps are replacing brighter rays, and the hubbub of the street is getting louder.

'Cabby for Viborg Way!' suddenly hears Iona. 'Cabby!'

Iona jumps and, through his snow-covered eyelashes, sees an officer in a greatcoat, with his hood over his head.

'Viborg way!' the officer repeats. 'Are you asleep, eh? Viborg way!'
With a nod of assent, Iona picks up the reins, in consequence of which layers of snow slip off the horse's back and neck. The officer seats himself in the sleigh, the cab driver smacks his lips to encourage his horse, stretches out his neck like a swan, sits up and, more from habit than necessity, brandishes his whip. The little horse also stretches its neck, bends its wooden-looking legs, and makes a move undecidedly.

'What are you doing, werewolf!' is the exclamation Iona hears from the dark mass moving to and fro, as soon as they have started.

'Where the devil are you going? To the r-r-right!'
'You do not know how to drive. Keep to the right!' calls the officer angrily. A coachman from a private carriage swears at him; a passerby, who has run across the road and rubbed his shoulder against the horse's nose, looks at him furiously as he sweeps the snow from his sleeve. Iona shifts about on his seat as if he was on needles, moves his elbows as if he were trying to keep his equilibrium, and gasps about like someone suffocating, who does not understand why and wherefore he is there.

'What scoundrels they all are!' jokes the officer; 'one would think they had all entered into an agreement to jostle you or fall under your horse.'

Iona looks around at the officer and moves his lips. He evidently wants to say something but the only sound that issues is a snuffle.

'What?' asks the officer. Iona twists his mouth into a smile and, with an effort, says hoarsely:
'My son, Barin, died this week.'
'Hm! What did he die of?'
Iona turns with his whole body towards his fare and says: 'And who knows! They say high fever. He was three days in the hospital and then died... God's will be done.'

"Turn round! The devil!' sounds from the darkness. 'Have you popped off, old doggie, eh? Use your eyes!'

'Go on, go on,' says the officer, 'otherwise we shall not get there by tomorrow. Hurry up a bit!'

1.  **What event that occurred before the story begins, influences the way the character Iona acts in this story?**

    Ⓐ  The death of his son
    Ⓑ  The winter storm
    Ⓒ  The officer's harsh comments
    Ⓓ  Iona's wife's sickness

2.  **Based on the plot of this story, what can you assume was The Lament mentioned in the title?**

    Ⓐ  The officer had to reach Viborg urgently.
    Ⓑ  Grief made the cabby confused.
    Ⓒ  The people were sad because the cabby was not driving carefully.
    Ⓓ  The horse was lost.

## Best Friend

Ever since they were kids, Julie and Max had been best friends. They went to kindergarten together. They went to summer camp together. They hung out together every weekend. But suddenly, things between the two had started to change.

Max had started playing on the football team and didn't have much time for Julie anymore. He was always busy, and he never seemed to make it to study hall, where the two used to swap stories about their favorite (or least favorite) teachers. In class, Julie noticed that Max never seemed to have his homework done on time anymore. She even noticed that he got a 'D' on his last paper. She knew something was going on with him – but what?

At first, Julie decided to play it cool and see how things went. She tried waiting in the hall for Max after class to see if she could ask if he was OK. But days went by, and he never had time to stop. He'd rush right past her in the hall, only to leave her feeling even worse about what was happening between them.

Even though she wasn't sure she could handle the situation herself, Julie didn't want to talk to her parents because she was afraid they would tell her not to hang out with Max anymore. She barely saw him as it was, so she knew it would just make things worse if her parents didn't approve of him. She didn't want to tell Max's parents either because she didn't want him to get in trouble. Still, it seemed like something needed to change.

Julie decided to go to one of her school counselors and let her know she was concerned. When she walked into Mrs. Smith's room, she was surprised to see that Max was already sitting there. "I'm sorry, I'll come back," Julie said.

"No, stay," said Max. "Maybe you can help."

Julie was surprised to find that Max had visited the counselor's office for the same reason she had: he was starting to feel overwhelmed with all of the things he was supposed to be doing as a student, an athlete, and a friend. He needed some guidance on how to determine what truly mattered and how to divide his time between all of the things that were important to him.

When she realized that Max was still the same old Max (just a little more stressed), Julie was relieved. She was also happy to know that he had come to a conclusion on his own, without her having to talk to someone else about it. She decided it was a sign they were both growing up.

3. **How does Max playing football affect his relationship with Julie in this story? Select those that apply.**

   Ⓐ It brings the two of them closer together.
   Ⓑ It gives the two something to talk about during study hall.
   Ⓒ It makes Julie wonder why he doesn't talk to her anymore.
   Ⓓ It makes him too busy to have time for Julie.

## Tryouts

For years, Sam had dreamed of being the best tennis player in the world. He went to tennis practice every single morning and night. He spent every summer at tennis camp, and he gave up long weekends at the beach to work on his game. Now, it seemed his hard work was finally paying off. He was invited to try out for the state tennis team!

Still, there was something that was bothering Sam. The tryouts for the tennis team were on the same day as his mom's birthday, and he knew his family was planning a huge surprise party for her. He didn't want to hurt his mom's feelings by missing the party, but he also didn't want to miss his one shot at being a champion tennis player just because the tryouts were on his mom's birthday. He was in a quandary; he didn't know what to do.

For days, Sam went to bed, worrying about the decision. If he went to the tryout, he worried he would seem selfish. If he stayed home, he would miss his one big shot at making the state team. In fact, despite the honor of being invited to try out, he hadn't even told his family about the opportunity. He was so stressed about deciding whether to go or not that he couldn't even think about sharing the news.

Weeks went by, and Sam was making no progress. Every day his coach asked him if he was ready for the tryout, and Sam couldn't even respond. Finally, Sam couldn't bear the stress any longer. He decided to talk to his grandfather about his predicament.

"You know, your mom wants you to be happy," he told Sam. "It would be a great birthday present for her to know you are making your dream come true."

Sam had never thought of it that way before, and after talking to his grandfather, he knew what he had to do. He immediately went home and sat down with his parents to let them know about the opportunity to try out for the state team. His parents were so excited that when he told them, apologetically, what day the tryouts were, they were so busy shrieking with excitement that he thought maybe they hadn't heard.

"But Mom, that means I'm going to miss your birthday," Sam said. "I am happy you are so nice about it, but I still feel really bad."

"Are you kidding?" his mom asked. "This is the best present I could ask for!"

**4.  Why was Sam's tryout a great birthday present for his mother? Write in the box below.**

```
┌─────────────────────────────────────────────────────────────────────┐
│                                                                       │
│                                                                       │
│                                                                       │
│                                                                       │
│                                                                       │
└─────────────────────────────────────────────────────────────────────┘
```

### *Fairy Tales by A Brothers' Grimm*
### (Excerpt)

A certain king once fell ill, and the doctor declared that only a sudden fright would restore him to health, but the king was not a man for anyone to play tricks on, except his fool. One day, when the fool was with him in his boat, he cleverly pushed the king into the water. Help had already been arranged, and the king was drawn ashore and put to bed. The fright, the bath, and the rest in bed cured the diseased king.

The king wanted to frighten the fool for his act, so he told him that he would be put to death. He directed the executioner privately not to use the axe but to let fall a single drop of water on the fool's neck. Amidst shouts and laughter, the fool was asked to rise and thank the king for his kindness. But the fool never moved; he was dead; killed by the master's joke.

5. **Based on the relationships between the characters and the plot of this story, who is the only person who can play a trick on the king?**

  Ⓐ The courtiers
  Ⓑ The prince
  Ⓒ The fool
  Ⓓ The doctor

### "Bruno the Bear"
### Excerpt from *The Bond of Love*

I will begin with Bruno, my wife's pet sloth bear. I got him for her by accident. Two years ago, we were passing through the cornfields near a small town in Iowa. People were driving away the wild pigs from the fields by shooting at them. Some were shot, and some escaped. We thought that everything was over when suddenly a black sloth bear came out panting in the hot sun.

Now I will not shoot a sloth bear wantedly, but unfortunately for the poor beast, one of my companions did not feel the same way about it and promptly shot the bear on the spot.

As we watched the fallen animal, we were surprised to see that the black fur on its back moved and left the prostrate body. Then we saw it was a baby bear that had been riding on its mother's back when the sudden shot had killed her. The little creature ran around its prostrate parent, making a pitiful noise. I ran up to it to attempt a capture. It scooted into the sugarcane field. Following it with my companions, I was at last able to grab it by the scruff of its neck while it snapped and tried to scratch me with its long, hooked claws.

We put it in one of the large jute-bags we had brought, and when I got back home, I duly presented it to my wife. She was delighted! She at once put a blue colored ribbon around its neck, and after discovering the cub was a 'boy,' she christened it Bruno.

Bruno soon took to drinking milk from a bottle. It was but a step further, and within a very few days, he started eating and drinking everything else. And everything is the right word, for he ate porridge made from any ingredients, vegetables, fruit, nuts, meat (especially pork), curry and rice regardless of condiments and chilies, bread, eggs, chocolates, sweets, pudding, ice-cream, etc., As for drink: milk, tea, coffee, lime juice, aerated water, buttermilk, beer, alcoholic liquor, and, in fact, anything liquid. It all went down with relish.

The bear became very attached to our two dogs and all the children living in and around our farm. He was left quite free in his younger days and spent his time playing, running into the kitchen, and going to sleep in our beds.

One day an accident befell him. I put down poison (barium carbonate) to kill the rats and mice that had got into my library. Bruno entered the library as he often did and ate some of the poison. Paralysis set into the extent that he could not stand on his feet. But he dragged himself on his stumps to my wife, who called me. I guessed what had happened.

Off I rushed him in the car to the vet's residence. A case of poisoning! Tame Bear—barium carbonate—what to do? Out came his medical books, and a feverish reference to index began: "What poison did you say, sir?" he asked, "Barium carbonate," I said.

"Ah yes—B—Ba—Barium Salts—Ah! Barium carbonate! Symptoms— paralysis—treatment—injections of . .. Just a minute, sir. I'll bring my syringe and the medicine." Said the doc. I dashed back to the car. Bruno was still floundering about on his stumps, but clearly, he was weakening rapidly; there was some vomiting, he was breathing heavily, with heaving flanks and gaping mouth. I was really scared and did not know what to do. I was feeling very guilty and was running in and out of the vet's house doing everything the doc asked me.

"Hold him, everybody!" In goes the hypodermic—Bruno squeals — 10 c.c. of the antidote enters his system without a drop being wasted. Ten minutes later: condition unchanged! Another 10 c.c. Injected! Ten minutes later: breathing less torturous— Bruno can move his arms and legs a little although he cannot stand yet. Thirty minutes later: Bruno gets up and has a great feed! He looks at us disdainfully, as much as to say, 'What's barium carbonate to a big black bear like me?' Bruno was still eating. I was really happy to see him recover.

The months rolled on, and Bruno had grown many times the size he was when he came. He had equaled the big dogs in height and had even outgrown them. But was just as sweet, just as mischievous, just as playful. And he was very fond of us all. Above all, he loved my wife, and she loved him too! And he could do a few tricks, too. At the command, 'Bruno, wrestle,' or 'Bruno, box,' he vigorously tackled anyone who came forward for a rough and tumble. Give him a stick and say 'Bruno, hold the gun,' and he pointed the stick at you. Ask him, 'Bruno, where's baby?' and he immediately produced and cradled affectionately a stump of wood which he had carefully concealed in his straw bed. But because of the neighborhoods' and our renters' children, poor Bruno, had to be kept chained most of the time.

Then my son and I advised my wife and friends advised her, too, to give Bruno to the zoo. He was getting too big to keep at home. After some weeks of such advice, she at last consented. Hastily, and before she could change her mind, a letter was written to the curator of the zoo. Did he want a tame bear for his collection? He replied, "Yes." The zoo sent a cage in a truck, a distance of hundred – eighty – seven miles, and Bruno was packed off. We all missed him greatly, but in a sense, we were relieved. My wife was inconsolable. She wept and fretted. For the first few days, she would not eat a thing. Then she wrote a number of letters to the curator. How was Bruno? Back came the replies, "Well, but fretting; he refuses food too."

After that, friends visiting the zoo were begged to make a point of seeing how Bruno was getting along. They reported that he was well but looked very thin and sad. All the keepers at the zoo said he was fretting. For three months, I managed to restrain my wife from visiting the zoo. Then she said one day, "I must see Bruno. Either you take me by car, or I will go myself by bus or train myself." So I took her by car. Friends had conjectured that the bear would not recognize her. I had thought so too. But while she was yet some yards from his cage, Bruno saw her and recognized her. He howled with happiness. She ran up to him, petted him through the bars, and he stood on his head in delight.

For the next three hours, she would not leave that cage. She gave him tea, lemonade, cakes, ice cream, and whatnot. Then 'closing time' came and we had to leave. My wife cried bitterly; Bruno cried bitterly; even the hardened curator and the keepers felt depressed. As for me, I had reconciled myself to what I knew was going to happen next.

"Oh please, sir," she asked the curator, "may I have my Bruno back"? Hesitantly, he answered, "Madam, he belongs to the zoo and is Government property now. I cannot give away Government property. But if my boss, the superintendent, agrees, certainly, you may have him back."

There followed the return journey home and a visit to the superintendent's office. A tearful pleading: "Bruno and I are both fretting for each other. Will you please give him back to me?" He was a kind-hearted man and consented. Not only that, but he wrote to the curator, telling him to lend us a cage for transporting the bear back home.

Back we went to the zoo again, armed with the superintendent's letter. Bruno was driven into a small cage and hoisted on top of the car; the cage was tied securely, and a slow and careful return journey back home was accomplished.

Once home, a squad of workers were engaged for special work around our yard. An island was made for Bruno. It was twenty feet long and fifteen feet wide and was surrounded by a dry moat, six feet wide and seven feet deep. A wooden box that once housed fowls was brought and put on the island for Bruno to sleep in at night. Straw was placed inside to keep him warm, and his 'baby,' the gnarled stump, along with his 'gun,' the piece of bamboo, both of which had been sentimentally preserved since he had been sent away to the zoo, were put back for him to play with. In a few days, the workers hoisted the cage on to the island, and Bruno was released. He was delighted; standing on his hind legs, he pointed his 'gun' and cradled his 'baby.' My wife spent hours sitting on a chair there while he sat on her lap. He was fifteen months old and pretty heavy too!

The way my wife reaches the island and leaves it is interesting. I have tied a rope to the overhanging branch of a maple tree with a loop at its end. Putting one foot in the loop, she kicks off with the other, to bridge the six-foot gap that constitutes the width of the surrounding moat. The return journey back is made the same way.

But who can say now that a sloth bear has no sense of affection, no memory, and no individual characteristics?

6. **What event in the plot of this story led Bruno to be taken to the Vet's house?**

   Ⓐ He ate too much food.
   Ⓑ He ate a rat poison called barium carbonate and was paralyzed.
   Ⓒ He broke his leg trying to wrestle.
   Ⓓ None of these.

## THE OLD MAN AND THE DEVILS - A Gaelic Folk Tale
### (Ed. Kate Douglas Wiggin)

A long time ago there was an old man who had a big lump on the right side of his face. One day he went into the mountain to cut wood when the rain began to pour and the wind to blow so very hard that, finding it impossible to return home, and filled with fear, he took refuge in the hollow of an old tree. While sitting there doubled up and unable to sleep, he heard the confused sound of many voices in the distance gradually approaching to where he was. He said to himself: "How strange! I thought I was all alone in the mountain, but I hear the voices of many people." So, taking courage, he peeped out and saw a great crowd of strange-looking beings. Some were red, and dressed in green clothes; others were black, and dressed in red clothes; some had only one eye; others had no mouth; indeed, it is quite impossible to describe their varied and strange looks. They kindled a fire so that it became as light as day. They sat down in two cross-rows, and began to drink wine and make merry just like human beings. They passed the wine cup around so often that many of them soon drank too much. One of the young devils got up and began to sing a merry song and to dance; so also many others; some danced well, others badly. One said: "We have had uncommon fun tonight, but I would like to see something new."

Then the old man, losing all fear, thought he would like to dance, and saying, "Let come what will, if I die for it, I will have a dance, too," crept out of the hollow tree and, with his cap slipped over his nose and his ax sticking in his belt, began to dance. The devils in great surprise jumped up, saying, "Who is this?" but the old man advancing and receding, swaying to and fro, and posturing this way and that way, the whole crowd laughed and enjoyed the fun, saying: "How well the old man dances! You must always come and join us in our sport; but, for fear you might not come, you must give us a pledge that you will." So the devils consulted together, and, agreeing that the lump on his face, which was a token of wealth, was what he valued most highly, demanded that it should be taken. The old man replied: "I have had this lump many years, and would not without good reason part with it; but you may have it, or an eye, or my nose either if you wish." So the devils laid hold of it, twisting and pulling, and took it off without giving him any pain, and put it away as a pledge that he would come back. Just then the day began to dawn, and the birds to sing, so the devils hurried away.

The old man felt his face and found it quite smooth, and not a trace of the lump left. He forgot all about cutting wood and hastened home. His wife, seeing him, exclaimed in great surprise, "What has happened to you?" So he told her all that had befallen him.

Now, among the neighbors, there was another old man who had a big lump on the left side of his face. Hearing all about how the first old man had got rid of his misfortune, he determined that he would also try the same plan. So he went and crept into the hollow tree, and waited for the devils to come. Sure enough, they came just as he was told, and they sat down, drank wine, and made merry just as they did before. The second old man, afraid and trembling, crept out of the hollow tree. The devils welcomed him, saying: "The old man has come; now let us see him dance." This old fellow was awkward, and did not dance as well as the other, so the devils cried out: "You dance badly, and are getting worse and worse; we will give you back the lump which we took from you as a pledge." Upon this, one of the devils brought the lump, and stuck it on the other side of his face; so the poor old fellow returned home with a lump on each side.

7. **Based on information in the selection, what event can you assume happened between the first man returning without the lump on his face and the second man heading to the tree in hopes of having his lump removed?**

 Ⓐ The people in town began gossiping about how the first man lost his lump.
 Ⓑ The old man's wife celebrated her husband losing his lump.
 Ⓒ The second old man prayed he would lose his lump.
 Ⓓ The devils decided to punish the next man who tried to dance with them.

## MY SHADOW
### by Robert Louis Stevenson

I have a little shadow that goes in and out with me,
And what can be the use of him is more than I can see.
He is very, very like me, from the heels up to the head;
And I see him jump before me, when I jump into my bed.
The funniest thing about him is the way he likes to grow—
Not at all like proper children, which is always very slow;
For he sometimes shoots up taller, like an India-rubber ball,
And he sometimes gets so little that there's none of him at all.

8. **The narrator of this poem is a child. How does this character affect the plot of the poem?**

 Ⓐ He is confused by his shadow, so he is constantly trying to avoid it.
 Ⓑ He is amazed by his shadow, so plays with it to try to understand it.
 Ⓒ He is frightened by his shadow, so he tries to "lose" it.
 Ⓓ He isn't affected at all by his shadow.

9. **How can you tell that when the poem talks about "Him/He" the literary element of personification is being used? Write in the box below.**

10. **What is the tone of this poem?**

 Ⓐ serious
 Ⓑ playful
 Ⓒ depressing
 Ⓓ funny

## Chapter 3

## Lesson 8: Relationship Between People And Events

1. **Which sentence below contains a conjunction indicating a possible relationship?**

   Ⓐ Due to the large number of offers, Mike had to increase his giveaway time limit.
   Ⓑ Kelsey is coming to dinner and a movie with me tonight.
   Ⓒ The oven did not cook right because the brownies were not completely done.
   Ⓓ The promise of a better life brought many immigrants to America.

2. **Which set of words lets the reader know a passage will include sequencing?**

   Ⓐ Finally, before, after that
   Ⓑ Consequently, as a result, therefore
   Ⓒ And, if, or
   Ⓓ Neither, because of that, and

3. **Which set of words lets the reader know a passage will include cause and effect?**

   Ⓐ Finally, before, after that
   Ⓑ Consequently, as a result, therefore
   Ⓒ And, if, or
   Ⓓ Neither, because of that, and

### The Assassination of President Lincoln
April 14, 1865

Shortly after 10 p.m. on April 14, 1865, actor, John Wilkes Booth entered the presidential box at Ford's Theatre in Washington D.C. and fatally shot President Abraham Lincoln. **As Lincoln slumped forward in his seat, Booth leapt onto the stage and escaped through the back door.** A doctor in the audience rushed over to examine the paralyzed president. Lincoln was then carried across the street to Petersen's Boarding House, where he died early the next morning.

Lincoln was the first president assassinated in U.S. history. Why did Booth do it? He thought it would aid the South, which had just surrendered to Federal forces. It had nearly the opposite effect, ending Lincoln's plans for a rather generous peace. Booth did not act alone. This "wanted" poster appeared everywhere, offering a reward for the arrest of Booth and his accomplices. The conspirators were all captured, and Booth was shot while trying to escape from Union soldiers.

The whole country grieved the death of President Lincoln. As the nine-car funeral train carried President Lincoln home for burial in Springfield, Illinois, people showed up at train stations all along the way to pay their respects.

"The Assassination of President Lincoln." The Assassination of President Lincoln. N.p., n.d. Web. 15 July 2013.

4. **In the bolded sentence above, what does the word "as" tell the reader?**

Ⓐ A doctor looked at the President.
Ⓑ Booth waited after shooting Lincoln.
Ⓒ The president slumped so he was shot.
Ⓓ Two events occurred at very nearly the same time.

5. **What happens second in the passage?**

Ⓐ Booth shot Lincoln
Ⓑ Booth entered the theater
Ⓒ Lincoln slumped
Ⓓ The doctor came to Lincoln's aid.

6. **What is the correct statement about the passage?**

Ⓐ Because Lincoln was untrustworthy, Booth shot him.
Ⓑ The country grieved Lincoln, and this is why they waited for the carriage with his body to go by.
Ⓒ The country grieved Lincoln, so they lined up at the train station to pay their respects.
Ⓓ There were no doctors in the theater so Lincoln could not be saved.

7. **What best describes the bolded sentence?**

Ⓐ flashback
Ⓑ sequence of events
Ⓒ compare contrast
Ⓓ cause and effect

8. **What happened at the end of the second paragraph? Write in the box below.**

## Chapter 3

## Lesson 9: When And Where?

### "Scouting for Boys"
### (Excerpt)

"Hi! Stop Thief!" shouted old Blenkinsopp as he rushed out of his little store near the village. "He's stolen my sugar. Stop him."

Stop whom? There was nobody in sight running away, "Who stole it?" asked the policeman.

"I don't know, but a whole bag of sugar is missing. It was there only a few minutes ago." The policeman tried to track the thief, but it looked a pretty impossible job for him to single out the tracks of the thief from among dozens of other footprints about the store. However, he presently started off hopefully, at a jog-trot, away out into the bush. In some places, he went over the hard stony ground, but he never checked his pace, although no footmarks could be seen. People wondered how he could possibly find the trail. Still, he trotted on. Old Blenkinsopp was feeling the heat and the pace

At length, he suddenly stopped and cast around, having evidently lost the trail. Then a grin came on his face as he pointed with his thumb over his shoulder up the tree near which he was standing. There, concealed among the branches, they saw a young man with the missing bag of sugar.

How had the policeman spotted him? His sharp eyes had detected some grains of sugar sparkling in the dust. The bag leaked, leaving a slight trail of these grains. He followed that trail, and when it came to an end in the bush, he noticed a string of ants going up a tree. They were after the sugar, and so was he, and between them, they brought about the capture of the thief.

Old Blenkinsopp was so pleased that he promptly opened the bag and spilled a lot of the sugar on the ground as a reward to the ants.

He also appreciated the policeman for his cleverness in using his eyes to see the grains of sugar and the ants, and in using his wits to know why the ants were climbing the tree.

1. **The opening sentence in the passage describes the setting of the story (or where it takes place). Mention it in the box below.**

## "The Lament"
## by Sravani

It is twilight. Thick wet snow is slowly twirling around the newly lighted street lamps and lying in soft thin layers on roofs, on horses' backs, on people's shoulders and hats. The cab driver, Iona Potapov, is quite white and looks like a phantom: he is bent double as far as a human body can bend double; he is seated on his box; he never makes a move. If a whole snowdrift fell on him, it seems as if he would not find it necessary to shake it off. His little horse is also quite white, and remains motionless; its immobility, its angularity, and its straight wooden-looking legs, even close by, give it the appearance of a gingerbread horse worth a kopek. It is, no doubt, plunged in deep thought. If you were snatched from the plough, from your usual gray surroundings, and were thrown into this slough full of monstrous lights, unceasing noise and hurrying people, you too would find it difficult not to think.

Iona and his little horse have not moved from their place for a long while. They left their yard before dinner and, up to now, not a fare. The evening mist is descending over the town, the white lights of the lamps are replacing brighter rays, and the hubbub of the street is getting louder.

'Cabby for Viborg Way!' suddenly hears Iona. 'Cabby!'

Iona jumps and, through his snow-covered eyelashes, sees an officer in a greatcoat, with his hood over his head.

'Viborg way!' the officer repeats. 'Are you asleep, eh? Viborg way!'

With a nod of assent, Iona picks up the reins, in consequence of which layers of snow slip off the horse's back and neck. The officer seats himself in the sleigh, the cab driver smacks his lips to encourage his horse, stretches out his neck like a swan, sits up and, more from habit than necessity, brandishes his whip. The little horse also stretches its neck, bends its wooden-looking legs, and makes a move undecidedly.

'What are you doing, werewolf!' is the exclamation Iona hears from the dark mass moving to and fro, as soon as they have started.

'Where the devil are you going? To the r-r-right!'

'You do not know how to drive. Keep to the right!' calls the officer angrily. A coachman from a private carriage swears at him; a passerby, who has run across the road and rubbed his shoulder against the horse's nose, looks at him furiously as he sweeps the snow from his sleeve. Iona shifts about on his seat as if he was on needles, moves his elbows as if he were trying to keep his equilibrium, and gasps about like someone suffocating, who does not understand why and wherefore he is there.
'What scoundrels they all are!' jokes the officer; 'one would think they had all entered into an agreement to jostle you or fall under your horse.'

Iona looks around at the officer and moves his lips. He evidently wants to say something but the only sound that issues is a snuffle.

'What?' asks the officer.

Iona twists his mouth into a smile and, with an effort, says hoarsely:
'My son, Barin, died this week.'
'Hm! What did he die of?'
Iona turns with his whole body towards his fare and says: 'And who knows! They say high fever. He was three days in the hospital and then died... God's will be done.'

"Turn round! The devil!' sounds from the darkness. 'Have you popped off, old doggie, eh? Use your eyes!'

'Go on, go on,' says the officer, 'otherwise we shall not get there by tomorrow. Hurry up a bit!'

"If you were snatched from the plough, from your usual gray surroundings, and were thrown into this slough full of monstrous lights, unceasing noise and hurrying people, you too would find it difficult not to think."

2. **Which detail in the above passage tells us this story is set in the winter?**

   Ⓐ It is twilight.
   Ⓑ His little horse is also quite white, and remains motionless;
   Ⓒ A thick wet snow is slowly twirling around the newly lighted street lamps and lying in soft thin layers on roofs, on horses' backs, on people's shoulders and hats.
   Ⓓ The cab driver, Iona Potapov, is quite white and looks like a phantom: he is bent double as far as a human body can bend double;

3. **What details in the story tells us that the setting is in Russia?**

   Ⓐ The name of the cab driver, Iona Potapov.
   Ⓑ A police officer asks for a cab ride.
   Ⓒ It is snowing heavily.
   Ⓓ The name of the place the officer wants to go.

## Best Friend

Ever since they were kids, Julie and Max had been best friends. They went to kindergarten together. They went to summer camp together. They hung out together every weekend. But suddenly, things between the two had started to change.

Max had started playing on the football team and didn't have much time for Julie anymore. He was always busy, and he never seemed to make it to study hall, where the two used to swap stories about their favorite (or least favorite) teachers. In class, Julie noticed that Max never seemed to have his homework done on time anymore. She even noticed that he got a 'D' on his last paper. She knew something was going on with him – but what?

At first, Julie decided to play it cool and see how things went. She tried waiting in the hall for Max after class to see if she could ask if he was OK. But days went by, and he never had time to stop. He'd rush right past her in the hall, only to leave her feeling even worse about what was happening between them.

Even though she wasn't sure she could handle the situation herself, Julie didn't want to talk to her parents because she was afraid they would tell her not to hang out with Max anymore. She barely saw him as it was, so she knew it would just make things worse if her parents didn't approve of him. She didn't want to tell Max's parents either because she didn't want him to get in trouble. Still, it seemed like something needed to change.

Julie decided to go to one of her school counselors and let her know she was concerned. When she walked into Mrs. Smith's room, she was surprised to see that Max was already sitting there.

"I'm sorry, I'll come back," Julie said.
"No, stay," said Max. "Maybe you can help."

Julie was surprised to find that Max had visited the counselor's office for the same reason she had: he was starting to feel overwhelmed with all of the things he was supposed to be doing as a student, an athlete, and a friend. He needed some guidance on how to determine what truly mattered and how to divide his time between all of the things that were important to him.

When she realized that Max was still the same old Max (just a little more stressed), Julie was relieved. She was also happy to know that he had come to a conclusion on his own, without her having to talk to someone else about it. She decided it was a sign they were both growing up.

4. **How would the outcome of the selection be different if the final scene was set in the principal's office instead of the guidance counselor's office?**

   Ⓐ Julie may not have been as sympathetic to Max because he would have been in trouble with the principal.
   Ⓑ Max would have been embarrassed because Julie saw him in the principal's office.
   Ⓒ The outcome of the selection wouldn't change if the setting changed.
   Ⓓ The outcome would change with any setting/ending different than the counselor's office.

LumosLearning.com

## THE LAND OF NOD by Robert Louis Stevenson

From breakfast on through all the day
At home among my friends I stay,
But every night I go abroad
Afar into the Land of Nod.

All by myself I have to go,
With none to tell me what to do—
All alone beside the streams
And up the mountain-sides of dreams.

The strangest things are there for me,
Both things to eat and things to see,
And many frightening sights abroad
Till morning in the Land of Nod.

Try as I like to find the way,
I never can get back by day,
Nor can remember plain and clear
The curious music that I hear.

**5.  What is the setting of this poem?**

Ⓐ  A child's bedroom
Ⓑ  A child's dreams
Ⓒ  The mountains
Ⓓ  The breakfast table

## THE WONDERFUL HAIR by A. H. Wraitslaw

There was a man who was very poor, but so well supplied with children that he was utterly unable to maintain them, and one morning more than once prepared to kill them, in order not to see their misery in dying of hunger, but his wife prevented him. One night a child came to him in his sleep, and said to him: "Man! I see that you are making up your mind to destroy and to kill your poor little children, and I know that you are distressed thereat; but in the morning you will find under your pillow a mirror, a red kerchief, and an embroidered pocket-handkerchief; take all three secretly and tell no-body; then go to such a hill; by it you will find a stream; go along it till you come to its fountain-head; there you will find a damsel as bright as the sun, with her hair hanging down over her back. Be on your guard, that the ferocious she-dragon do not coil around you; do not converse with her if she speaks; for if you converse with her, she will poison you, and turn you into a fish or something else, and will then devour you but if she bids you examine her head, examine it, and as you turn over her hair, look, and you will find one hair as red as blood; pull it out and run back again; then, if she suspects and begins to run after you, throw her first the embroidered pocket-handkerchief, then the kerchief, and, lastly, the mirror; then she will find occupation for herself. And sell that hair to some rich man; but don't let them cheat you, for that hair is worth countless wealth; and you will thus enrich yourself and maintain your children."

When the poor man awoke, he found everything under his pillow, just as the child had told him in his sleep; and then he went to the hill. When there, he found the stream, went on and on alongside of it, till he came to the fountain-head. Having looked about him to see where the damsel was, he espied her above a piece of water, like sunbeams threaded on a needle, and she was embroidering at a frame on stuff, the threads of which were young men's hair. As soon as he saw her, he made a reverence to her, and she stood on her feet and questioned him: "Whence are you, unknown young man?" But he held his tongue. She questioned him again: "Who are you? Why have you come?" and much else of all sorts; but he was as mute as a stone, making signs with his hands, as if he were deaf and wanted help. Then she told him to sit down on her skirt. He did not wait for any more orders, but sat down, and she bent down her head to him, that he might examine it. Turning over the hair of her head, as if to examine it, he was not long in finding that red hair, and separated it from the other hair, pulled it out, jumped off her skirt and ran away back as he best could. She noticed it, and ran at his heels full speed after him. He looked around, and seeing that she was about to overtake him, threw, as he was told, the embroidered pocket-handkerchief on the way, and when she saw the pocket-handkerchief she stooped and began to overhaul it in every direction, admiring the embroidery, till he had got a good way off. Then the damsel placed the pocket-handkerchief in her bosom, and ran after him again. When he saw that she was about to overtake him, he threw the red kerchief, and she again occupied herself, admiring and gazing, till the poor man had again got a good way off. Then the damsel became exasperated, and threw both the pocket-handkerchief and the kerchief on the way, and ran after him in pursuit. Again, when he saw that she was about to overtake him, he threw the mirror. When the damsel came to the mirror, the like of which she had never seen before, she lifted it up, and when she saw herself in it, not knowing that it was herself, but thinking that it was somebody else, she, as it were, fell in love with herself in the mirror, and the man got so far off that she was no longer able to overtake him. When she saw that she could not catch him, she turned back, and the man reached his home safe and sound. After arriving at his home, he showed his wife the hair, and told her all that had happened to him, but she began to jeer and laugh at him. But he paid no attention to her, and went to a town to sell the hair. A crowd of all sorts of people and merchants collected round him; one offered a sequin, another two, and so on, higher and higher, till they came to a hundred gold sequins. Just then the emperor heard of the hair, summoned the man into his presence, and said to him that he would give him a thousand sequins for it, and he sold it to him. What was the hair? The emperor split it in two from top to bottom, and found registered in it in writing many remarkable things, which happened in the olden time since the beginning of the world. Thus the man became rich and lived on with his wife and children. And that child, that came to him in his sleep, was an angel sent by the Lord God, whose will it was to aid the poor man, and to reveal secrets which had not been revealed till then.

6. **What details from the story do help the reader see that it takes place in a rural (country) setting? Select those that apply.**

   Ⓐ The characters live near a stream.
   Ⓑ He is going to sell hair in a local market.
   Ⓒ He has many children.
   Ⓓ He is to go into the woods/forest.

## "The Smith and the Fairies" : A Gaelic Folk Tale (Ed. Kate Douglas Wiggin)

Years ago there lived in Crossbrig a smith of the name of MacEachern. This man had an only child, a boy of about thirteen or fourteen years of age, cheerful, strong, and healthy. All of a sudden he fell ill; took to his bed and moped whole days away. No one could tell what was the matter with him, and the boy himself could not, or would not, tell how he felt. He was wasting away fast; getting thin, old, and yellow; and his father and all his friends were afraid that he would die.

At last one day, after the boy had been lying in this condition for a long time, getting neither better nor worse, always confined to bed, but with an extraordinary appetite—one day, while sadly revolving these things, and standing idly at his forge, with no heart to work, the smith was agreeably surprised to see an old man, well known for his sagacity and knowledge of out-of-the-way things, walk into his workshop. Forthwith he told him the occurrence which had clouded his life.

The old man looked grave as he listened; and after sitting a long time pondering over all he had heard, gave his opinion thus: "It is not your son you have got. The boy has been carried away by the 'Daione Sith,' and they have left a Sibhreach in his place."
"Alas! and what then am I to do?" said the smith. "How am I ever to see my own son again?"
"I will tell you how," answered the old man. "But, first, to make sure that it is not your own son you have got, take as many empty egg-shells as you can get, go into his room, spread them out carefully before his sight, then proceed to draw water with them, carrying them two and two in your hands as if they were a great weight, and arrange them when full, with every sort of earnestness around the fire."

The smith accordingly gathered as many broken egg-shells as he could get, went into the room, and proceeded to carry out all his instructions.
He had not been long at work before there arose from the bed a shout of laughter, and the voice of the seeming sick boy exclaimed, "I am eight hundred years of age, and I have never seen the like of that before." The smith returned and told the old man.
"Well, now," said the sage to him, "did I not tell you that it was not your son you had: your son is in Borracheill in a digh there (that is, a round green hill frequented by fairies). Get rid as soon as possible of this intruder, and I think I may promise you your son. You must light a very large and bright fire before the bed on which this stranger is lying. He will ask you, 'What is the use of such a fire as that?' Answer him at once, 'You will see that presently!' and then seize him, and throw him into the middle of it. If it is your own son you have got, he will call out to you to save him; but if not, the thing will fly through the roof."
The smith again followed the old man's advice: kindled a large fire, answered the question put to him as he had been directed to do, and seizing the child flung him in without hesitation. The Sibhreach gave an awful yell, and sprang through the roof, where a hole had been left to let the smoke out.

On a certain night the old man told him the green round hill, where the fairies kept the boy, would be open, and on that date the smith, having provided himself with a Bible, a dirk, and a crowing cock, was to proceed to the hill. He would hear singing and dancing, and much merriment going on, he had been told, but he was to advance boldly; the Bible he carried would be a certain safeguard to him against any danger from the fairies. On entering the hill he was to stick the dirk in the threshold, to prevent the hill from closing upon him; "and then," continued the old man, "on entering you will see a spacious apartment before you, beautifully clean, and there, standing far within, working at a forge, you will also see your own son. When you are questioned, say you come to seek him, and will not go without him."

Not long after this, the time came round, and the smith sallied forth, prepared as instructed. Sure enough as he approached the hill, there was a light where light was seldom seen before. Soon after, a sound of piping, dancing, and joyous merriment reached the anxious father on the night wind.

Overcoming every impulse to fear, the smith approached the threshold steadily, stuck the dirk into it as directed, and entered. Protected by the Bible he carried on his breast, the fairies could not touch him; but they asked him, with a good deal of displeasure, what he wanted there. He answered, "I want my son, whom I see down there, and I will not go without him."

Upon hearing this the whole company before him gave a loud laugh, which wakened up the cock he carried dozing in his arms, who at once leaped up on his shoulders, clapped his wings lustily, and crowed loud and long.

The fairies, incensed, seized the smith and his son, and throwing them out of the hill, flung the dirk after them, and in an instant all was dark.

For a year and a day the boy never did a turn of work, and hardly ever spoke a word; but at last one day, sitting by his father and watching him finishing a sword he was making for some chief, and which he was very particular about, he suddenly exclaimed, "That is not the way to do it;" and taking the tools from his father's hands he set to work himself in his place, and soon fashioned a sword, the like of which was never seen in the country before.

From that day the young man wrought constantly with his father, and became the inventor of a peculiarly fine and well-tempered weapon, the making of which kept the two smiths, father and son, in constant employment, spread their fame far and wide, and gave them the means in abundance, as they before had the disposition, to live content with all the world and very happily with each other.

7. **Which detail from the story is NOT a clue that the story is set in the past?**

   Ⓐ There are no longer smiths working today.
   Ⓑ People in the story believe there are fairies in the woods.
   Ⓒ The smith carries a Bible with him because he believes it will protect him.
   Ⓓ The smith and his son make swords for people in town.

### *The Two Melons* A Chinese Folk Tale (Ed. Kate Douglas Wiggin)

An honest and poor old woman was washing clothes at a pool when a bird that a hunter had disabled by a shot in the wing fell down into the water before her. She gently took up the bird, carried it home with her, dressed its wound, and fed it until it was well when it soared away. Some days later, it returned, put before her an oval seed, and departed again. The woman planted the seed in her yard, and when it came up, she recognized the leaf as that of a melon. She made a trellis for it, and gradually a fruit formed on it, and grew to great size.

Toward the end of the year, the old dame was unable to pay her debts, and her poverty so weighed upon her that she became ill. Sitting one day at her door, feverish and tired, she saw that the melon was ripe and looked luscious, so she determined to try its unknown quality. Taking a knife, she severed the melon from its stalk and was surprised to hear it chink in her hands. On cutting it in two, she found it full of silver and gold pieces, with which she paid her debts and bought supplies for many days.

Among her neighbors was a busybody who craftily found out how the old woman had so suddenly become rich. Thinking there was no good reason why she should not herself be equally fortunate, she washed clothes at the pool, keeping a sharp lookout for birds until she managed to hit and maim one of a flock that was flitting over the water. She then took the disabled bird home and treated it with care until its wing healed, and it flew away. Shortly afterward, it came back with a seed in its beak, laid it before her, and again took flight. The woman quickly planted the seed, saw it come up and spread its leaves, made a trellis for it, and had the gratification of seeing a melon form on its stalk. In the prospect of her future wealth, she ate rich food, bought fine garments, and got so deeply into debt that, before the end of the year, she was harried by duns. But the melon grew apace, and she was delighted to find that, as it ripened, it became of vast size and that when she shook it, there was a great rattling inside. At the end of the year, she cut it down, and divided it, expecting it to be a coffer of coins; but there crawled out of it two old, lame, hungry beggars, who told her they would remain and eat at her table as long as they lived.

8. **Where and when can you infer this story takes place?**

   Ⓐ In the past in a bustling city
   Ⓑ In the past in a poor village
   Ⓒ In the present in a farming community
   Ⓓ In the present in a bustling city

### Jane Eyre (Excerpt)
### by Charlotte Bronte

The red-room was a square chamber, very seldom slept in, I might say never, indeed, unless when a chance influx of visitors at Gateshead Hall rendered it necessary to turn to account all the accommodation it contained: yet it was one of the largest and stateliest chambers in the mansion. A bed supported on massive pillars of mahogany, hung with curtains of deep red damask, stood out like a tabernacle in the centre; the two large windows, with their blinds always drawn down, were half shrouded in festoons and falls of similar drapery; the carpet was red; the table at the foot of the bed was covered with a crimson cloth; the walls were a soft fawn color with a blush of pink in it; the wardrobe, the toilet-table, the chairs were of darkly polished old mahogany. Out of these deep surrounding shades rose high, and glared white, the piled-up mattresses and pillows of the bed, spread with a snowy Marseilles counterpane. Scarcely less prominent was an ample cushioned easy-chair near the head of the bed, also white, with a footstool before it; and looking, as I thought, like a pale throne.

This room was chill because it seldom had a fire; it was silent, because remote from the nursery and kitchen; solemn because it was known to be so seldom entered. The house-maid alone came here on Saturdays, to wipe from the mirrors and the furniture a week's quiet dust: and Mrs. Reed herself, at far intervals, visited it to review the contents of a certain secret drawer in the wardrobe, where were stored divers parchments, her jewel-casket, and a miniature of her deceased husband; and in those last words lies the secret of the red-room--the spell which kept it so lonely in spite of its grandeur.

9. **Where can you infer this story takes place?**

   Ⓐ In a hotel in the present
   Ⓑ In a home in the future
   Ⓒ In a large home in the past
   Ⓓ In a country cottage in the present

10. **Which line or lines from the excerpt best support the time in which this story is set?**

   Ⓐ This room was chilled, because it seldom had a fire; it was silent, because removed from the nursery and kitchen; solemn because it was known to be so seldom entered.
   Ⓑ The red-room was a square chamber, very seldom slept in, I might say never, indeed, unless when a chance influx of visitors at Gateshead Hall rendered it necessary to turn to account all the accommodation it contained
   Ⓒ A bed supported on massive pillars of mahogany, hung with curtains of deep red damask, stood out like a tabernacle in the centre; the two large windows, with their blinds always drawn down, were half shrouded in festoons and falls of similar drapery;
   Ⓓ Scarcely less prominent was an ample cushioned easy-chair near the head of the bed, also white, with a footstool before it; and looking, as I thought, like a pale throne.

## Chapter 3

## Lesson 10: Who Or What?

### "Bruno the Bear"
### Excerpt from The Bond of Love

I will begin with Bruno, my wife's pet sloth bear. I got him for her by accident. Two years ago, we were passing through the cornfields near a small town in Iowa. People were driving away the wild pigs from the fields by shooting at them. Some were shot, and some escaped. We thought that everything was over when suddenly a black sloth bear came out panting in the hot sun.

Now I will not shoot a sloth bear wantedly, but unfortunately for the poor beast, one of my companions did not feel the same way about it and promptly shot the bear on the spot.

As we watched the fallen animal, we were surprised to see that the black fur on its back moved and left the prostrate body. Then we saw it was a baby bear that had been riding on its mother's back when the sudden shot had killed her. The little creature ran around its prostrate parent, making a pitiful noise. I ran up to it to attempt a capture. It scooted into the sugarcane field. Following it with my companions, I was at last able to grab it by the scruff of its neck while it snapped and tried to scratch me with its long, hooked claws.

We put it in one of the large jute-bags we had brought, and when I got back home, I duly presented it to my wife. She was delighted! She at once put a blue colored ribbon around its neck, and after discovering the cub was a 'boy,' she christened it Bruno.

Bruno soon took to drinking milk from a bottle. It was but a step further, and within a very few days, he started eating and drinking everything else. And everything is the right word, for he ate porridge made from any ingredients, vegetables, fruit, nuts, meat (especially pork), curry and rice regardless of condiments and chilies, bread, eggs, chocolates, sweets, pudding, ice-cream, etc., As for drink: milk, tea, coffee, lime juice, aerated water, buttermilk, beer, alcoholic liquor, and, in fact, anything liquid. It all went down with relish.

The bear became very attached to our two dogs and all the children living in and around our farm. He was left quite free in his younger days and spent his time playing, running into the kitchen, and going to sleep in our beds.

One day an accident befell him. I put down poison (barium carbonate) to kill the rats and mice that had got into my library. Bruno entered the library as he often did and ate some of the poison. Paralysis set into the extent that he could not stand on his feet. But he dragged himself on his stumps to my wife, who called me. I guessed what had happened.

Off I rushed him in the car to the vet's residence. A case of poisoning! Tame Bear—barium carbonate— what to do? Out came his medical books, and a feverish reference to index began: "What poison did you say, sir?" he asked, "Barium carbonate," I said.

"Ah yes—B—Ba—Barium Salts—Ah! Barium carbonate! Symptoms— paralysis—treatment—injections of . .. Just a minute, sir. I'll bring my syringe and the medicine." Said the doc. I dashed back to the car. Bruno was still floundering about on his stumps, but clearly, he was weakening rapidly; there was some vomiting, he was breathing heavily, with heaving flanks and gaping mouth. I was really scared and did not know what to do. I was feeling very guilty and was running in and out of the vet's house doing everything the doc asked me.

"Hold him, everybody!" In goes the hypodermic—Bruno squeals — 10 c.c. of the antidote enters his  system without a drop being wasted. Ten minutes later: condition unchanged! Another 10 c.c. Injected! Ten minutes later: breathing less torturous— Bruno can move his arms and legs a little although he cannot stand yet. Thirty minutes later: Bruno gets up and has a great feed! He looks at us disdainfully, as much as to say, 'What's barium carbonate to a big black bear like me?' Bruno was still eating. I was really happy to see him recover.

The months rolled on, and Bruno had grown many times the size he was when he came. He had equaled the big dogs in height and had even outgrown them. But was just as sweet, just as mischievous, just as playful. And he was very fond of us all. Above all, he loved my wife, and she loved him too! And he could do a few tricks, too. At the command, 'Bruno, wrestle,' or 'Bruno, box,' he vigorously tackled anyone who came forward for a rough and tumble. Give him a stick and say 'Bruno, hold the gun,' and he pointed the stick at you. Ask him, 'Bruno, where's baby?' and he immediately produced and cradled affectionately a stump of wood which he had carefully concealed in his straw bed. But because of the neighborhoods' and our renters' children, poor Bruno, had to be kept chained most of the time.

Then my son and I advised my wife and friends advised her, too, to give Bruno to the zoo. He was getting too big to keep at home. After some weeks of such advice, she at last consented. Hastily, and before she could change her mind, a letter was written to the curator of the zoo. Did he want a tame bear for his collection? He replied, "Yes." The zoo sent a cage in a truck, a distance of hundred – eighty – seven miles, and Bruno was packed off. We all missed him greatly, but in a sense, we were relieved. My wife was inconsolable. She wept and fretted. For the first few days, she would not eat a thing. Then she wrote a number of letters to the curator. How was Bruno? Back came the replies, "Well, but fretting; he refuses food too."

After that, friends visiting the zoo were begged to make a point of seeing how Bruno was getting along. They reported that he was well but looked very thin and sad. All the keepers at the zoo said he was fretting. For three months, I managed to restrain my wife from visiting the zoo. Then she said one day, "I must see Bruno. Either you take me by car, or I will go myself by bus or train myself." So I took her by car. Friends had conjectured that the bear would not recognize her. I had thought so too. But while she was yet some yards from his cage, Bruno saw her and recognized her. He howled with happiness. She ran up to him, petted him through the bars, and he stood on his head in delight.

For the next three hours, she would not leave that cage. She gave him tea, lemonade, cakes, ice cream, and whatnot. Then 'closing time' came and we had to leave. My wife cried bitterly; Bruno cried bitterly; even the hardened curator and the keepers felt depressed. As for me, I had reconciled myself to what I knew was going to happen next.

"Oh please, sir," she asked the curator, "may I have my Bruno back"? Hesitantly, he answered, "Madam, he belongs to the zoo and is Government property now. I cannot give away Government property. But if my boss, the superintendent, agrees, certainly, you may have him back."

There followed the return journey home and a visit to the superintendent's office. A tearful pleading: "Bruno and I are both fretting for each other. Will you please give him back to me?" He was a kind-hearted man and consented. Not only that, but he wrote to the curator, telling him to lend us a cage for transporting the bear back home.

Back we went to the zoo again, armed with the superintendent's letter. Bruno was driven into a small cage and hoisted on top of the car; the cage was tied securely, and a slow and careful return journey back home was accomplished.

Once home, a squad of workers were engaged for special work around our yard. An island was made for Bruno. It was twenty feet long and fifteen feet wide and was surrounded by a dry moat, six feet wide and seven feet deep. A wooden box that once housed fowls was brought and put on the island for Bruno to sleep in at night. Straw was placed inside to keep him warm, and his 'baby,' the gnarled stump, along with his 'gun,' the piece of bamboo, both of which had been sentimentally preserved since he had been sent away to the zoo, were put back for him to play with. In a few days, the workers hoisted the cage on to the island, and Bruno was released. He was delighted; standing on his hind legs, he pointed his 'gun' and cradled his 'baby.' My wife spent hours sitting on a chair there while he sat on her lap. He was fifteen months old and pretty heavy too!

The way my wife reaches the island and leaves it is interesting. I have tied a rope to the overhanging branch of a maple tree with a loop at its end. Putting one foot in the loop, she kicks off with the other, to bridge the six-foot gap that constitutes the width of the surrounding moat. The return journey back is made the same way.

But who can say now that a sloth bear has no sense of affection, no memory, and no individual characteristics?

**1. What motivated the narrator to keep Bruno chained up?**

Ⓐ because he had grown big
Ⓑ because he was very playful and this scared some of the children in the neighborhood
Ⓒ because he was very dangerous
Ⓓ because he was a bear

## Best Friend

Ever since they were kids, Julie and Max had been best friends. They went to kindergarten together. They went to summer camp together. They hung out together every weekend. But suddenly, things between the two had started to change.

Max had started playing on the football team and didn't have much time for Julie anymore. He was always busy, and he never seemed to make it to study hall, where the two used to swap stories about their favorite (or least favorite) teachers. In class, Julie noticed that Max never seemed to have his homework done on time anymore. She even noticed that he got a 'D' on his last paper. She knew something was going on with him – but what?

At first, Julie decided to play it cool and see how things went. She tried waiting in the hall for Max after class to see if she could ask if he was OK. But days went by, and he never had time to stop.

He'd rush right past her in the hall, only to leave her feeling even worse about what was happening between them.

Even though she wasn't sure she could handle the situation herself, Julie didn't want to talk to her parents because she was afraid they would tell her not to hang out with Max anymore. She barely saw him as it was, so she knew it would just make things worse if her parents didn't approve of him. She didn't want to tell Max's parents either because she didn't want him to get in trouble. Still, it seemed like something needed to change. Julie decided to go to one of her school counselors and let her know she was concerned.

When she walked into Mrs. Smith's room, she was surprised to see that Max was already sitting there.

"I'm sorry, I'll come back," Julie said.
"No, stay," said Max. "Maybe you can help."

Julie was surprised to find that Max had visited the counselor's office for the same reason she had: He was starting to feel overwhelmed with all of the things he was supposed to be doing as a student, an athlete, and a friend. He needed some guidance on how to determine what truly mattered and how to divide his time between all of the things that were important to him. When she realized that Max was still the same old Max (just a little more stressed), Julie was relieved. She was also happy to know that he had come to a conclusion on his own, without her having to talk to someone else about it. She decided it was a sign they were both growing up.

2.  **What two events in the story contributed to Max being overwhelmed?**

   Ⓐ counselor's advice
   Ⓑ football commitments
   Ⓒ friendship expectations
   Ⓓ summer camp

3. **Which two of the following reasons led to Julie getting worried about Max?**

   Ⓐ He was getting bad grades.
   Ⓑ He was partying a lot.
   Ⓒ He wasn't reading books.
   Ⓓ He was too busy for her.

4. **Who are the two main characters of the above story? Write in the box below.**

---

### "Scouting for Boys"
### (Excerpt)

"Hi! Stop Thief!" shouted old Blenkinsopp as he rushed out of his little store near the village. "He's stolen my sugar. Stop him."

Stop whom? There was nobody in sight running away, "Who stole it?" asked the policeman.

"I don't know, but a whole bag of sugar is missing. It was there only a few minutes ago." The policeman tried to track the thief, but it looked a pretty impossible job for him to single out the tracks of the thief from among dozens of other footprints about the store. However, he presently started off hopefully, at a jog-trot, away out into the bush. In some places, he went over the hard stony ground, but he never checked his pace, although no footmarks could be seen. People wondered how he could possibly find the trail. Still, he trotted on. Old Blenkinsopp was feeling the heat and the pace

At length, he suddenly stopped and cast around, having evidently lost the trail. Then a grin came on his face as he pointed with his thumb over his shoulder up the tree near which he was standing. There, concealed among the branches, they saw a young man with the missing bag of sugar.

How had the policeman spotted him? His sharp eyes had detected some grains of sugar sparkling in the dust. The bag leaked, leaving a slight trail of these grains. He followed that trail, and when it came to an end in the bush, he noticed a string of ants going up a tree. They were after the sugar, and so was he, and between them, they brought about the capture of the thief.

Old Blenkinsopp was so pleased that he promptly opened the bag and spilled a lot of the sugar on the ground as a reward to the ants.

He also appreciated the policeman for his cleverness in using his eyes to see the grains of sugar and the ants, and in using his wits to know why the ants were climbing the tree.

LumosLearning.com                                                        145

5. **Why did the old man rush out of the store?**

    Ⓐ to stop the thief who had stolen his sugar
    Ⓑ to catch the ants
    Ⓒ to go for a walk
    Ⓓ to leave the shop

6. **What character, along with the policeman, helped to catch the thief?**

    Ⓐ the shopkeeper
    Ⓑ the ants
    Ⓒ the villagers
    Ⓓ the shopkeeper's wife

## Tryouts

For years, Sam had dreamed of being the best tennis player in the world. He went to tennis practice every single morning and night. He spent every summer at tennis camp, and he gave up long weekends at the beach to work on his game. Now, it seemed his hard work was finally paying off. He was invited to try out for the state tennis team!

Still, there was something that was bothering Sam. The tryouts for the tennis team were on the same day as his mom's birthday, and he knew his family was planning a huge surprise party for her. He didn't want to hurt his mom's feelings by missing the party, but he also didn't want to miss his one shot at being a champion tennis player. He was in a quandary; he didn't know what to do.

For days, Sam went to bed, worrying about the decision. If he went to the tryout, he worried he would seem selfish. If he stayed home, he would miss his one big shot at making the state team. In fact, despite the honor of being invited to try out, he hadn't even told his family about the opportunity. He was so stressed about deciding whether to go or not that he couldn't even think about sharing the news.

Weeks went by, and Sam was making no progress. Every day his coach asked him if he was ready for the tryout, and Sam couldn't even respond. Finally, Sam couldn't bear the stress any longer. He decided to talk to his grandfather about his predicament.

"You know, your mom wants you to be happy," he told Sam. "It would be a great birthday present for her to know you are making your dream come true."

Sam had never thought of it that way before, and after talking to his grandfather, he knew what he had to do. He immediately went home and sat down with his parents to let them know about the opportunity to try out for the state team. When Sam apologetically told his parents what day the tryouts were, they were so busy shrieking with excitement that he thought maybe they hadn't heard.

"But Mom, that means I'm going to miss your birthday," Sam said. "I am happy you are so nice about it, but I still feel really bad."

"Are you kidding?" his mom asked. "This is the best present I could ask for!"

7. **What character trait(s) did Sam NOT display in talking to his parents honestly about his tryout and his quandary?**

   Ⓐ Integrity – he understood the right thing to do in the situation
   Ⓑ Honesty – he explained why he wanted to go and why he felt bad about it
   Ⓒ Maturity – he was willing to talk to them even though he knew he might not like their answer
   Ⓓ Being Proactive- he was hesitant and waited so long to ask for guidance.

8. **Which of the following statements best characterizes Sam?**

   Ⓐ Sam is very selfish.
   Ⓑ Sam does not care about what others feel. He just wants to do what he likes.
   Ⓒ Sam is very concerned about others to the point where he would sacrifice his own happiness for someone else's.
   Ⓓ Sam can't make decisions easily.

9. **How does Sam's character change as the story progresses?**

   Ⓐ Sam goes from being selfish to caring.
   Ⓑ Sam goes from being confident to self-doubting.
   Ⓒ Sam goes from being concerned to confident.
   Ⓓ Sam goes from being angry to happy.

## Excerpt from *Tales of A Brothers' Grimm*

A certain king once fell ill, and the doctor declared that only a sudden fright would restore him to health, but the king was not a man for anyone to play tricks on, except his fool. One day, when the fool was with him in his boat, he cleverly pushed the king into the water. Help had already been arranged, and the king was drawn ashore and put to bed. The fright, the bath, and the rest in bed cured the diseased king.

The king wanted to frighten the fool for his act, so he told him that he would be put to death. He directed the executioner privately not to use the axe but to let fall a single drop of water on the fool's neck. Amidst shouts and laughter, the fool was asked to rise and thank the king for his kindness. But the fool never moved; he was dead; killed by the master's joke.

**10. How was the king's view of jokes after the fool's death likely different than that of the fool when he was alive?**

Ⓐ Both had the same view of jokes. Jokes were cruel and unkind.

Ⓑ The fool thought jokes were funny, but the king did not find them amusing.

Ⓒ The fool realized jokes can sometimes backfire, but the king always thought they would work out in his favor.

Ⓓ The king realized that jokes can sometimes not work out the way you intend for them to play out, but because the fool always had success with his jokes, the king did not consider the fact that his joke might backfire.

## Chapter 3

## Lesson 11: Based On A True Story - History And Fiction

**"Paul Revere's Ride" (Excerpt)**
**Henry Wadsworth Longfellow**

Listen my children and you shall hear
Of the midnight ride of Paul Revere,
On the eighteenth of April, in Seventy-five;
Hardly a man is now alive
Who remembers that famous day and year.
He said to his friend, "If the British march
By land or sea from the town to-night,
Hang a lantern aloft in the belfry arch
Of the North Church tower as a signal light,--
One if by land, and two if by sea;
And I on the opposite shore will be,
Ready to ride and spread the alarm
Through every Middlesex village and farm,
For the country folk to be up and to arm."
Then he said "Good-night!" and with muffled oar
Silently rowed to the Charlestown shore,
Just as the moon rose over the bay,
Where swinging wide at her moorings lay
The Somerset, British man-of-war;
A phantom ship, with each mast and spar
Across the moon like a prison bar,
And a huge black hulk, that was magnified
By its own reflection in the tide.

It was twelve by the village clock
When he crossed the bridge into Medford town.
He heard the crowing of the cock,
And the barking of the farmer's dog,
And felt the damp of the river fog,
That rises after the sun goes down.
It was one by the village clock,
When he galloped into Lexington.
He saw the gilded weathercock
Swim in the moonlight as he passed,
And the meeting-house windows, black and bare,
Gaze at him with a spectral glare,
As if they already stood aghast

At the bloody work they would look upon.
It was two by the village clock,
When he came to the bridge in Concord town.
He heard the bleating of the flock,
And the twitter of birds among the trees,
And felt the breath of the morning breeze
Blowing over the meadow brown.
And one was safe and asleep in his bed
Who at the bridge would be first to fall,
Who that day would be lying dead,
Pierced by a British musket ball.
You know the rest. In the books you have read
How the British Regulars fired and fled,---
How the farmers gave them ball for ball,
From behind each fence and farmyard wall,
Chasing the redcoats down the lane,
Then crossing the fields to emerge again
Under the trees at the turn of the road,
And only pausing to fire and load.

**The Real Story of Revere's Ride**
From the Paul Revere House official Website
In 1774 and the Spring of 1775 Paul Revere was employed by the Boston Committee of Correspondence and the Massachusetts Committee of Safety as an express rider to carry news, messages, and copies of resolutions as far away as New York and Philadelphia.

On the evening of April 18, 1775, Paul Revere was sent for by Dr. Joseph Warren and instructed to ride to Lexington, Massachusetts, to warn Samuel Adams and John Hancock that British troops were marching to arrest them. After being rowed across the Charles River to Charlestown by two associates, Paul Revere borrowed a horse from his friend Deacon John Larkin. While in Charlestown, he verified that the local "Sons of Liberty" committee had seen his pre-arranged signals. (Two lanterns had been hung briefly in the bell-tower of Christ Church in Boston, indicating that troops would row "by sea" across the Charles River to Cambridge, rather than marching "by land" out Boston Neck. Revere had arranged for these signals the previous weekend, as he was afraid that he might be prevented from leaving Boston).

On the way to Lexington, Revere "alarmed" the country-side, stopping at each house, and arrived in Lexington about midnight. As he approached the house where Adams and Hancock were staying, a sentry asked that he not make so much noise. "Noise!" cried Revere, "You'll have noise enough before long. The regulars are coming out!" After delivering his message, Revere was joined by a second rider, William Dawes, who had been sent on the same errand by a different route. Deciding on their own to continue on to Concord, Massachusetts, where weapons and supplies were hidden, Revere and Dawes were joined by a third rider, Dr. Samuel Prescott. Soon after, all three were arrested by a British patrol. Prescott escaped almost immediately, and Dawes soon after. Revere was held for some time and then released. Left without a horse, Revere returned to Lexington in time to witness part of the battle on the Lexington Green.

1. **According to the poem, what was the purpose of Revere's ride?**

   Ⓐ To alert everyone in the county that the British were approaching.
   Ⓑ To warn Samuel Adams and John Hancock that the British were approaching.
   Ⓒ To make it back to Boston in time for the battle.
   Ⓓ To reach Lexington before the British troops to awaken the members of the militia.

2. **According to the non-fiction passage, what was the purpose of Revere's ride?**

   Ⓐ To alert everyone in the county that the British were approaching.
   Ⓑ To warn Samuel Adams and John Hancock that the British were approaching.
   Ⓒ To make it back to Boston in time for the battle.
   Ⓓ To reach Lexington before the British troops to awaken the members of the militia.

3. **What information from the non-fiction passage does the poem exclude?**

   Ⓐ The description of the signals in the church steeple.
   Ⓑ That Revere was arrested and held by the British.
   Ⓒ That Revere reached the town of Lexington.
   Ⓓ That the British soldiers were coming by sea.

4. **Which excerpt from the non-fiction passage conflicts most with the poem?**

   Ⓐ Left without a horse, Revere returned to Lexington in time to witness part of the battle on the Lexington Green.
   Ⓑ Paul Revere borrowed a horse from his friend, Deacon John Larkin.
   Ⓒ Two lanterns had been hung briefly in the bell-tower of Christ Church in Boston, indicating that troops would row "by sea" across the Charles River to Cambridge, rather than marching "by land" out Boston Neck.
   Ⓓ On the way to Lexington, Revere "alarmed" the country-side, stopping at each house, and arrived in Lexington about midnight.

5. **Who is the writer of the above poem? Mention in the box below.**

# THE BAND OF THE TITANIC
## By Florence Earle Coates
### "These are the immortal,—the fearless"—Upanishads

UP, lads! they say we've struck a berg, though there's no danger yet,—
Our noble liner was not built to wreck!—
But women may have felt a shock they're needing to forget,
And when there's trouble, men should be on deck.

Come!—now's the time! They're wanting us to brighten them a bit;
Play up, my lads—as lively as you can!
Give them a merry English air! they want no counterfeit
Like that down-hearted tune you just began!...

I think the Captain's worried, lads: maybe the thing's gone wrong;
Well, we will show them all is right with us!
Of Drake and the Armadas now we'll play them such a song
Shall make them of the hero emulous.

When boats are being lowered, lads, your place and mine are here,—
Oh, we were never needed more than now!
When others go, it is for us those left behind to cheer,
And I am glad, my lads, that we know how!

If it is Death that's calling us, we'll make a brave response;
Play up, play up!—ye may not play again;
The prize that Nelson won at last, the chance that comes but once,
Is ours, my lads!—the chance to die like men!

From The Worcester Evening Gazette
April 20, 1912
New York, April 19. Of all the heroes who went to their death when the Titanic dived to its ocean grave, none, in the opinion of Miss Hilda Slater, a passenger in the last boat to pull off, deserved greater credit than the members of the vessel's orchestra. According to Miss Slater, the orchestra played until the last. When the vessel took its final plunge the strains of a lively air, mingled gruesomely with the cries of those who realized that they were face to face with death.

"It was terrible," said Miss Slater, who had come from her home in England to visit a brother, an architect in this city. "From the moment the vessel struck, or as soon as the members of the orchestra could be collected, there was a steady round of lively airs. It did much to keep up the spirits of everyone and probably served as much as the efforts of the officers trying to prevent panic."

When the ship struck the iceberg, Miss Slater went on deck. She was ordered to go back to bed, which she did on being assured there was no danger. A half-hour later, she heard confusion on deck and heard someone cry, "Order everyone to don life belts."

After dressing again, Miss. Slater returned to the deck and was ordered to the boat deck aloft.

"When I got there," she said, "I found an indescribable scene. A number of the steerage men passengers had attempted to seize one of the boats, and there was a brisk revolver fire: many men fell under it. The prompt and drastic action of the officers restored order."

"There were many touching scenes as the boats put off. I saw Col. John Jacob Astor hand his young wife into a boat tenderly and then asked an officer whether he might also go. When permission was refused, he stepped back and coolly took out his cigarette case. "Good-bye, dearie" he called gaily, as he lighted a cigarette and leaned over the rail. "I'll join you later." Another man, a Frenchman, I think, approached one of the boats about to be lowered. He had with him, two little boys. An officer waved him back sternly. "Bless you," he said, "I don't want to go, but for God's sake take the boys. Their mother is waiting for them in New York." The boys were taken aboard."
From The Worcester Evening Gazette
April 20, 1912
New York, April 19- Mrs. John Murray Brown of Acton, Mass, who with her sister, Mrs. Robert C. Cornell and Mrs. E.D. Appleton, was saved, was in the last life-boat to get safely away from the Titanic.

"The band played marching from deck to deck, and as the ship went under, I could still hear the music." Mrs. Brown said. "The musicians were up to their knees in water when last I saw them. We offered assistance to Capt. Smith, but he refused."

"Mrs. Astor was in the life-boat with my sister, Mrs. Cornell. I heard Col. Astor tell her he would wait with the men. Our boat was almost dragged down by the suction."

6.  **Who is the writer of the poem "The Band Of The Titanic"? Mention in the box below.**

7.  **What detail from the newspaper articles supports the attitude assigned to the musicians in the last stanza of the poem?**

    Ⓐ  "The band played marching from deck to deck, and as the ship went under I could still hear the music. Mrs. Brown said."
    Ⓑ  "The musicians were up to their knees in water when last I saw them."
    Ⓒ  "From the moment the vessel struck, or as soon as the members of the orchestra could be collected, there was a steady round of lively airs. It did much to keep up the spirits of everyone and probably served as much as the efforts of the officers trying to prevent panic."
    Ⓓ  "Another man, a Frenchman, I think, approached one of the boats about to be lowered. He had with him two little boys. An officer waved him back sternly."

8.  **What detail from the newspaper articles supports the information in the second stanza of the poem?**

    Ⓐ  When the vessel took its final plunge, the strains of a lively air mingled gruesomely with the cries of those who realized that they were face to face with death.
    Ⓑ  "The band played marching from deck to deck, and as the ship went under I could still hear the music." Mrs. Brown said.
    Ⓒ  Of all the heroes who went to their death when the Titanic dived to its ocean grave, none, in the opinion of Miss. Hilda Slater, a passenger in the last boat to pull off, deserved greater credit than the members of the vessel's orchestra.
    Ⓓ  When the ship struck the iceberg, Miss Slater went on deck. She was ordered to go back to bed, which she did on being assured there was no danger.

9.  **What do both the poem and newspaper articles suggest the ship's band did for the victims and survivors?**

    Ⓐ  Provided entertainment while the passengers awaited rescue
    Ⓑ  Helped organize the lifeboats so that only women and children had places
    Ⓒ  Helped people from becoming hysterical while the lifeboats were lowered
    Ⓓ  Helped lower the lifeboats into the water

10. **Why would readers consider Mrs. Brown and Miss Slater accurate reporters of what was happening on board the Titanic just before the ship sank?**

    Ⓐ  They were personal friends of the members of the band.
    Ⓑ  They were on the ship until it sank and were rescued from the water.
    Ⓒ  They were on lifeboats as the ship was sinking.
    Ⓓ  Their stories offer identical details.

## Chapter 3

## Lesson 12: How Is It Built? Analyzing Structure

**Bushmen**

With so much technology around us each day, it is hard to imagine that anyone in the world would live without television, let alone a cell phone or radio. Still, there are a few cultures that maintain an extremely primitive lifestyle, nearly untouched by the modern world. One of those is commonly known as the Bushmen of Kalahari.

The Bushmen, also known as the "Basarwa" or "San" is found throughout southern Africa in regions of the Kalahari Desert. Nomadic hunters and gatherers by nature, they roam the region living in small kinship groups and, relatively isolated from the rest of society, have developed an extremely unique culture not otherwise seen or understood by modern man.

Unlike English, which is built on a complex system of sounds and letters, the Bushmen speak an extremely unique language made exclusively of clicking sounds. The sounds are created with a sucking action from the tongue, and even the click language itself can vary widely from tribe to tribe, making it extremely difficult to communicate with non-Bush people.

In addition to language, the Bushmen have a very different way of living. Similar to Eskimos, groups of Bushmen will live in "kinship" societies. Led by their elders, they travel together, with women in the group gathering food while men hunt for it. Children, on the other hand, have no duties other than playing. In fact, leisure is an extremely important part of the Bushmen society. Dance, music, and humor are essential, with a focus on family rather than technology or development. Because of this, some people associate the Bush culture with a backward kind of living or low status.

Because of the increased speed of advancement and urban development, the Bushmen culture is in danger. Some have already been forced to switch from hunting to farming due to modernization programs in their countries. Others have been forced to move to certain areas of their countries so that modernization can continue to occur there. With so much development, it's clear that though the Bushmen culture is very rich, it is also in danger of extinction. It is unclear how long the Bush culture will continue.

http://en.wikibooks.org/wiki/Cultural_Anthropology/Print_version'

**1. How are the paragraphs in this selection organized?**

Ⓐ by topic
Ⓑ from broad ideas to narrow ideas
Ⓒ chronologically
Ⓓ compare and contrast

# Baseball Card Collecting

Looking for a new hobby? Do you like baseball? If you answered "yes" to these two questions, baseball card collecting might be a fun pastime for you to begin! Ever since candy and gum manufacturers started putting cards with pictures of popular baseball players into the packages in the 1800s to encourage young people to buy their sweets, kids have been collecting baseball cards. Now, more than 200 years later, baseball card collecting has become a popular hobby for children and adults alike.

## What You Need to Be a Baseball Card Collector

The main thing you need to start a baseball card collection is cards, of course! Baseball cards are usually sold in packs of four or more cards. Large chain stores like Walmart and Target, as well as drug stores, are the easiest places to find packs of baseball cards. You can also find cards at special baseball card shops. You should plan on spending around $2.99 for each pack of baseball cards you purchase. Once you've started your collection by buying packs of cards, you'll probably find that there are one or two specific cards you want that you haven't been able to get in packs. The best places to get single cards are the baseball card shows held at malls or convention centers or on the Internet. You can also trade cards with another baseball card collector. A lot of times, a friend has the card you're looking for. Because you might also have a card he or she wants, trading is a great way to build the collection that you want. Plus, it doesn't cost you a cent!

As a baseball card collector, you'll not only need cards, but also a place to put them. Baseball cards can become very valuable. You may get a card in a pack today that is worth ten or twenty times the price you paid for it years down the line. The price that you can sell a baseball card is based on the condition that it is in. For this reason, you want to be sure to have a safe place to store your cards where they won't get damaged. There are lots of different options for storing baseball cards. If you have just a few important cards that you want to protect, you can purchase sleeves to store them in. Sleeves are firm plastic wrappers that are slightly larger than a card. You simply slip the card into the opening on the sleeve, and it is protected from wetness and bending. If you have several cards to store, consider buying boxes or albums. At baseball card shops, you can buy boxes that are specially designed to store baseball cards. For serious baseball card collectors with very valuable cards, cases that lock are the ideal spot to store your cards.

Once you've collected cards for a while, you'll want a way to keep track of what cards you have in your collection. Those with small collections can use a notebook where they write down the players' names and dates of the cards they have. For those with larger collections, the computer is the best place to keep track of their collections. While you can create your own database of cards using a software program on your computer, there are also special baseball card software programs that make it much easier. Beckett, the company that publishes a most popular guide to baseball card values, sells a computer program with the names of cards already loaded into it. You simply need to go in and click on the names of cards to record those that are part of your collection.

## Types of Baseball Cards You Can Collect

There are four main companies that produce baseball cards: Topps, Upper Deck, Fleer, and Donruss/

Playoff. The most popular and easiest cards to find in stores are those made by Topps and Upper Deck. Each of these companies sells sets of cards. You can either purchase a full set from a baseball card store or show, or you can put together a set by buying enough packs of cards to collect each card in the set. The basic set put out each year by each company is made up of 500 or more cards. Cards feature posed pictures of Major League Baseball players as well as action shots. Within the basic set, there are several subsets that each has a special theme. For example, a card set might have a special subset of homerun heroes within the larger basic set they sell that year. If you buy individual packs of baseball cards to build your set, you'll have a chance at getting insert cards. These are special cards that are printed in limited quantities and are inserted into packs. Insert cards are usually worth more money than basic cards because there are fewer of them produced each year.

For serious baseball collectors, there are premium and specialty cards available. Premium cards come in sets and are printed by the main baseball card companies. These cards are more expensive but feature extra perks. For example, parallel sets of premium cards are the same as the basic set but are fancier. They might have bolder colors or special borders. In addition to premium sets, serious baseball card collectors like to collect rookie cards. A rookie card is a player's first baseball card. The year that the player is placed on a team's roster, he becomes a rookie. Rookie cards become very valuable when the player goes on to have a successful career. Autographed baseball cards are another great find for devoted baseball card collectors. There are two types of autographed cards: those with autographs signed on the actual card and those with autographs cut from other sources that are glued onto the card. This second type is known as cut autos. Cut autos are usually created for players who are no longer living.

A new type of baseball card has just come out in the last few years and may totally change card collecting in the future. Digital baseball cards are now available. These cards don't come printed on paper like traditional baseball cards. Instead, they are purchased and stored on the Internet. One of the major companies, Topps, has already had great success with its line of computer based cards called eTopps.

Whatever type of cards you choose to collect, you're sure to find hours of enjoyment in with your new hobby.

http://en.wikibooks.org/wiki/Cultural_Anthropology/Print_version'

2.  **If you wanted to find information about how to start a baseball card collection, which section of this selection would you want to read?**

    Ⓐ  what you need to be a baseball card collector
    Ⓑ  types of baseball cards you can collect
    Ⓒ  what companies make baseball cards
    Ⓓ  looking for a new hobby

## Table of Contents for <u>Flowers of the Farm</u>

I.      Introduction
II.     In the Coppice
III.    Flowers on the Walls
IV.     Three Handsome Weeds
V.      Clover
VI.     In "Ashmead"
VII.    In the Hay-field
VIII.   In the Hay-field (continued)
IX.     In the Corn-field
X.      In the Corn-field (continued)
XI.     On the Chase
XII.    In the Lanes

**3.  Based on this table of contents, what can you tell about how this book is organized?**

Ⓐ  The book is organized by types of flowers.
Ⓑ  The book is organized by locations where the flowers can be found.
Ⓒ  The book is organized chronologically.
Ⓓ  The book is organized by location and type of flower found on the farm.

### All about Skunks

Skunks are animals that people both love and hate. To look at them you'd think they are cuddly little critters. They have cute faces that look almost like those of cats and long black and white fur that seems like it would be soft to pet. You might even think, "Flower on the movie <u>Bambi</u> is sweet and Pepe LePew on cartoons doesn't seem so bad. Certainly I could walk up to a skunk and play with it." Yet getting too close to a skunk is a mistake…a big stinky mistake. Though they may look cute and sweet, they hardly smell so! Skunks produce one of the most powerful odors of all animals.

Black and White with a Long Bushy Tail

Skunks are easy to spot because almost all of them look the same. Most of the 12 species or types of skunks have black, bushy fur with a white stripe running down their long tails. There are a few types of skunks that have brown, grey or red fur and one that has what looks like spots instead of a stripe (but is actually an uneven stripe), but for the most part all skunks look pretty much the same. While their appearances may be very much alike, their sizes can be quite different. A skunk can be anywhere from 15.6 inches long to 37 inches long and can weigh between 1.1 pounds and 18 pounds. Skunks are mostly found in Canada, the United States and Mexico though there are a few kinds that live in the Philippines and Indonesia.

Life as a Skunk

For the most part, skunks like to live by themselves. It's not very often that you'll see a group of skunks together. Usually, they only travel in groups when the weather is cold. This way they can sleep close together to stay warm.

Skunks are also nocturnal animals. This means that they sleep during the day and are active when it is dark outside. Skunks cannot see very well, but they have excellent senses of smell and hearing. It's not surprising that skunks would rather move around during the night knowing that sight is not their best sense. In fact, most skunks are killed when they happen to wander on to roads and are hit by cars. They cannot see where they are and walk into these dangerous areas.

Skunk Chow

Skunks are omnivores meaning that they eat both plants and animals. They can be found eating nuts, berries, roots, leaves, grasses, and even some types of fungi (mushroom-like plants). For animals, they enjoy dining on rodents such as mice and rats, insects, earthworms, frogs, lizards, toads and birds. Sometimes when they are unable to find live animals to eat, they become scavengers eating dead animals left behind. When they live close to people's homes, skunks sometimes will even get into trash cans eating garbage.

When skunks eat, they do not limit themselves to small meals. They like to "pig out" on whatever food they can find. When there is a large amount of food available skunks get very fat very quickly.

Oooh, that Smell!

What's the first thing you think of when you see a skunk? If you answered "stink" then you're like most people. Many of us connect skunks with their smell. In fact, the name "skunk" comes from the Algon-quin Indian word "seganuku" which means "one who squirts". The stinky odor that you smell when skunks are around comes from a liquid that they can spray from two spots near their tails. This "skunk juice" is a mixture of sulfur chemicals. Sulfur is a mineral that smells a lot like rotten eggs which is why skunk spray is so stinky. Watch out if you get any of this juice on you because it is not easy to get off! Skunk spray is very difficult to remove from clothes, skin, and hair. Though lots of pet owners swear that you can get a skunk's smell out of a dog's hair by washing him in tomato juice, the best way to remove the scent is by washing the stinky area with a mixture of hydrogen peroxide, baking soda, and dishwashing soap. This mixture changes the chemicals in the skunk spray so that it no longer stinks.

Not only does skunk juice smell bad, but it also stings. A person who happens to get this fluid on his skin will feel like he's been stung by a bee. The burning feeling caused by skunk spray is so strong that if you were to get it in your eyes you might become blind for a short period of time!
Even though it might seem to people who have been sprayed by skunks that the reason for their stinky smell is to annoy us, there is actually a much more important reason why these animals make and squirt their juice. Skunks use their spray to protect themselves from predators (other animals who are trying to attack them). When the average skunk believes that another animal is about to hurt him he will warn it to get away by first stomping his front legs or running forwards and then backwards. Some

types of skunks will also hiss or stand up on their front legs. If the predator does not back away, the skunk shoots a cloud of his smelly juice into the air in front of the other animal so that it will have to walk through it to get to him. Skunks are able to spray their juice up to 15 feet. When the predator comes near the cloud of spray he usually is so bothered by the smell that he leaves the skunk alone. The odor from the spray is so powerful that it even keeps bears from attacking skunks!

While skunks are able to use this smelly liquid to protect themselves, they try not to use it too often. They only have enough juice in their bodies at a time to spray 5 or 6 times. It takes a skunk's body at least 2 weeks to make more juice. Luckily, once a predator has been sprayed once by a skunk he doesn't usually forget the event. Many animals will stay away from skunks because they remember their horrible smell. As soon as they see a white stripe on a black body they will run away!

Beyond the Stink

Skunks aren't just stinky animals. They can be very helpful to people. Because they enjoy eating insects and rats sometimes people will purposely put skunks in their yards, on their farms, or in their barns to help keep the number of pesky critters down. Some people even enjoy keeping skunks as pets!

http://www.pbs.org/wnet/nature/is-that-skunk-do-skunks-make-good-pets/4569/

4. **If you wanted to find information about how to get the smell of skunk spray out of your dog's fur, which section should you read?**

   Ⓐ Black and White with a Long Bushy Tail
   Ⓑ Life as a Skunk
   Ⓒ Skunk Chow
   Ⓓ Oooh, that Smell!

5. **What three things do not indicate the purpose of providing separate headings in this selection?**

   Ⓐ To relate an interesting fact about skunks
   Ⓑ Discuss what the whole selection is about
   Ⓒ To mention the title of another article about skunks
   Ⓓ To brief on the main idea of the paragraphs below the heading

## The Great Round World and What's Going On In It
### magazine article -- Anonymous author

Blondin was a Frenchman, his father having been one of Napoleon's soldiers.

A story is told of him that when he was five years old he saw an acrobat performing on a tight-rope. He was so pleased with what he saw, that when he got home he stretched a rope between two posts, and, as soon as his mother was out of the way, took his father's fishing-rod, and, using it as a balancing pole, made his first appearance as a tight-rope walker.

He was trained for an acrobat and tight-rope walking, and came to this country with a troupe of pantomimists.

While he visited Niagara Falls, the idea at once struck him that, if he dared to cross those terrible waters on a rope, his fortune would be made. He made up his mind to try it, and stayed in the village of Niagara for weeks, until he had learned just how it would be possible for him to perform the feat.

Then he set about getting the scheme well advertised, and securing plenty of money for himself if he succeeded in accomplishing it.

On August 17th, 1859, he made the trip across the Falls in the presence of 50,000 spectators. This performance made him famous.

His rope was 175 feet above the waters.

He was not satisfied with merely walking across; he crossed again blindfolded, and then carrying a man on his back, and once again wheeling a barrow before him.

In the summer of 1860 he crossed once more in the presence of the Prince of Wales, and carried a man on his back, whom he set down on the rope six times, while he rested.

He died in London, at the age of seventy-three.

**6.  How is this selection organized?**

   Ⓐ  Chronological Order
   Ⓑ  Order of Importance
   Ⓒ  Causes and Effects
   Ⓓ  Comparison-Contrast

**Advertisement from <u>The Great Round World and What's Going On In It</u> magazine -- Anonymous author**

FOUR FAMOUS BOOKS

Every boy and girl is interested in what is going on about them. The authors of this series have gathered together the most interesting kind of information and have told it in a most entertaining way.

Copies will be sent post-paid to any address upon receipt of the price named.

1. Foods and Beverages, by E.A. Beal, M.D. Contains reading lessons on the various kinds of Foods and their hygienic values; on Grains, Fruits, and useful Plants, with elementary botanical instruction relating thereto; and on other common subjects of interest and importance to all, old and young. 281 pages. Cloth, 60 cents.

2. Every-Day Occupations, by H. Warren Clifford, S.D. Quantities of useful facts entertainingly told, relating to work and workers. How Leather is Tanned; How Silk is Made; The Mysteries of Glass-Making, of Cotton Manufacture, of Cloth-Making, of Ship and House Building; The Secrets of the Dyer's Art and the Potter's Skill—all and more are described and explained in detail with wonderful clearness. 330 pages. Cloth, 60 cents.

3. Man and Materials, by Wm. G. Parker, M.E. Shows how man has raised himself from savagery to civilization by utilizing the raw material of the earth. This brings for the first time the wonderful natural resources of the United States to the notice of American children. The progress of the Metal-Working arts simply described and very attractively illustrated. 323 pages. Cloth, 60 cents.

4. Modern Industries and Commerce, by Robert Louis, Ph.D. Treats of commerce and the different means of conveyance used in different eras. Highways, Canals. Tunnels, Railroads, and the Steam Engine are discussed in an entertaining way. Other subjects are Paper Manufacture, Newspapers, Electric Light, Atlantic Cable, the Telephone, and the principal newer commercial applications of Electricity, etc. 329 pages. Cloth, 60 cents.

**7. How does the way the author has structured this advertisement help the reader understand the information in it?**

Ⓐ  The headings organize the topics in the selection.
Ⓑ  The book titles help the reader locate information about specific books.
Ⓒ  The ad is organized from the most interesting to the least interesting book which helps the reader know which books are best to purchase.
Ⓓ  The author numbers the items.

# The Great Barrier Reef

Located off the northeastern coast of Australia is the most complex and diverse ecosystem in the world. The Great Barrier Reef is comprised of more than 3,000 individual coral reefs and is home to a plethora of species of plants and animals.

Geology of Great Barrier Reef

Formation of the Great Barrier Reef began millions of years ago. Volcanic activity created what is known as the Coral Sea Basin and a series of raised islands surrounding the basin. As the sea level changed over time, so did life living in the basin and on the islands. Over time coral reefs grew, died and were buried under sediment from volcanic eruptions. This layer of rich sediment built up over time, forming shelves. The earliest individual coral located on in the raised area now known as the Great Barrier Reef is thought to have formed a half-million years ago. Around 600,000 years ago, complete corals began forming in the area, and the origin of the oldest of those still living today dates back 20,000 years. Sea levels in the area continued to rise until approximately 6,000 years ago. At that point, the water level evened out, creating the ideal conditions for the formation of a fusion of coral and other plant and animal life. The shallow grounds created by years of volcanic activity and sedimentary build up combined with the warm waters and high levels of sunlight provide the perfect environment for the Great Barrier Reef to form and thrive

Life in the Great Barrier Reef

Within the Great Barrier Reef, there are several habitats. Consistent throughout the entire 1616-mile formation are coral reefs. What we consider a piece of coral is actually a collection of several individual coral polyps. Each coral is actually a number of polyps. Coral polyps are living creatures that encase themselves in hard, protective shells made of calcium carbonate. These shells band together, forming colonies. The colonies together are known as reefs. Within the Great Barrier Reef, there are millions of coral featuring a multitude of colors and textures. There are more than 400 species of hard and soft corals living in the Reef.

Housed within the reefs is a vastly diverse collection of animal life, many of which are endangered. Within its waters, the Great Barrier Reef provides homes to 5,000 species of mollusks and 125 species of sharks, stingrays, and skates. In addition, there are more than 1,500 species of fish, including the colorful clownfish. Thirty species of whales, dolphins, and porpoises live in the Great Barrier Reef, including humpback whales which use its warm, shallow waters as breeding grounds before journeying to Hawaii to give birth. Six endangered species of marine turtles also use the area to reproduce. The loggerhead turtle, one of the most highly protected endangered species, lives and breeds in the Great Barrier Reef. Over the last 40 years, the number of these turtles has decreased so rapidly that there are only 3% of the number of the creatures alive today. Housed around this extremely diverse collection of animal life are 2,195 species of plants. Above water 215 species of birds live on the Great Barrier Reef.

Environmental Threats

Because of the diversity, complexity, and uniqueness of the ecosystem, the Great Barrier Reef was placed under the protection of the Australian federal parks system, was named a World Heritage Site in 1981, and has been called one of the Seven Natural Wonders of the World. Still, life in the Reef is at risk.

*Coral Bleaching*

One of the greatest threats to the Great Barrier Reef is climate change, also known as global warming. Three times over the last ten years, the water in the seas surrounding the Great Barrier Reef has risen 1 or more degrees Celsius. While this may not seem that significant, any temperature increase threatens the coral reefs. When the water becomes warmer, the coral become stressed. This stress causes them to force Zooxanthellae, algae living in coral shells essential to the sustenance of the coral polyp, out of their shells. Without this algae, the coral is unable to use photosynthesis to form its color, which is why the phenomenon is known as "coral bleaching". Once the algae are absent, the coral's white skeleton shows, and the coral begins dying, stops reproducing, and becomes vulnerable to disease. The Great Barrier Reef experienced episodes of coral bleaching in 1998, 2002, and 2006. Scientists estimate that the 2002 temperature increase caused 60 to 95% of the Reef's coral to become bleached. Because water temperatures are likely to continue to rise, researchers predict that episodes of coral bleaching will continue to occur. Therefore, the Great Barrier Reef Marine Park Authority has formed a response plan aimed at detecting and responding to future occurrences.

*Crown of Thorns Starfish*

Another natural threat to the Great Barrier Reef is the Crown of Thorns Starfish. This creature which is a naturally occurring species feeds on coral. While a small number of starfish pose no major threat to the vast collection of coral reefs, when they rapidly multiply, they place the Reef at risk. Eradicating these creatures (by forcing them to migrate out of the area) takes anywhere between 1 and 15 years.

Over the last 40 years, there have been three major outbreaks of Crown of Thorn Starfish. During those periods large portions of the coral reefs were damaged. These outbreaks combined with episodes of coral bleaching have had dramatic impacts on the coral forming the foundation of the Great Barrier Reef as well as threatening marine and bird species living in the Reef.

Human Impact

Not all of the destruction of the Great Barrier Reef has come from natural sources. Human actions have also negatively impacted the area. Water pollution has threatened life in the Reef. A series of rivers feed the sea where the Reef is located. These rivers have flooded farm lands upstream siphoning large amounts of pesticides used on cattle and sugar cane farms surrounding the rivers. These waters then empty into the seas polluting the waters that the ecosystem.

In addition, land development poses risks to the Great Barrier Reef. Because of its beauty and diversity, the area attracts a huge number of visitors. Though the Reef is protected by the Australian Parks

Authority, the tourism industry has built up commercial areas on the lands surrounding the area.

This coastal development threatens the delicate ecosystem adjacent to it.

Beyond this, boats have damaged the Reef. Fishing boats have stripped the area of a number of key species of fish including the Giant Triton. While fishing of certain types of fish has been limited, the boats legitimately fishing in the area pose a potential threat to the entire collection of life located in the Great Barrier Reef. Because the boats carry large amounts of oil necessary for their operation, they always hold the possibility of creating a hazardous situation by spilling the oil into the area's waters.

8.  **How is this selection organized?**

    Ⓐ  Using headings
    Ⓑ  Using subheadings
    Ⓒ  Using graphics
    Ⓓ  Using topics

9.  **If the writer wanted to add the example of people dumping their beach garbage into the reef to the selection, what section would it best fit into?**

    Ⓐ  Geology of Great Barrier Reef
    Ⓑ  Life in the Great Barrier Reef
    Ⓒ  Coral Bleaching
    Ⓓ  Human Impact

### Summer Safety Tips for your Pets

Never leave your pets in a parked car.

In the heat of summer, there is no safe amount of time to leave your pet in a parked car. Even if you leave the engine running and the air conditioning on, the temperature inside the vehicle can go up very quickly. According to the Humane Society, on an 85 degree day, the temperature in a car with the windows slightly open can go up to 102 degrees in ten minutes or less. In less than an hour, that temperature can go up to 120 degrees or more! Your pet could suffer permanent organ damage or worse from exposure to high temperatures. If you plan to go somewhere where your pet is not allowed inside, leave him home!

Pets feel humidity too.

Unlike humans, animals don't sweat from pores all over their bodies. Animals pant or breathe rapidly to eliminate heat and moisture from their bodies. If there is a lot of moisture in the air, panting is less effective, and the pet could become overheated and have no way to release that heat. A dehumidifier or air conditioner will remove moisture from the air and make your pet's natural cooling mechanism more effective.

Fans don't help animals very much.

When a human stands in front of a fan, the air current rushes over his or her skin and helps evaporate the moisture from sweating. Evaporation helps a human feel cooler. Dogs only sweat from the pads on the bottoms of their feet. Standing in front of a fan doesn't help a dog, since there isn't a large amount of evaporation going on.

Limit exercise on hot days.

Do you feel like running when the temperature is high? Why not? Generally, exercising in extreme heat makes you thirsty and very tired. Too much exercise could lead to heat stroke, a dangerous condition when your body isn't able to cool down. Your pets can suffer the same consequences. When it is extremely hot outside, try to exercise your pet only in the morning or evening when the temperature is cooler and cut down the amount of time your pet spends running around.

http://www.petfinder.com/dogs/dog-care/leaving-pet-parked-car-deadly/

**10. How is this article organized?**

- Ⓐ By subtopic
- Ⓑ Chronologically
- Ⓒ By order of importance
- Ⓓ Alphabetically

## Chapter 3

## Lesson 13: Finding Patterns - Comparing And Contrasting

**THE WONDERFUL HAIR by A. H. Wraitslaw**

There was a man who was very poor, but so well supplied with children that he was utterly unable to maintain them, and one morning more than once prepared to kill them, in order not to see their misery in dying of hunger, but his wife prevented him. One night a child came to him in his sleep, and said to him: "Man! I see that you are making up your mind to destroy and to kill your poor little children, and I know that you are distressed thereat; but in the morning you will find under your pillow a mirror, a red kerchief, and an embroidered pocket-handkerchief; take all three secretly and tell no-body; then go to such a hill; by it you will find a stream; go along it till you come to its fountain-head; there you will find a damsel as bright as the sun, with her hair hanging down over her back. Be on your guard, that the ferocious she-dragon do not coil around you; do not converse with her if she speaks; for if you converse with her, she will poison you, and turn you into a fish or something else, and will then devour you but if she bids you examine her head, examine it, and as you turn over her hair, look, and you will find one hair as red as blood; pull it out and run back again; then, if she suspects and begins to run after you, throw her first the embroidered pocket-handkerchief, then the kerchief, and, lastly, the mirror; then she will find occupation for herself. And sell that hair to some rich man; but don't let them cheat you, for that hair is worth countless wealth; and you will thus enrich yourself and maintain your children."

When the poor man awoke, he found everything under his pillow, just as the child had told him in his sleep; and then he went to the hill. When there, he found the stream, went on and on alongside of it, till he came to the fountain-head. Having looked about him to see where the damsel was, he espied her above a piece of water, like sunbeams threaded on a needle, and she was embroidering at a frame on stuff, the threads of which were young men's hair. As soon as he saw her, he made a reverence to her, and she stood on her feet and questioned him: "Whence are you, unknown young man?" But he held his tongue. She questioned him again: "Who are you? Why have you come?" and much else of all sorts; but he was as mute as a stone, making signs with his hands, as if he were deaf and wanted help. Then she told him to sit down on her skirt. He did not wait for any more orders, but sat down, and she bent down her head to him, that he might examine it. Turning over the hair of her head, as if to examine it, he was not long in finding that red hair, and separated it from the other hair, pulled it out, jumped off her skirt and ran away back as he best could. She noticed it, and ran at his heels full speed after him. He looked around, and seeing that she was about to overtake him, threw, as he was told, the embroidered pocket-handkerchief on the way, and when she saw the pocket-handkerchief she stooped and began to overhaul it in every direction, admiring the embroidery, till he had got a good way off. Then the damsel placed the pocket-handkerchief in her bosom, and ran after him again.

When he saw that she was about to overtake him, he threw the red kerchief, and she again occupied herself, admiring and gazing, till the poor man had again got a good way off. Then the damsel became exasperated, and threw both the pocket-handkerchief and the kerchief on the way, and ran after him in pursuit. Again, when he saw that she was about to overtake him, he threw the mirror. When the damsel came to the mirror, the like of which she had never seen before, she lifted it up, and when she saw herself in it, not knowing that it was herself, but thinking that it was somebody else, she, as it were, fell in love with herself in the mirror, and the man got so far off that she was no longer able to overtake him. When she saw that she could not catch him, she turned back, and the man reached his home safe and sound. After arriving at his home, he showed his wife the hair, and told her all that had happened to him, but she began to jeer and laugh at him.

But he paid no attention to her, and went to a town to sell the hair. A crowd of all sorts of people and merchants collected round him; one offered a sequin, another two, and so on, higher and higher, till they came to a hundred gold sequins. Just then the emperor heard of the hair, summoned the man into his presence, and said to him that he would give him a thousand sequins for it, and he sold it to him. What was the hair? The emperor split it in two from top to bottom, and found registered in it in writing many remarkable things, which happened in the olden time since the beginning of the world. Thus the man became rich and lived on with his wife and children. And that child, that came to him in his sleep, was an angel sent by the Lord God, whose will it was to aid the poor man, and to reveal secrets which had not been revealed till then.

1. **How is the outcome of this selection different than what the little boy predicted when he spoke to his father through a dream?**

   Ⓐ The father is not able to earn a great deal of money by selling the damsel's hair.
   Ⓑ The damsel comes after the father and attacks him.
   Ⓒ The boy's prediction is accurate. There is no difference.
   Ⓓ The father is not happy with the boy's instructions.

### "The Smith and the Fairies": A Gaelic Folk Tale (Ed. Kate Douglas Wiggin)

Years ago there lived in Crossbrig a smith of the name of MacEachern. This man had an only child, a boy of about thirteen or fourteen years of age, cheerful, strong, and healthy. All of a sudden he fell ill; took to his bed and moped whole days away. No one could tell what was the matter with him, and the boy himself could not, or would not, tell how he felt. He was wasting away fast; getting thin, old, and yellow; and his father and all his friends were afraid that he would die.

At last one day, after the boy had been lying in this condition for a long time, getting neither better nor worse, always confined to bed, but with an extraordinary appetite—one day, while sadly revolving these things, and standing idly at his forge, with no heart to work, the smith was agreeably surprised to see an old man, well known for his sagacity and knowledge of out-of-the-way things, walk into his workshop. Forthwith he told him the occurrence which had clouded his life.

The old man looked grave as he listened; and after sitting a long time pondering over all he had heard, gave his opinion thus: "It is not your son you have got. The boy has been carried away by the 'Daione Sith,' and they have left a Sibhreach in his place."
"Alas! and what then am I to do?" said the smith. "How am I ever to see my own son again?"

"I will tell you how," answered the old man. "But, first, to make sure that it is not your own son you have got, take as many empty egg-shells as you can get, go into his room, spread them out carefully before his sight, then proceed to draw water with them, carrying them two and two in your hands as if they were a great weight, and arrange them when full, with every sort of earnestness around the fire." The smith accordingly gathered as many broken egg-shells as he could get, went into the room, and proceeded to carry out all his instructions.

He had not been long at work before there arose from the bed a shout of laughter, and the voice of the seeming sick boy exclaimed, "I am eight hundred years of age, and I have never seen the like of that before." The smith returned and told the old man.

"Well, now," said the sage to him, "did I not tell you that it was not your son you had: your son is in Borracheill in a digh there (that is, a round green hill frequented by fairies). Get rid as soon as possible of this intruder, and I think I may promise you your son. You must light a very large and bright fire before the bed on which this stranger is lying. He will ask you, 'What is the use of such a fire as that?' Answer him at once, 'You will see that presently!' and then seize him, and throw him into the middle of it. If it is your own son you have got, he will call out to you to save him; but if not, the thing will fly through the roof."

The smith again followed the old man's advice: kindled a large fire, answered the question put to him as he had been directed to do, and seizing the child flung him in without hesitation. The Sibhreach gave an awful yell, and sprang through the roof, where a hole had been left to let the smoke out.

On a certain night the old man told him the green round hill, where the fairies kept the boy, would be open, and on that date the smith, having provided himself with a Bible, a dirk, and a crowing cock, was to proceed to the hill. He would hear singing and dancing, and much merriment going on, he had been told, but he was to advance boldly; the Bible he carried would be a certain safeguard to him against any danger from the fairies. On entering the hill he was to stick the dirk in the threshold, to prevent the hill from closing upon him; "and then," continued the old man, "on entering you will see a spacious apartment before you, beautifully clean, and there, standing far within, working at a forge, you will also see your own son. When you are questioned, say you come to seek him, and will not go without him."

Not long after this, the time came round, and the smith sallied forth, prepared as instructed. Sure enough as he approached the hill, there was a light where light was seldom seen before. Soon after, a sound of piping, dancing, and joyous merriment reached the anxious father on the night wind.

Overcoming every impulse to fear, the smith approached the threshold steadily, stuck the dirk into it as directed, and entered. Protected by the Bible he carried on his breast, the fairies could not touch him; but they asked him, with a good deal of displeasure, what he wanted there. He answered, "I want my son, whom I see down there, and I will not go without him."

Upon hearing this the whole company before him gave a loud laugh, which wakened up the cock he carried dozing in his arms, who at once leaped up on his shoulders, clapped his wings lustily, and crowed loud and long.

The fairies, incensed, seized the smith and his son, and throwing them out of the hill, flung the dirk after them, and in an instant all was dark.

For a year and a day the boy never did a turn of work, and hardly ever spoke a word; but at last one day, sitting by his father and watching him finishing a sword he was making for some chief, and which he was very particular about, he suddenly exclaimed, "That is not the way to do it;" and taking the tools from his father's hands he set to work himself in his place, and soon fashioned a sword, the like of which was never seen in the country before.

From that day the young man wrought constantly with his father, and became the inventor of a peculiarly fine and well-tempered weapon, the making of which kept the two smiths, father and son, in constant employment, spread their fame far and wide, and gave them the means in abundance, as they before had the disposition, to live content with all the world and very happily with each other.

2.  **How is the fairy pretend version of the smith's son different than the smith's actual son?**

    Ⓐ  The fairy is a trickster, while the real son is cheerful, strong, and a healthy young man.
    Ⓑ  The fairy is cruel to the father, while the real son is kind to his father.
    Ⓒ  The fairy and the son are alike.
    Ⓓ  The fairy and the father are alike.

### The Two Melons A Chinese Folk Tale (Ed. Kate Douglas Wiggin)

An honest and poor old woman was washing clothes at a pool, when a bird that a hunter had disabled by a shot in the wing, fell down into the water before her. She gently took up the bird, carried it home with her, dressed its wound, and fed it until it was well, when it soared away. Some days later it returned, put before her an oval seed, and departed again. The woman planted the seed in her yard and when it came up she recognized the leaf as that of a melon. She made a trellis for it, and gradually a fruit formed on it, and grew to great size.

Toward the end of the year, the old dame was unable to pay her debts, and her poverty so weighed upon her that she became ill. Sitting one day at her door, feverish and tired, she saw that the melon was ripe, and looked luscious; so she determined to try its unknown quality. Taking a knife, she severed the melon from its stalk, and was surprised to hear it chink in her hands. On cutting it in two, she found it full of silver and gold pieces, with which she paid her debts and bought supplies for many days.

Among her neighbors was a busybody who craftily found out how the old woman had so suddenly become rich. Thinking there was no good reason why she should not herself be equally fortunate, she washed clothes at the pool, keeping a sharp lookout for birds until she managed to hit and maim one of a flock that was flitting over the water. She then took the disabled bird home, and treated it with care till its wing healed and it flew away. Shortly afterward it came back with a seed in its beak, laid it before her, and again took flight. The woman quickly planted the seed, saw it come up and spread its leaves, made a trellis for it, and had the gratification of seeing a melon form on its stalk.

In prospect of her future wealth, she ate rich food, bought fine garments, and got so deeply into debt that, before the end of the year, she was harried by duns. But the melon grew apace, and she was delighted to find that, as it ripened, it became of vast size, and that when she shook it there was a great rattling inside. At the end of the year she cut it down, and divided it, expecting it to be a coffer of coins; but there crawled out of it two old, lame, hungry beggars, who told her they would remain and eat at her table as long as they lived.

3.  **How are the busybody neighbor and the honest old woman different?**

   Ⓐ  They are not different. They are both poor and hungry.
   Ⓑ  The honest old woman acts out of selflessness while the busybody neighbor acts out of self interest.
   Ⓒ  The honest old woman is much poorer than the busybody neighbor.
   Ⓓ  The honest old woman minds her own business while the busybody neighbor is concerned with everyone else's business.

4.  **Select two themes discussed in the story from the options below.**

   Ⓐ  Greed
   Ⓑ  Surprises
   Ⓒ  The rewards of genuine kindness
   Ⓓ  Being physically strong

### "Love Between Brothers and Sisters" by Isaac Watts

Whatever brawls disturb the street,
There should be peace at home;
Where sisters dwell and brothers meet,
Quarrels should never come.

Birds in their little nests agree;
And 'tis a shameful sight,
When children of one family
Fall out and chide and fight.

5.  **Which statement contrasts with the author's viewpoint in this poem?**

   Ⓐ  Brothers and sisters should try their hardest to love one another.
   Ⓑ  Nothing good can come from siblings arguing with one another.
   Ⓒ  There's no harm in siblings occasionally not getting along with one another.
   Ⓓ  It is natural for siblings to have arguments.

## TO MAKE AN AMBLONGUS PIE
### by Edward Lear

Take 4 pounds (say 4½ pounds) of fresh Amblongusses, and put them in a small pipkin.

Cover them with water, and boil them for 8 hours incessantly; after which, add 2 pints of new milk, and proceed to boil for 4 hours more.

When you have ascertained that the Amblongusses are quite soft, take them out, and place them in a wide pan, taking care to shake them well previously.

Grate some nutmeg over the surface, and cover them carefully with powdered gingerbread, curry-powder, and a sufficient quantity of Cayenne pepper.

Remove the pan into the next room, and place it on the floor. Bring it back again, and let it simmer for three-quarters of an hour. Shake the pan violently till all the Amblongusses have become of a pale purple color.

Then, having prepared the paste, insert the whole carefully, adding at the same time a small pigeon, 2 slices of beef, 4 cauliflowers, and any number of oysters.

Watch patiently till the crust begins to rise, and add a pinch of salt from time to time.

Serve up in a clean dish, and throw the whole out of the window as fast as possible.

6.  **How is this recipe different than a typical recipe? Select two options.**

    Ⓐ  This recipe is nonsense while real recipes are intended to be made.
    Ⓑ  The directions in this recipe are mentioned as a paragraph and not as steps like a typical recipe.
    Ⓒ  This recipe uses exotic ingredients while typical recipes use common ingredients.
    Ⓓ  This recipe is written such that it is much more time consuming than a typical recipe.


### Best Friend

Max had started playing on the football team and didn't have much time for Julie anymore. He was always busy, and he never seemed to make it to study hall, where the two used to swap stories about their favorite (or least favorite) teachers. In class, Julie noticed that Max never seemed to have his homework done on time anymore. She even noticed that he got a 'D' on his last paper. She knew something was going on with him – but what?
At first, Julie decided to play it cool and see how things went. She tried waiting in the hall for Max after class to see if she could ask if he was OK. But days went by, and he never had time to stop. He'd rush right past her in the hall, only to leave her feeling even worse about what was happening between them.

Even though she wasn't sure she could handle the situation herself, Julie didn't want to talk to her parents because she was afraid they would tell her not to hang out with Max anymore. She barely saw him as it was, so she knew it would just make things worse if her parents didn't approve of him. She didn't want to tell Max's parents either because she didn't want him to get in trouble. Still, it seemed like something needed to change. Julie decided to go to one of her school counselors and let her know she was concerned.

When she walked into Mrs. Smith's room, she was surprised to see that Max was already sitting there.

"I'm sorry, I'll come back," Julie said.
"No, stay," said Max. "Maybe you can help."

Julie was surprised to find that Max had visited the counselor's office for the same reason she had: He was starting to feel overwhelmed with all of the things he was supposed to be doing as a student, an athlete, and a friend. He needed some guidance on how to determine what truly mattered and how to divide his time between all of the things that were important to him. When she realized that Max was still the same old Max (just a little more stressed), Julie was relieved. She was also happy to know that he had come to a conclusion on his own, without her having to talk to someone else about it. She decided it was a sign they were both growing up.

7. **Even though Julie and Max are interested in different things once they enter high school, what remains the same about the two of them?**

   Ⓐ They both care about each other.
   Ⓑ They are both interested in sports.
   Ⓒ They both want to do well in school.
   Ⓓ They both need help in their classes.

## A VALENTINE TO CATHERINE
### by Evaleen Stein

If you will be my True-Love,
I'll tell you what I'll do,
I'll ask a little bluebird
To sing a song to you.

When first you see a violet
And softly pricking through
The garden-bed come crocuses
And golden tulips, too,

Then watch! for he'll be coming,
The little bird of blue;
He'll sing, "I love you, Sweetheart,
It's true, true, true!"

8. **How is this Valentine poem unlike the valentines people exchange on Valentine's Day today?**

   Ⓐ The poem and valentines show love for the people they are given to.
   Ⓑ The poem and valentines have "I love you" written in them.
   Ⓒ The poem uses a bird to convey a valentine message.
   Ⓓ There is no difference in either types of cards.

### From "The Strike of the Fireworks" by Carolyn Wells

'Twas the night before the Fourth of July, the people slept serene;
The fireworks were stored in the old town hall that stood on the village green.
The steeple clock tolled the midnight hour, and at its final stroke,
The fire in the queer old-fashioned stove lifted its voice and spoke;
"The earth and air have naught to do, the water, too, may play,
And only fire is made to work on Independence Day.

9. **How is the scene described in this stanza of the poem typical of a Fourth of July celebration?**

   Ⓐ The people in town go to bed early on the Fourth of July.
   Ⓑ There is a fireworks celebration held in the town on the Fourth of July.
   Ⓒ There is a bonfire on the Fourth of July.
   Ⓓ There is a town clock that strikes midnight.

**"Base Details"**
**Siegfried Sassoon**

IF I were fierce, and bald, and short of breath,
I'd live with scarlet Majors at the Base,
And speed glum heroes up the line to death.

You'd see me with my puffy petulant face,
Guzzling and gulping in the best hotel,
Reading the Roll of Honour. 'Poor young chap,'
I'd say—'I used to know his father well;
Yes, we've lost heavily in this last scrap.'

And when the war is done and youth stone dead,
I'd toddle safely home and die—in bed.

**10. Which statements are inferred by this poem?**

Ⓐ He is young and may still be fighting in the war.
Ⓑ He is old and gray and on the opposite side of the war.
Ⓒ People have died tragically in the war.
Ⓓ The speaker is being sarcastic in the poem.

## Lesson 14: Comparing Media

**Fall Leaves**
**USDA Forest Service**

We almost always think of trees as being green, but there is one time of year when their leaves turn a myriad orange, red, yellow, and brown: the beautiful and chilly days of fall. Those living in the Eastern or Northern United States come to anticipate the change in color starting in September or October every single year. But what causes the leaves to change color, and why? Just like many animals that hibernate for the winter, trees experience a unique change during the winter months. During summer, for instance, plants use the process of photosynthesis to transform carbon dioxide found in the air into organic compounds like sugars using energy from the sun. During the winter, however, there is less light to go around, and their ability to create food from the photosynthesis process is limited. What does that have to do with a leaf's color? The substance that allows trees to turn carbon dioxide into food (chlorophyll) is also the cause of the leaf's green sheen. As the photosynthesis process wanes in the colder months due to the lack of sun, so does its greenish hue, allowing other elements present in the leaf to show through. Believe it or not, the yellows and oranges that appear in fall have actually been there all year in the form of nutrients like carotene (also found in carrots). The intense green color of the chlorophyll had simply overshadowed them. But what about the reds and browns? And what causes the leaves to fall away after they change color? The bright reds and purples in each leaf come from a strong antioxidant that many trees create on their own because of their protective qualities. The antioxidant helps protect the trees from the sun, lower their freezing levels, and protect them from frost. As winter comes, so does the need for the antioxidant (similar to the way a dog gets more fur during winter to stay warmer). As for the leaves falling, that is another story. At the base of each leaf, there is a layer of cells that carry food and water from the leaf to the tree during the summer months to keep it fed. In the fall, that layer actually starts to harden, preventing the passage of nutrients. Because of this, the nutrients and waste that previously passed from the leaf into the tree become trapped in the leaf with no fresh water to clean it. Not only does this cause the leaf to turn brown, eventually, but it also causes the cells within it to harden so much that the leaf tears and blows away. Thus the pile of leaves you enjoyed jumping in as a child.

Because each tree, and each leaf, contains a unique amount of nutrients depending on how well-nourished it was over the spring and summer, the way each leaf breaks down during the winter months is also quite different. The result is the unique and complex facet of colors we see in each neighborhood or forest each fall.

http://www.sciencemadesimple.com/leaves.htm

1. **If this passage was turned into a video documentary, what would it include to help you understand how the leaves change color?**

   Ⓐ Time-lapse video of the leaves changing color
   Ⓑ Paintings by artists depicting fall leaves
   Ⓒ Pictures of animals that hibernate during the winter
   Ⓓ Subtitles of the text on the screen

2. **You've been asked to turn this passage into a slide show presentation. Which graphic would you use to help explain the process of leaves changing color?**

   Ⓐ A picture of leaves that have changed color
   Ⓑ A picture of animals hibernating
   Ⓒ A diagram of the process leaves go through when changing color
   Ⓓ A diagram explaining when leaves change color around the world

3. **A naturalist is presenting this information to a class of students. Which visual aid could she bring to help students understand the information in the passage?**

   Ⓐ A picture of leaves that have changed color
   Ⓑ A pile of leaves of different colors
   Ⓒ A photograph of a pile of leaves
   Ⓓ A diagram explaining the process

### History of Olympics
### From *Ancient Olympics Guide*

Even though the modern Olympic Games are held every four years, they bear little resemblance to the athletic contests held at Olympia in Greece in ancient times. The games were open to competitors from all over Greece, and the contests included chariot racing, horse racing, running, wrestling, boxing, and the pentathlon, a contest involving jumping, quoit throwing, javelin throwing, running, and wrestling. Scholars date the earliest contests at 776 B.C., more than two and a half thousand years ago. The first trophies that were won consisted not of gold medals and cups but of simple crowns of olive leaves. Women and slaves were admitted neither as contestants nor as spectators. The classical games ceased to be held probably about A.D.393.

Much of the credit for the revival of the Games held at Athens in 1896 goes to Baron Pierre de Coubertin, a French classical scholar, who greatly admired the sporting ideals of the ancient Greeks. As an educationist and lover of amateurism, he looked upon physical exercise as an essential feature of a balanced education. Forty-two events were contested, and new disciplines such as cycling, hurdling, high jump, shooting, and gymnastics were introduced. One of the most popular events of the modern Olympics is the marathon. This very tiring twenty-six-mile foot race over an open course is the supreme test of the runners' endurance. The marathon was not a part of the ancient Olympics, although it originated in Greece. And, finally, a more recent development in the Olympics is the introduction of the winter games, which were started in 1924. They are held separately from the summer games but in the same year. The Winter Olympics provide competition in skiing, speed and figure skating, ice hockey, and rifle shooting. Such cold weather sports could never have developed in the warm climate of Greece

4. **The History Channel is making a documentary based on this passage. What would be most helpful for them to include?**

   Ⓐ Footage from recent Olympic games
   Ⓑ Video of the original Olympic games
   Ⓒ Images showing the different Olympic sports from the beginning until now.
   Ⓓ Interviews with current Olympic athletes

5. **A gym teacher wants students to understand this passage better. What can the teacher do to make this passage more interactive?**

   Ⓐ Play a video about the Olympics
   Ⓑ Have students play some of the sports
   Ⓒ Show students pictures of the Olympics
   Ⓓ Bring in an Olympic athlete to talk to students

6. **A news station has turned this piece into a special news report. When should they NOT air it?**

   Ⓐ Around the next summer or winter Olympic games
   Ⓑ Right before the Super Bowl
   Ⓒ Sometime in the Fall
   Ⓓ Sometime in the Spring

### Egyptian Pyramids

Today, we have high-tech cranes and other machines to help us create massive skyscrapers and other modern works of architecture. Still, some of the most breathtaking architecture in the world, such as the ancient pyramids of Egypt, were created before those high-tech machines even existed. So how did those ancient civilizations create them?

Believe it or not, though they are one of the most studied and admired relics in history, there is no evidence to tell historians exactly how the Ancient Egyptians built the pyramids. Thus, they have been left to create their own theories as to how Egyptians created such amazing and awe-inspiring works of art.

According to one theory, the Egyptians placed logs under the large stone blocks in order to roll or transport them to the pyramid building location. Large groups of men would work to push or pull them into place (although historians also disagree on whether these men were slaves or skilled artisans). Still more, once the men moved the blocks to the pyramid location, they needed to lift them to ever-increasing heights to reach the top levels of the pyramid as it grew. Without modern cranes, many scientists have been baffled as to how they were able to do it. Some believe they used a ramp system that would allow them to roll the blocks upward around or through the pyramids; others believe they must have used a combination of pulleys and lifts. Still, most agree that once they did, they used a mixture of gravel and limestone to help fill any crevices and hold the mound together.

With such a primitive yet impressive building process, it's obvious that the pyramids must have taken a great deal of time to build. With an estimated 2 million blocks weighing an average of 2.5 million tons each, the Great Pyramid of Giza, for instance, is estimated to have taken some 20 years to build. At 481 feet tall, it held the record of tallest building for 3,800 years – not bad for a building created almost entirely by hand.

Even though scientists don't know exactly how the Egyptians did it, they do know that the method the Egyptians used to build pyramids changed over time. In the early days, the pyramids were made completely of stone, with limestone used to create the main body and higher quality limestone being used for the smooth outer casing. Later on, the pyramids were made mostly of mud brick with a limestone casing. Though they were likely much easier to build, they didn't stand up nearly as well over time, leaving archaeologists with even fewer clues about their creation.

http://en.wikipedia.org/wiki/Egyptian_pyramid_construction_techniques

7. **This passage is being displayed as part of a museum exhibit. What would it most likely NOT be accompanied by? Select those that apply.**

   Ⓐ Pictures of modern-day construction trucks
   Ⓑ Pictures of Egyptians building the pyramids
   Ⓒ Relics from Ancient Egypt
   Ⓓ Items from Egyptian kings

8. **If creating a documentary based on this passage, what would the director most likely use in the opening sequence related to the opening of the passage? Select those that apply.**

   Ⓐ Experts talking about the pyramids
   Ⓑ Illustrations of the pyramids
   Ⓒ Illustrations of Egyptian kings who got pyramids built
   Ⓓ Illustrations of modern-day houses

9. **If this passage was turned into a play, what would it most likely be about?**

   Ⓐ A specific modern-day construction worker
   Ⓑ A factual account of how pyramids were built
   Ⓒ A specific pyramid-builder or group of pyramids
   Ⓓ An interpretive dance of the building of pyramids

### From <u>Guiseppi Verdi</u>
### by Thomas Trapper

Whenever the organ man came into the village of Roncole, in Italy (where Verdi was born, October 10, 1813), Verdi could not be kept indoors. But he followed the wonderful organ and the wonderful man who played it, all day long, as happy as he could be.

When Guiseppi was seven years old, his father, though only a poor innkeeper, bought him a spinet, a sort of small piano. So faithfully did the little boy practice that the spinet was soon quite worn out and new jacks, or hammers, had to be made for it. This was done by Stephen Cavaletti, who wrote a message on one of the jacks telling that he made them anew and covered them with leather, and fixed the pedal, doing all for nothing, because the little boy, Guiseppi Verdi, showed such willingness to practice and to learn. Thus the good Stephen thought this was pay enough.

**10. If turned into a media production, this passage would most likely be…?**

- Ⓐ A story on the local news
- Ⓑ A play at the local theater
- Ⓒ A slideshow presentation
- Ⓓ A song about Verdi

## Chapter 3

## Lesson 15: How It's Made And What It Means

### "Do Not Go Gentle into that Good Night"
### Dylan Thomas

Do not go gentle into that good night,
Old age should burn and rave at close of day;
Rage, rage against the dying of the light.

Though wise men at their end know dark is right,
Because their words had forked no lightning they
Do not go gentle into that good night.

Good men, the last wave by, crying how bright
Their frail deeds might have danced in a green bay,
Rage, rage against the dying of the light.

Wild men who caught and sang the sun in flight,
And learn, too late, they grieved it on its way,
Do not go gentle into that good night.

Grave men, near death, who see with blinding sight
Blind eyes could blaze like meteors and be gay,
Rage, rage against the dying of the light.

And you, my father, there on the sad height,
Curse, bless me now with your fierce tears, I pray.
Do not go gentle into that good night.
Rage, rage against the dying of the light.

1. **Which three characteristics of this poem indicates it is a villanelle?**

   Ⓐ There are nineteen lines.
   Ⓑ The poem has five tercets.
   Ⓒ The subject of the poem is death.
   Ⓓ There is a quatrain at the end.

2. **Which answer does not use repetition to develop the tone of this poem?**

    Ⓐ The word rage is repeated to develop the idea that one can fight back against death.
    Ⓑ The word men is repeated to remind the subject about whom he is writing.
    Ⓒ The word gentle is repeated to remind the reader how to behave.
    Ⓓ The word me is repeated to establish the focus of the poem.

3. **How is end rhyme used to make connections between the stanzas?**

    Ⓐ Every other line rhymes.
    Ⓑ Each stanza uses the same rhyme scheme.
    Ⓒ The rhyme scheme changes every other stanza.
    Ⓓ The last line of each stanza rhymes with the first line of the next stanza.

## Ethan Frome
## Edith Wharton

I had the story, bit by bit, from various people, and, as generally happens in such cases, each time it was a different story.

If you know Starkfield, Massachusetts, you know the post-office. If you know the post-office you must have seen Ethan Frome drive up to it, drop the reins on his hollow-backed bay and drag himself across the brick pavement to the white colonnade; and you must have asked who he was.

It was there that, several years ago, I saw him for the first time; and the sight pulled me up sharp. Even then he was the most striking figure in Starkfield, though he was but the ruin of a man. It was not so much his great height that marked him, for the "natives" were easily singled out by their lank longitude from the stockier foreign breed: it was the careless powerful look he had, in spite of a lameness checking each step like the jerk of a chain. There was something bleak and unapproachable in his face, and he was so stiffened and grizzled that I took him for an old man and was surprised to hear that he was not more than fifty-two. I had this from Harmon Gow, who had driven the stage from Bettsbridge to Starkfield in pre-trolley days and knew the chronicle of all the families on his line.

"He's looked that way ever since he had his smash-up; and that's twenty four years ago come next February," Harmon threw out between reminiscent pauses.

The "smash-up" it was—I gathered from the same informant—which, besides drawing the red gash across Ethan Frome's forehead, had so shortened and warped his right side that it cost him a visible effort to take the few steps from his buggy to the post-office window. He used to drive in from his farm every day at about noon, and as that was my own hour for fetching my mail I often passed him in the porch or stood beside him while we waited on the motions of the distributing hand behind the grating. I noticed that, though he came so punctually, he seldom received anything but a copy of the Bettsbridge Eagle, which he put without a glance into his sagging pocket. At intervals, however, the post-master would hand him an envelope addressed to Mrs. Zenobia —or Mrs. Zeena-Frome, and usually bearing conspicuously in the upper left-hand corner the address of some manufacturer of patent medicine and the name of his specific. These documents my neighbour would also pocket without a glance, as if too much used to them to wonder at their number and variety, and would then turn away with a silent nod to the post-master.

4. **What does this prologue to the story, Ethan Frome, suggest about the story that is about to be told?**

Ⓐ That it is a true story.
Ⓑ That the story is based in part on rumors heard about town.
Ⓒ That the narrator is not certain of the accuracy of all of the details she is about to present.
Ⓓ That the narrator has known the subject of the story for a long time.

5. **Why might the author have included this prologue?**

Ⓐ To relieve herself of any responsibility for the story's accuracy.
Ⓑ To explain how she became familiar with the story she is about to tell.
Ⓒ To explain the importance of accuracy in the story that will follow.
Ⓓ To hint at how the story will end.

### Excerpt from Romeo and Juliet
### By William Shakespeare

PROLOGUE

Two households, both alike in dignity,
In fair Verona, where we lay our scene,
From ancient grudge break to new mutiny,
Where civil blood makes civil hands unclean.
From forth the fatal loins of these two foes
A pair of star-cross'd lovers take their life;
Whose misadventured piteous overthrows
Do with their death bury their parents' strife.
The fearful passage of their death-mark'd love,
And the continuance of their parents' rage,
Which, but their children's end, nought could remove,
Is now the two hours' traffic of our stage;
The which if you with patient ears attend,
What here shall miss, our toil shall strive to mend.

SCENE I. Verona. A public place.

*Enter SAMPSON and GREGORY, of the house of Capulet, armed with swords and bucklers*

SAMPSON
Gregory, o' my word, we'll not carry coals.
GREGORY
No, for then we should be colliers.
SAMPSON
I mean, an we be in choler, we'll draw.
GREGORY
Ay, while you live, draw your neck out o' the collar.
SAMPSON
I strike quickly, being moved.
GREGORY
But thou art not quickly moved to strike.
SAMPSON
A dog of the house of Montague moves me.
GREGORY
To move is to stir; and to be valiant is to stand:
therefore, if thou art moved, thou runn'st away.
SAMPSON
A dog of that house shall move me to stand: I will
take the wall of any man or maid of Montague's.
GREGORY
That shows thee a weak slave; for the weakest goes
to the wall.
SAMPSON
True; and therefore women, being the weaker vessels,
are ever thrust to the wall: therefore I will push
Montague's men from the wall, and thrust his maids
to the wall.
GREGORY
The quarrel is between our masters and us their men.
SAMPSON
'Tis all one, I will show myself a tyrant: when I
have fought with the men, I will be cruel with the
maids, and cut off their heads.
GREGORY
The heads of the maids?
SAMPSON
Ay, the heads of the maids, or their maidenheads;
take it in what sense thou wilt.
GREGORY
They must take it in sense that feel it.
SAMPSON
Me they shall feel while I am able to stand: and
'tis known I am a pretty piece of flesh.

GREGORY

'Tis well thou art not fish; if thou hadst, thou
hadst been poor John. Draw thy tool! here comes
two of the house of the Montagues.

SAMPSON

My naked weapon is out: quarrel, I will back thee.

GREGORY

How! turn thy back and run?

SAMPSON

Fear me not.

GREGORY

No, marry; I fear thee!

SAMPSON

Let us take the law of our sides; let them begin.

GREGORY

I will frown as I pass by, and let them take it as
they list.

SAMPSON

Nay, as they dare. I will bite my thumb at them;
which is a disgrace to them, if they bear it.

*Enter ABRAHAM and BALTHASAR*

**6. What is the difference between the format of the prologue and the rest of this excerpt?**

Ⓐ The prologue is written in verse, the rest in prose.
Ⓑ The prologue is written in prose, the rest in verse.
Ⓒ The prologue uses iambic tetrameter and the rest of the excerpt uses iambic pentameter.
Ⓓ There is a difference in the spacing of the lines for easier reading.

### "Stopping by Woods on a Snowy Evening"
### By Robert Frost

Whose woods these are I think I know.
His house is in the village though;
He will not see me stopping here
To watch his woods fill up with snow.

My little horse must think it queer
To stop without a farmhouse near
Between the woods and frozen lake
The darkest evening of the year.

He gives his harness bells a shake
To ask if there is some mistake.

The only other sound's the sweep
Of easy wind and downy flake.

The woods are lovely, dark and deep.
But I have promises to keep,
And miles to go before I sleep,
And miles to go before I sleep.

Robert Frost, "Stopping by Woods on a Snowy Evening" from The Poetry of Robert Frost, edited by Edward Connery Lathem. Copyright 1923, © 1969 by Henry Holt and Company, Inc., renewed 1951, by Robert Frost. Reprinted with the permission of Henry Holt and Company, LLC.

Source: The Random House Book of Poetry for Children (1983). Retrieved 13, July, 2013.http://www.poetryfoundation.org/poem/171621.

7. **What is the rhyme scheme of the first stanza? Write in the box below.**

"...He gives his harness bells a shake
As if to ask if there is some mistake..."

8. **What is the effect of this use of personification?**

Ⓐ The author likes to use horses in his poetry to show the time in history that the poem was written.
Ⓑ To show the reader that the horse and the man are very close.
Ⓒ The horse's communication emphasizes how odd it would be to stop in the woods at that time.
Ⓓ The horse shakes because he is cold and wants the man to hurry.

9. **What is the rhyme scheme of this poem?**

Ⓐ abaa
abba
aaba
cccc

Ⓑ aaba
bbcb
ccdc
dddd

Ⓒ abcd
abcd
abcd
abcd

Ⓓ abaad
abaab
abcdeb
abdec

## "The Road Not Taken"
### BY ROBERT FROST

Two roads diverged in a yellow wood,
And sorry I could not travel both
And be one traveler, long I stood
And looked down one as far as I could
To where it bent in the undergrowth;

Then took the other, as just as fair,
And having perhaps the better claim,
Because it was grassy and wanted wear;
Though as for that the passing there
Had worn them really about the same,

And both that morning equally lay
In leaves no step had trodden black.
Oh, I kept the first for another day!
Yet knowing how way leads on to way,
I doubted if I should ever come back.

I shall be telling this with a sigh
Somewhere ages and ages hence:
Two roads diverged in a wood, and I—
I took the one less traveled by,
And that has made all the difference.

## 10. Which line in the last stanza indicates a time in the future?

Ⓐ  no step had trodden black
Ⓑ  two roads diverged
Ⓒ  yellow wood
Ⓓ  somewhere ages and ages hence

## Lesson 16: A Matter Of Attitude

**From THE HISTORY OF THE SEVEN FAMILIES OF THE LAKE PIPPLE-POPPLE. by Edward Lear**

The Parrots lived upon the Soffsky-Poffsky trees, which were beautiful to behold, and covered with blue leaves; and they fed upon fruit, artichokes, and striped beetles.

The Storks walked in and out of the Lake Pipple-Popple and ate frogs for breakfast and buttered toast for tea, but on account of the extreme length of their legs, they could not sit down, and so they walked about continually. The Geese, having webs to their feet, caught quantities of flies, which they ate for dinner.

The Owls anxiously looked after mice, which they caught, and made into sago-puddings. The Guinea Pigs toddled about the gardens and ate lettuces and Cheshire cheese.

The Cats sate still in the sunshine and fed upon sponge biscuits. The Fishes lived in the lake and fed chiefly on boiled periwinkles. And all these seven families lived together in the utmost fun and felicity.

1.  **How do the author's descriptions of the animals' habitats affect the tone of the story? Select those that apply.**

    Ⓐ  They make the animals appear hungry all the time.
    Ⓑ  They create a tone of silliness.
    Ⓒ  They create a tone of nonsense.
    Ⓓ  They create an angry tone.

### THE WONDERFUL HAIR by A. H. Wraitslaw

There was a man who was very poor, but so well supplied with children that he was utterly unable to maintain them, and one morning more than once prepared to kill them, in order not to see their misery in dying of hunger, but his wife prevented him. One night a child came to him in his sleep, and said to him: "Man! I see that you are making up your mind to destroy and to kill your poor little children, and I know that you are distressed thereat; but in the morning you will find under your pillow a mirror, a red kerchief, and an embroidered pocket-handkerchief; take all three secretly and tell no-body; then go to such a hill; by it, you will find a stream; go along it till you come to its fountain-head; there you will find a damsel as bright as the sun, with her hair hanging down over her back. Be on your guard, that the ferocious she-dragon do not coil around you; do not converse with her if she speaks; for if you converse with her, she will poison you, and turn you into a fish or something else, and will then devour you but if she bids you examine her head, examine it, and as you turn over her hair, look, and you will find one hair as red as blood; pull it out and run back again; then, if she suspects and begins to run after you, throw her first the embroidered pocket-handkerchief, then the kerchief, and, lastly, the mirror; then she will find occupation for herself. And sell that hair to some rich man; but don't let them cheat you, for that hair is worth countless wealth; and you will thus en-rich yourself and maintain your children." When the poor man awoke, he found everything under his pillow, just as the child had told him in his sleep; and then he went to the hill. When there, he found the stream, went on and on alongside of it, till he came to the fountain-head. Having looked about him to see where the damsel was, he espied her above a piece of water, like sunbeams threaded on a needle, and she was embroidering at a frame on stuff, the threads of which were young men's hair. As soon as he saw her, he made a reverence to her, and she stood on her feet and questioned him: "Whence are you, unknown young man?" But he held his tongue. She questioned him again: "Who are you? Why have you come?" and much else of all sorts; but he was as mute as a stone, making signs with his hands, as if he were deaf and wanted help. Then she told him to sit down on her skirt. He did not wait for any more orders, but sat down, and she bent down her head to him, that he might examine it. Turning over the hair of her head, as if to examine it, he was not long in finding that red hair, and separated it from the other hair, pulled it out, jumped off her skirt and ran away back as he best could. She noticed it, and ran at his heels full speed after him. He looked around, and seeing that she was about to overtake him, threw, as he was told, the embroidered pocket-hand-kerchief on the way, and when she saw the pocket-handkerchief she stooped and began to overhaul it in every direction, admiring the embroidery, till he had got a good way off. Then the damsel placed the pocket-handkerchief in her bosom and ran after him again. When he saw that she was about to overtake him, he threw the red kerchief, and she again occupied herself, admiring and gazing, till the poor man had again got a good way off. Then the damsel became exasperated, and threw both the pocket-handkerchief and the kerchief on the way, and ran after him in pursuit. Again, when he saw that she was about to overtake him, he threw the mirror. When the damsel came to the mirror, the like of which she had never seen before, she lifted it up, and when she saw herself in it, not knowing that it was herself, but thinking that it was somebody else, she, as it were, fell in love with herself in the mirror, and the man got so far off that she was no longer able to overtake him. When she saw that she could not catch him, she turned back, and the man reached his home safe and sound. After arriving at his home, he showed his wife the hair and told her all that had happened to him, but she began to jeer and laugh at him. But he paid no attention to her and went to a town to sell the hair. A crowd of all sorts of people and merchants collected round him; one offered a sequin, another two, and so on, higher and higher, till they came to a hundred gold sequins. Just then, the emperor heard of the hair, summoned the man into his presence, and said to him that he would give him a thousand sequins for it, and he sold it to him. What was the hair? The emperor split it in two from top to bottom and found registered in it in writing many remarkable things, which happened in the olden time since the beginning of the world. Thus the man became rich and lived on with his wife and children. And that child, that came to him in his sleep was an angel sent by the Lord God, whose will it was to aid the poor man and to reveal secrets which had not been revealed till then.

2.  **What is the tone at the end of this story?**

Ⓐ Serious
Ⓑ Joyful
Ⓒ Angry
Ⓓ Confused

## "Base Details"
## by Siegfried Sassoon

IF I were fierce, and bald, and short of breath,
I'd live with scarlet Majors at the Base,
And speed glum heroes up the line to death.

You'd see me with my puffy petulant face,
Guzzling and gulping in the best hotel,
Reading the Roll of Honour. 'Poor young chap,'
I'd say—'I used to know his father well;
Yes, we've lost heavily in this last scrap.'

And when the war is done and youth stone dead,
I'd toddle safely home and die—in bed.

3. **What is the narrator's tone toward the officers at the base? Select those that apply.**

   Ⓐ  He respects the decisions they make about the war.
   Ⓑ  He looks forward to moving up the ranks and becoming an officer.
   Ⓒ  He does not consider them worthy of respect.
   Ⓓ  He believes the officers are fat and greedy and don't value the young soldiers.

4. **From which line from the poem can you infer the narrator is disgusted with the officers?**

   Ⓐ  I'd toddle safely home and die - in bed.
   Ⓑ  If I were fierce, and bald, and short of breath,
       I'd live with scarlet Majors at the base...
   Ⓒ  You'd see me with my puffy petulant face,
       Guzzling and gulping in the best hotel.
   Ⓓ  Yes, we've lost heavily in this last scrap.


## From *The Moribund* by Guy de Maupassant

The warm autumn sun was beating down on the farmyard. Under the grass, which had been cropped close by the cows, the earth soaked by recent rains, was soft and sank in under the feet with a soggy noise, and the apple trees, loaded with apples, were dropping their pale green fruit in the dark green grass.

Four young heifers, tied in a line, were grazing, and at times, looking toward the house and lowing. The fowls made a colored patch on the dung-heap before the stable, scratching, moving about and cackling, while two roosters crowed continually, digging worms for their hens, whom they were calling with a loud clucking.

The wooden gate opened, and a man entered. He might have been forty years old, but he looked at least sixty, wrinkled, bent, walking slowly, impeded by the weight of heavy wooden shoes full of straw. His long arms hung down on both sides of his body. When he got near the farm, a yellow cur, tied at the foot of an enormous pear tree, beside a barrel which served as his kennel, began at first to wag his tail and then to bark for joy. The man cried:

"Down, Finot!"

The dog was quiet.

**A peasant woman came out of the house. Her large, flat, bony body was outlined under a long woollen jacket drawn in at the waist. A gray skirt, too short, fell to the middle of her legs, which were encased in blue stockings. She, too, wore wooden shoes, filled with straw. The white cap, turned yellow, covered a few hairs which were plastered to the scalp, and her brown, thin, ugly, toothless face had that wild, animal expression which is often to be found on the faces of the peasants.**

The man asked:

"How is he gettin' along?"

The woman answered:

"The priest said it's the end--that he will never live through the night."

Both of them went into the house.

After passing through the kitchen, they entered a low, dark room, barely lighted by one window, in front of which a piece of calico was hanging.

The big beams turned brown with age and smoke, crossed the room from one side to the other, supporting the thin floor of the garret, where an army of rats ran about day and night.

The moist, lumpy earthen floor looked greasy, and, at the back of the room, the bed made an indistinct white spot. A harsh, regular noise, a difficult, hoarse, wheezing breathing, like the gurgling of water from a broken pump, came from the darkened couch where an old man, the father of the peasant woman, was dying.

The man and the woman approached the dying man and looked at him with calm, resigned eyes. The son-in-law said:

"I guess it's all up with him this time; he will not last the night."

The woman answered:

"He's been gurglin' like that ever since midday." They were silent. The father's eyes were closed, his face was the color of the earth and so dry that it looked like wood. Through his open mouth came his harsh, rattling breath, and the gray linen sheet rose and fell with each respiration.

5.   In the paragraph in bold, what is the author's tone toward the woman? Select two options.

   Ⓐ  sympathy
   Ⓑ  repulsed
   Ⓒ  anger
   Ⓓ  longing

## Excerpt from *Little Women*
## By Louisa May Alcott

"Christmas won't be Christmas without any presents," grumbled Jo, lying on the rug. "It's so dreadful to be poor!" sighed Meg, looking down at her old dress.

"I don't think it's fair for some girls to have plenty of pretty things, and other girls nothing at all," added little Amy, with an injured sniff.

"We've got Father and Mother, and each other," said Beth contentedly from her corner.

The four young faces on which the firelight shone brightened at the cheerful words, but darkened again as Jo said sadly, "We haven't got Father, and shall not have him for a long time." She didn't say "perhaps never," but each silently added it, thinking of Father far away, where the fighting was.

Nobody spoke for a minute; then Meg said in an altered tone, "You know the reason Mother proposed not having any presents this Christmas was because it is going to be a hard winter for everyone; and she thinks we ought not to spend money for pleasure, when our men are suffering so in the army. We can't do much, but we can make our little sacrifices, and ought to do it gladly. But I am afraid I don't." And Meg shook her head, as she thought regretfully of all the pretty things she wanted.

"But I don't think the little we should spend would do any good. We've each got a dollar, and the army wouldn't be much helped by our giving that. I agree not to expect anything from Mother or you, but I do want to buy UNDINE AND SINTRAM for myself. I've wanted it so long," said Jo, who was a bookworm.

"I planned to spend mine in new music," said Beth, with a little sigh, which no one heard but the hearth brush and kettle holder.

"I shall get a nice box of Faber's drawing pencils. I really need them," said Amy decidedly.

"Mother didn't say anything about our money, and she won't wish us to give up everything. Let's each buy what we want, and have a little fun. I'm sure we work hard enough to earn it," cried Jo, examining the heels of her shoes in a gentlemanly manner.

"I know I do--teaching those tiresome children nearly all day, when I'm longing to enjoy myself at home," began Meg, in the complaining tone again.

"You don't have half such a hard time as I do," said Jo. "How would you like to be shut up for hours with a nervous, fussy old lady, who keeps you trotting, is never satisfied, and worries you till you're ready to fly out the window or cry?"

"It's naughty to fret, but I do think washing dishes and keeping things tidy is the worst work in the world. It makes me cross, and my hands get so stiff, I can't practice well at all." And Beth looked at her rough hands with a sigh that anyone could hear that time.

"I don't believe any of you suffer as I do," cried Amy, "for you don't have to go to school with impertinent girls, who plague you if you don't know your lessons, and laugh at your dresses, and label your father if he isn't rich, and insult you when your nose isn't nice."

"If you mean libel, I'd say so, and not talk about labels, as if Papa was a pickle bottle," advised Jo, laughing.

"I know what I mean, and you needn't be satirical about it. It's proper to use good words and improve your vocabulary," returned Amy, with dignity.

"Don't peck at one another, children. Don't you wish we had the money Papa lost when we were little, Jo? Dear me! How happy and good we'd be if we had no worries!" said Meg, who could remember better times.

"You said the other day you thought we were a deal happier than the King children, for they were fighting and fretting all the time, in spite of their money."

"So I did, Beth. Well, I think we are. For though we do have to work, we make fun of ourselves, and are a pretty jolly set, as Jo would say."

"Jo does use such slang words!" observed Amy, with a reproving look at the long figure stretched on the rug.

Jo immediately sat up, put her hands in her pockets, and began to whistle.

"Don't, Jo. It's so boyish!"
"That's why I do it."
"I detest rude, unladylike girls!"
"I hate affected, niminy-piminy chits!"

"Birds in their little nests agree," sang Beth, the peacemaker, with such a funny face that both sharp voices softened to a laugh, and the "pecking" ended for that time.

"Really, girls, you are both to be blamed," said Meg, beginning to lecture in her elder-sisterly fashion. "You are old enough to leave off boyish tricks, and to behave better, Josephine. It didn't matter so much when you were a little girl, but now you are so tall, and turn up your hair, you should remember that you are a young lady."

"I'm not! And if turning up my hair makes me one, I'll wear it in two tails till I'm twenty," cried Jo, pulling off her net, and shaking down a chestnut mane. "I hate to think I've got to grow up and be Miss March, and wear long gowns, and look as prim as a China Aster! It's bad enough to be a girl, anyway, when I like boy's games and work and manners! I can't get over my disappointment in not being a boy. And it's worse than ever now, for I'm dying to go and fight with Papa. And I can only stay home and knit, like a poky old woman!"

And Jo shook the blue army sock till the needles rattled like castanets, and her ball bounded across the room.

**6. Why does Beth compare her sisters to birds in a nest?**

Ⓐ Because they are "pecking" at each other, but not really hurting one another.
Ⓑ Because they all need to learn to "fly" on their own and give their parents some relief.
Ⓒ Because they are gifted musically and should sing together.
Ⓓ Because they are always hungry and calling for someone to feed them.

**7. From the passage above, what does the author want the reader to know about Jo?**

Ⓐ That she enjoys buying and reading books
Ⓑ That she is selfish
Ⓒ That she knows exactly what she wants and how to get it.
Ⓓ That she is smarter than the other sisters

## Excerpt from *War of the Worlds*
## H.G. Wells

The Martians seem to have calculated their descent with amazing subtlety—their mathematical learning is evidently far in excess of ours—and to have carried out their preparations with a well-nigh perfect unanimity. Had our instruments permitted it, we might have seen the gathering trouble far back in the nineteenth century. Men like Schiaparelli watched the red planet—it is odd, by the way, that for countless centuries Mars has been the star of war—but failed to interpret the fluctuating appearances of the markings they mapped so well. All that time the Martians must have been getting ready.

**8. In the excerpt above, what is the author's tone toward the Martians?**

Ⓐ He is impressed by their intelligence and planning.
Ⓑ He finds them inferior to Earth's scientists.
Ⓒ He is afraid of what they will do.
Ⓓ He looks forward to learning from them.

**9. In the excerpt above, what is the author's tone toward the scientists of Earth?**

Ⓐ He forgives them for not seeing the building threat. Their instruments were too primitive. (forgiveness)
Ⓑ He blames them for not developing instruments to identify the building threat on Mars. (anger)
Ⓒ He believes they identified Mars as a source of war early on but didn't share what they knew. (distrustful)
Ⓓ He believes they could have been able to interpret the changes to the surface of the planet and determined what the Martians were planning. (annoyed)

## "Dreams"
## By Langston Hughes

Hold fast to dreams
For if dreams die
Life is a broken-winged bird
That cannot fly.

Hold fast to dreams
For when dreams go
Life is a barren field
Frozen with snow.

**10. What point is the poet making with the comparison in the first stanza?**

Ⓐ  Without dreams, people cannot make progress in their lives.
Ⓑ  Life without dreams is cold and barren.
Ⓒ  Like a bird with a broken wing, life is fragile and must be protected.
Ⓓ  Even if one cannot fly, he or she can still have a rewarding life.

## Chapter 3

## Lesson 17: Getting Technical

Scientists in South Korea have developed a type of artificial skin that will allow robots to feel slight vibrations. This skin, developed by weaving together extremely small nano hairs made of polymer or plastic, is more sensitive than human skin. When vibration is applied to this artificial skin, the nano hairs bend against each other to generate an electrical current. Sensors within the skin evaluate the current and using that information determine the source of the vibration.

Researchers are excited about the potential for this new development. The artificial skin could be used to cover prosthetic limbs to help those who have lost a limb experience more realistic sensations and function more naturally.

http://en.wikipedia.org/wiki/Neuroplasticity

1. **What can we assume about the nano hairs described in this article? Select what applies.**

   Ⓐ  They are made of natural or organic material.
   Ⓑ  They are made of plastic or polymer.
   Ⓒ  They generate electricity.
   Ⓓ  They were invented by North Korean scientists.

2. **Based on this article, what can you assume prosthetic means- natural or artificial? Write in the box below.**

3. **What is a sensor?**

   Ⓐ  A device used to transmit a message
   Ⓑ  A means by which the body perceives an external stimulus; one of the faculties of sight, smell, hearing, taste, and touch.
   Ⓒ  A device that detects or measures a physical property and records, indicates, or otherwise responds to it.
   Ⓓ  An artificial limb used by those who have suffered an accident or disease.

## An Advertisement for SIMPLE LESSONS IN THE STUDY OF NATURE By I.G. OAKLEY (from <u>The Great Round World and What's Going On In It</u> magazine)

This is a handy little book, which many a teacher who is looking for means to offer children genuine nature study may be thankful to get hold of.

Nature lessons, to be entitled to that name, must deal with what can be handled and scrutinized at leisure by the child, pulled apart, and even wasted. This can be done with the objects discussed in this book; they are under the feet of childhood—**grass, feathers, a fallen leaf, a budding twig, or twisted shell**; these things cannot be far out of the way, even within the stony limits of a city.

Nor are the lessons haphazard dashes at the nearest living thing; on the contrary, they are virtually fundamental, whether with respect to their relation to some of the classified sciences, or with reference to the development of thought and power of expression in the child himself.

The illustrations are few, and scarcely more than figures; it is not meant to be a pretty picture-book, yet is most clearly and beautifully printed and arranged, for its material is to be that out of which pictures are made. It will be found full of suggestions of practical value to teachers who are carrying the miscellaneous work of ungraded schools, and who have the unspeakable privilege of dealing with their pupils untrammeled by cast-iron methods and account-keeping examination records.

*Sample copy, 50 Cents, post-paid*

WILLIAM BEVERLEY HARISON
3 & 5 W. 18th St. • • • New York City

**4. What category do the items in bold all fit into?**

Ⓐ They are all animals.
Ⓑ They are all located in the author's backyard.
Ⓒ They are all items a child is likely to walk on when outside.
Ⓓ They are all plants.

### <u>The Great Round World and What's Going On In It</u>
#### magazine article -- Anonymous author

Did you ever see a house move?
If you have not, you have missed a very funny sight.

Imagine driving along a country road, and meeting a three-story house making a journey along the highway to new quarters.
There is a good deal of this to be seen just now at Katonah, New York.
A year or so ago the Croton water-shed water, which is in use in New York City, was found to be impure.

A commission was appointed to go and examine the Croton Water-Shed. This meant that they were to examine the little streams, and brooks, and rivers, and lakes, which supplied the water to our aqueduct, and see what the trouble was.

They found that along the banks of these streams and lakes, in villages and out in the country, a great many dwelling-houses and shanties had been built, the occupants of which were in the habit of throwing all sorts of rubbish into the water, making it unfit for drinking.

As a consequence of this, all of the houses were ordered to be torn down or moved away, and one small village of shanties was destroyed. Among others, the inhabitants of Katonah were ordered to move, that the banks of the stream might be cleared of dwellings.

Katonah has a railroad depot, and a post office, and thinks a good deal of itself.

When the Water-Shed Commission said that it must move or be destroyed, the residents of Katonah gathered together, and decided that rather than be wiped off the face of the map, it would pick up its houses and move itself.

So a new Katonah was established, about a quarter of a mile away from the old one, and just outside the Water-Shed on which it was forbidden to build, for fear of spoiling the water for New York. For several months past there has been a procession of houses moving from old Katonah to new.

5.  **What two things can you assume when water is described as impure?**

    Ⓐ  it is brown-colored
    Ⓑ  it is unsafe to drink
    Ⓒ  it is from a stream
    Ⓓ  it is polluted

## The Great Round World and What's Going On In It
### magazine article -- Anonymous author

The news comes from Hamburg that the strike of the dock laborers is over.
The strikers have been beaten because of their lack of money.
In No. 7 of The Great Round World you will find an account of the strike, and if you will also refer to No. 10, you will see that it was thought that the strikers could not hold out very much longer.

The money the strikers expected to receive from other labor unions to help them was so slow in coming that the men and their families were in want, and no man is likely to stand out for the benefit of others when his own children are suffering from cold and hunger.

The men have gone back to their old employers and asked for work. The pity of it all is, however, that during the strike others have been taken on in their places, and the employers have now no work to give them.

After holding out since the end of October, and refusing the masters' offer to give them $1.10 a day, and let all future troubles be settled by arbitration, the strikers have had to give in without gaining a single point. It is very sad.

6. **What does a strike mean in reference to workers?**

  Ⓐ A place where people in Hamburg work
  Ⓑ A protest where workers refuse to go to work until their needs are met
  Ⓒ A long list of people who are out of work.
  Ⓓ A missed hit in baseball

## Skunk Chow

Skunks are <u>omnivores</u>. They can be found eating nuts, berries, roots, leaves, grasses, and even some types of fungi (mushroom-like plants). For animals, they enjoy dining on rodents such as mice and rats, insects, earthworms, frogs, lizards, toads, and birds. Sometimes when they are unable to find live animals to eat, they become scavengers eating dead animals left behind. When they live close to people's homes, skunks sometimes will even get into trash cans, eating garbage.

When skunks eat, they do not limit themselves to small meals. They like to "pig out" on whatever food they can find. When there is a large amount of food available, skunks get very fat very quickly.

http://en.wikipedia.org/wiki/Skunk

7. **Based on information in the selection, what does the underlined term mean?**

  Ⓐ An animal that eats only plants
  Ⓑ An animal that eats nuts and berries
  Ⓒ An animal that eats plants and meat
  Ⓓ An animal that is usually awake only at night

## Skunk Chow

Skunks are omnivores. They can be found eating nuts, berries, roots, leaves, grasses, and even some types of fungi (mushroom-like plants). For animals, they enjoy dining on rodents such as mice and rats, insects, earthworms, frogs, lizards, toads, and birds. Sometimes when they are unable to find live animals to eat, they become <u>scavengers</u> eating dead animals left behind. When they live close to people's homes, skunks sometimes will even get into trash cans, eating garbage.

When skunks eat, they do not limit themselves to small meals. They like to "pig out" on whatever food they can find. When there is a large amount of food available, skunks get very fat very quickly.

http://en.wikipedia.org/wiki/Skunk

**8. Based on information in the selection, what does the underlined term mean?**

   Ⓐ An animal that eats only plants
   Ⓑ An animal that eats nuts and berries
   Ⓒ An animal that eats plants and meat
   Ⓓ An animal that is usually awake only at night

## Advertisement from <u>The Great Round World and What's Going On In It</u> magazine -- Anonymous author

*Photographs in relief.*

A new plan in regard to photographs has been invented.

It is to take a photograph, similar to the one that is to be embossed, and, after cutting it in a certain way, press the portions outward so that it shall stand in relief.

An open mask of the same shape as the photograph is then used, and the two photographs are dampened and pressed tightly together until the face and figure stand out from the card, and the picture looks as if it had been carved in wood.

This is a very ingenious invention, but the work is very difficult, and can only be done by people who are regularly trained to do it.

**9. What is the meaning of relief as it is used in this selection?**

   Ⓐ To feel as if a weight has been taken off your shoulders
   Ⓑ Embossed
   Ⓒ Sticking outward from the paper
   Ⓓ Sunk into the paper

## <u>The Great Round World and What's Going On In It</u>
### magazine article -- Anonymous author

At last, beyond any further question, Major William McKinley has been elected President of the United States.

The last formality was complied with when, on February 11th, at one o'clock, the **Senate** of the United States, headed by the Vice-President, filed into the **House of Representatives** to count the vote of the Electoral College, cast in the manner described in The Great Round World, No. 13.

As the Senators entered the House of Representatives, all the Congressmen rose and remained standing while their visitors filed in, two by two.

The little procession was preceded by the officers of the Senate, who carried the ballot boxes.

The work of counting was then commenced by the tellers, and ere long, it was officially announced that William McKinley was the choice of the people for President of the United States.

**10. What do the bold terms in this selection have in common?**

Ⓐ  They are all places William McKinley has worked.
Ⓑ  They are all parts of the U.S. government.
Ⓒ  They are people who work for the President of the U.S.
Ⓓ  The Supreme Court

## Chapter 3

## Lesson 18: What's The Author's Point?

**Fall Leaves**
**USDA Forest Service**

We almost always think of trees as being green, but there is one time of year when their leaves turn a myriad orange, red, yellow, and brown: the beautiful and chilly days of fall. Those living in the Eastern or Northern United States come to anticipate the change in color every year starting in September or October. What causes the leaves to change color, and why?

Just like many animals that hibernate for the winter, trees experience a unique change during the winter months. During summer, plants use the process of photosynthesis to transform carbon dioxide found in the air into organic compounds like sugars using energy from the sun. During the winter, however, there is less light to go around, and their ability to create food from the photosynthesis process is limited. What does that have to do with a leaf's color? The substance that allows trees to turn carbon dioxide into food (chlorophyll) is also the cause of the leaf's green sheen. As the photosynthesis process wanes in the colder months due to the lack of sun, so does its greenish hue, allowing other elements present in the leaf to show through. Believe it or not, the yellows and oranges that appear in fall have actually been there all year in the form of nutrients like carotene (also found in carrots). The intense green color of the chlorophyll had simply overshadowed them.

But what about the reds and browns? And what causes the leaves to fall away after they change color? The bright reds and purples in each leaf come from a strong antioxidant that many trees create on their own because of their protective qualities. The antioxidant helps protect the trees from the sun, lower their freezing levels, and protect them from frost. As winter comes, so does the need for the antioxidant (similar to the way a dog gets more fur during winter to stay warm).

As for the leaves falling, that is another story. At the base of each leaf, there is a layer of cells that carry food and water from the leaf to the tree during the summer months to keep it fed. In the fall, that layer actually starts to harden, preventing the passage of nutrients. Because of this, the nutrients and waste that previously passed from the leaf into the tree become trapped in the leaf with no fresh water to clean it. Not only does this cause the leaf to turn brown, eventually it causes the cells within it to harden so much that the leaf tears and blows away. Thus the pile of leaves you enjoyed jumping in as a child.

Because each tree, and each leaf, contains a unique amount of nutrients depending on how well-nourished it was over the spring and summer, the way each leaf breaks down during the winter months is also quite different. The result is the unique and complex facet of colors we see in neighborhoods and forests each fall.

1. **For the information in this selection to be considered reliable, it would need to be written by....**

   Ⓐ a journalist
   Ⓑ a student
   Ⓒ a scientist
   Ⓓ an environmental activist

## Egyptian Pyramids

Today, we have high-tech cranes and other machines to help us create massive skyscrapers and other modern works of architecture. Still, some of the most breathtaking architecture in the world, such as the ancient pyramids of Egypt, were created before those high-tech machines even existed. So how did those ancient civilizations create them?

Believe it or not, though they are one of the most studied and admired relics in history, there is no evidence to tell historians exactly how the Ancient Egyptians built the pyramids. Thus, they have been left to create their own theories as to how Egyptians created such amazing and awe-inspiring works of art.

According to one theory, the Egyptians placed logs under the large stone blocks in order to roll or transport them to the pyramid building location. Large groups of men would work to push or pull them into place (although historians also disagree on whether these men were slaves or skilled artisans). Still more, once the men moved the blocks to the pyramid location, they needed to lift them to ever-increasing heights to reach the top levels of the pyramid as it grew. Without modern cranes, many scientists have been baffled as to how they were able to do it. Some believe they used a ramp system that would allow them to roll the blocks upward around or through the pyramids; others believe they must have used a combination of pulleys and lifts. Still, most agree that once they did, they used a mixture of gravel and limestone to help fill any crevices and hold the mound together.

With such a primitive yet impressive building process, it's obvious that the pyramids must have taken a great deal of time to build. With an estimated 2 million blocks weighing an average of 2.5 million tons each, the Great Pyramid of Giza, for instance, is estimated to have taken some 20 years to build. At 481 feet tall, it held the record of tallest building for 3,800 years – not bad for a building created almost entirely by hand.

Even though scientists don't know exactly how the Egyptians did it, they do know that the method the Egyptians used to build pyramids changed over time. In the early days, the pyramids were made completely of stone, with limestone used to create the main body and higher quality limestone being used for the smooth outer casing. Later on, the pyramids were made mostly of mud brick with a limestone casing. Though they were likely much easier to build, they didn't stand up nearly as well over time, leaving archaeologists with even fewer clues about their creation.

2. **How could you verify whether or not the information in this selection is accurate? Select two options.**

Ⓐ by interviewing the author of the essay
Ⓑ by reading genuine researches on the Egyptian pyramids
Ⓒ by consulting Egyptian historians and experts on pyramids
Ⓓ by going to Egypt on holiday

## From <u>The Great Round World and What's Going On In It</u> magazine

The Czar of Russia is quite ill, and everyone feels sorry that he should be sick now when his advice and assistance is so badly needed to settle the worrying Turkish question, which has so troubled Europe.

The young Czar Nicholas, who was crowned with so much pomp and glory at Moscow last August, seems unable to carry on the government of Russia.
Many people say he is too weak to govern, and that there are going to be troubles and revolts in Russia.

The truth of the matter seems to be, that the young Czar is a gentle, kind-hearted man, who will not govern Russia in the stern, cruel way that his forefathers have done, and who is therefore thought to be weak and incapable.

While he is making a part of his people love him for his goodness, by far the larger half, who have, under the old rule, been able to make money and gain great power, are furious against him.

Poor young Nicholas is not only hated by the people who were most friendly to his father, but by the Nihilists, who look upon him as their natural enemy, and, between the two parties, it is said that the Czar goes about in constant fear of his life.

Nicholas never wanted to be a ruler. Those who know him say that he has become grave and sad in the few months since he came to the throne.
It is said that he is of too gentle a disposition to be able to keep his ministers in order and that they quarrel fiercely in his presence, and show very little respect for him.

According to all accounts, his health is giving way under the constant worry, and it is reported that he received a shock a few weeks ago, which so completely upset him, that it brought on his present illness.

He was walking in his gardens, and wishing to speak to one of the men who were at work; he signaled to him to come to him. The gardener, proud of his sovereign's notice, ran towards him at full speed. But a sentry, who had not noticed the Czar's signal, fearing that the man was going to harm the Emperor, fired his gun at him, and he fell dead at the Czar's feet.

Nicholas was terribly overcome by the dreadful mistake.

Some people say that his present illness is due to anxiety about the Czarina, who is also ill, and again others say that the wound which Nicholas received when he was traveling in Japan is the cause.

He was struck by a crazy Japanese, and would have been killed, had not Prince George of Greece, the son of the present King of Greece, who was with him, warded off the blow. As it was, the blow was heavy enough to form a lump on the young man's skull, which has caused him great pain, and which some people declare is troubling him now.

Whatever the cause, the Czar is ill, and in no state to attend to anything but his own affairs. It is a sad pity just at this moment when Europe needs him so badly.

3.  **Which statement from this selection is a fact?**

    (A) Many people say he is too weak to govern, and that there are going to be troubles and revolts in Russia.
    (B) The truth of the matter seems to be, that the young Czar is a gentle, kind-hearted man, who will not govern Russia in the stern, cruel way that his forefathers have done, and who is there fore thought to be weak and incapable.
    (C) According to all accounts, his health is giving way.
    (D) Nicholas was terribly overcome by the dreadful mistake.

4.  **What would be the best source to use to determine whether the eighth paragraph of this selection is factual or is an opinion- an eyewitness article on the event or a newspaper article by someone who dislikes the Czar?**

magazine -- Anonymous author

School and College Text-Books
AT WHOLESALE PRICES
**At my New Store (FEBRUARY 1ST)**
*3 & 5 West 18th Street The St. Ann Building*

With the greatly increased facilities, I can now offer to my customers the convenience of an assortment of text books and supplies more complete than any other in any store in this city. Books will be classified according to subject. Teachers and students are invited to call and refer to the shelves when in search of information; every convenience and assistance will be rendered to them.

Reading Charts, miscellaneous Reference Charts, Maps, Globes, Blackboards, and School Supplies at net prices singly or in quantity.
All books removed from old store (more or less damaged by removal) will be closed out at low prices.

*Mail orders promptly attended to*
*All books, etc., subject to approval*
William Beverley Harrison, 3 & 5 West 18th Street
FORMERLY 59 FIFTH AVENUE

5. **Which statement from this ad is NOT a fact?**

Ⓐ I can now offer to my customers the convenience of an assortment of text-books and supplies more complete than any other in any store in this city.
Ⓑ Teachers and students are invited to call and refer to the shelves when in search of information.
Ⓒ All books removed from old store (more or less damaged by removal) will be closed out at low prices.
Ⓓ Mail orders promptly attended to.

**An Advertisement for SIMPLE LESSONS IN THE STUDY OF NATURE By I.G. OAKLEY from <u>The Great Round World and What's Going On In It</u> magazine -- Anonymous author**

This is a handy little book, which many a teacher who is looking for means to offer children genuine nature study may be thankful to get hold of.

Nature lessons, to be entitled to that name, must deal with what can be handled and scrutinized at leisure by the child, pulled apart, and even wasted. This can be done with the objects discussed in this book; they are under the feet of childhood—grass, feathers, a fallen leaf, a budding twig, or twisted shell; **these things cannot be far out of the way, even within the stony limits of a city.**

Nor are the lessons haphazard dashes at the nearest living thing; on the contrary, they are virtually fundamental, whether with respect to their relation to some of the classified sciences, or with reference to the development of thought and power of expression in the child himself.

The illustrations are few, and scarcely more than figures; it is not meant to be a pretty picture-book, yet is most clearly and beautifully printed and arranged, for its material is to be that out of which pictures are made. It will be found full of suggestions of practical value to teachers who are carrying the miscellaneous work of ungraded schools, and who have the unspeakable privilege of dealing with their pupils untrammeled by cast-iron methods and account-keeping examination records.

*Sample copy, 50 Cents, post-paid*

_____

WILLIAM BEVERLEY HARISON
3 & 5 W. 18th St. • • • New York City

**6.  How could you determine whether or not the statement in bold is true?**

Ⓐ  Purchase the book
Ⓑ  Call the author and ask him if this statement is a fact or an opinion
Ⓒ  Buy the book and follow the lessons in your own backyard
Ⓓ  Buy the book and follow the lessons in several different settings

**<u>The Great Round World and What's Going On In It</u> magazine article -- Anonymous author**

Did you ever see a house move?

If you have not, you have missed a very funny sight.

Imagine driving along a country road, and meeting a three-story house making a journey along the highway to new quarters.

There is a good deal of this to be seen just now at Katonah, New York.

A year or so ago the Croton water-shed water, which is in use in New York City, was found to be impure.

A commission was appointed to go and examine the Croton Water-Shed. This meant that they were to examine the little streams, and brooks, and rivers, and lakes, which supplied the water to our aqueduct, and see what the trouble was.

They found that along the banks of these streams and lakes, in villages and out in the country, a great many dwelling-houses and shanties had been built, the occupants of which were in the habit of throwing all sorts of rubbish into the water, making it unfit for drinking.

In consequence of this, all of the houses were ordered to be torn down or moved away, and one small village of shanties was destroyed. Among others, the inhabitants of Katonah were ordered to move, that the banks of the stream might be cleared of dwellings.

Katonah has a railroad depot, and a post office, and thinks a good deal of itself.

When the Water-Shed Commission said that it must move or be destroyed, the residents of Katonah gathered together, and decided that rather than be wiped off the face of the map, it would pick up its houses and move itself.

So a new Katonah was established, about a quarter of a mile away from the old one, and just outside the Water-Shed on which it was forbidden to build, for fear of spoiling the water for New York.

For several months past there has been a procession of houses moving from old Katonah to new.

7.  **Which statement from this article contains an opinion?**

    Ⓐ  Katonah has a railroad depot, and a post-office.
    Ⓑ  When the Water-Shed Commission said that it must move or be destroyed, the residents of Katonah gathered together, and decided that rather than be wiped off the face of the map, it would pick up its houses and move itself.
    Ⓒ  Did you ever see a house move? If you have not, you have missed a very funny sight.
    Ⓓ  A year or so ago the Croton water-shed water, which is in use in New York City, was found to be impure.

## The Great Round World and What's Going On In It
### magazine article -- Anonymous author

The news comes from Hamburg that the strike of the dock laborers is over.

The strikers have been beaten because of their lack of money.

In No. 7 of The Great Round World, you will find an account of the strike, and if you will also refer to No. 10, you will see that it was thought that the strikers could not hold out very much longer.

The money the strikers expected to receive from other labor unions to help them was so slow in coming that the men and their families were in want, and no man is likely to stand out for the benefit of others when his own children are suffering from cold and hunger.

The men have gone back to their old employers and asked for work. The pity of it all is, however, that during the strike others have been taken on in their places, and the employers have now no work to give them.

After holding out since the end of October, and refusing the masters' offer to give them $1.10 a day, and let all future troubles be settled by arbitration, the strikers have had to give in without gaining a single point. It is very sad.

8.  **According to this selection, if readers want to gather more information to determine whether or not the labor strike should have taken place, where should they look?**

    Ⓐ  In newspapers from Hamburg
    Ⓑ  In past issues of the magazine this article was published in
    Ⓒ  In an encyclopedia
    Ⓓ  In other magazines

## The Great Round World and What's Going On In It
### magazine article -- Anonymous author

Blondin was a Frenchman, his father having been one of Napoleon's soldiers. A story is told of him that when he was five years old he saw an acrobat performing on a tight-rope.

He was so pleased with what he saw, that when he got home he stretched a rope between two posts, and, as soon as his mother was out of the way, took his father's fishing-rod, and, using it as a balancing pole, made his first appearance as a tight-rope walker.

He was trained for an acrobat and tight-rope walking, and came to this country with a troupe of pantomimists.

While he visited Niagara Falls, the idea at once struck him that, if he dared to cross those terrible waters on a rope, his fortune would be made. He made up his mind to try it, and stayed in the village of Niagara for weeks, until he had learned just how it would be possible for him to perform the feat.

Then he set about getting the scheme well advertised, and securing plenty of money for himself if he succeeded in accomplishing it.

On August 17th, 1859, he made the trip across the Falls in the presence of 50,000 spectators. This performance made him famous.

His rope was 175 feet above the waters.

He was not satisfied with merely walking across; he crossed again blindfolded, and then carrying a man on his back, and once again wheeling a barrow before him.

In the summer of 1860 he crossed once more in the presence of the Prince of Wales, and carried a man on his back, whom he set down on the rope six times, while he rested.

He died in London, at the age of seventy-three.

9. **Which of the following does the author express in this article?**

   Ⓐ His opinions about Blondin
   Ⓑ Factual information about Blondin
   Ⓒ Both his opinions of Blondin and factual information
   Ⓓ Blondin's input

### Advertisement from <u>The Great Round World and What's Going On In It</u> magazine -- Anonymous author

FOUR FAMOUS BOOKS

Every boy and girl is interested in what is going on about them. The authors of this series have gathered together the most interesting kind of information and have told it in a most entertaining way.

Copies will be sent post-paid to any address upon receipt of price named.

1. Foods and Beverages, by E.A. Beal, M.D. Contains reading lessons on the various kinds of Foods and their hygienic values; on Grains, Fruits, and useful Plants, with elementary botanical instruction relating thereto; and on other common subjects of interest and importance to all, old and young. 281 pages. Cloth, 60 cents.

2. Every-Day Occupations, by H. Warren Clifford, S.D. Quantities of useful facts entertainingly told, relating to work and workers. How Leather is Tanned; How Silk is Made; The Mysteries of Glass-Making, of Cotton Manufacture, of Cloth-Making, of Ship and House Building; The Secrets of the Dyer's

Art and the Potter's Skill—all and more are described and explained in detail with wonderful clearness. 330 pages. Cloth, 60 cents.

3. Man and Materials, by Wm. G. Parker, M.E. Shows how man has raised himself from savagery to civilization by utilizing the raw material of the earth. Brings for the first time the wonderful natural resources of the United States to the notice of American children. The progress of the Metal-Working arts simply described and very attractively illustrated. 323 pages. Cloth, 60 cents.

4. Modern Industries and Commerce, by Robert Louis, Ph.D. Treats of commerce and the different means of conveyance used in different eras. Highways, Canals. Tunnels, Railroads, and the Steam Engine are discussed in an entertaining way. Other subjects are Paper Manufacture, Newspapers, Electric Light, Atlantic Cable, the Telephone, and the principal newer commercial applications of Electricity, etc. 329 pages. Cloth, 60 cents.

**10. Which of the following does the author express in this advertisement?**

   Ⓐ  his opinions about the books.
   Ⓑ  factual information about the books
   Ⓒ  both factual information about the books and the author's opinion of the books
   Ⓓ  readers' viewpoints

# Answer Key and Detailed Explanations

## Chapter 3: Comprehension Skills

# Lesson 1: Prove It! (with Evidence From The Text)

| Question No. | Answer | Detailed Explanations |
|---|---|---|
| 1 | B | Answer choice two is the best answer. This answer is the best one because it shows that there were so many footprints that the police-man could not figure out exactly which prints belonged to the thief and which prints belonged to other customers.<br>The first answer is incorrect because if the prints were marked, there would be no point in searching for the thief.<br>The third answer choice can't be correct because the story clearly tells the reader that there are several footprints.<br>The last answer choice does not make sense. Why would someone clean the footprints when a crime had been committed? |
| 2 | his grand-father | His grandfather helps Sam make the choice. |
| 3 | A and B | The two signs that Sam's parents raised him well are-<br><br>He understood that family and tennis were both priorities he needed to balance in his life.<br>He sought guidance from his grandfather instead of running from the problem. |
| 4 | C | Answer choice three is correct. The answer is in the passage and can be found in the third paragraph.<br><br>The first two choices are not mentioned in the story, and although they make sense for today, this passage does not indicate that was an option.<br><br>The last choice is in the story, a ride in the boat, but what is expected to cure the king is a sudden fright (something unexpected), not a ride in a boat. |
| 5 | The Pig or Piggy-Wig | The poem states-<br>"But what shall we do for a ring?"<br>They sailed away for a year and a day,<br>To the land where the Bong-tree grows,<br>And there in a wood a Piggy-wig stood,<br>With a ring at the end of his nose". |
| 6 | A | Answer choice one is correct. In the last part of the poem, the frog tells the boys that the rocks hit them in the head. |

| Question No. | Answer | Detailed Explanations |
|---|---|---|
| 7 | D | Answer choice four is correct. Answer choices one and two are things boys might do, but the poem does not mention them doing so in this piece.<br>Answer choice three seems possible because the frogs complain of getting hit on the head, and claiming it "'tis death to us." However, the boys are not TRYING to kill the frogs. They are throwing stones in the water. |
| 8 | A | Answer choice one is correct. In the sixth line of the poem, there are quotation marks that indicate someone is talking. "The wolf once met...and began 'Your servant'...." section tells the reader that the wolf began speaking, therefore the best answer is choice number one. |
| 9 | B | The evidence is given therefore B is the correct choice. |
| 10 | | The secret of the poem is about losing loved ones. The lines from the poem that relates to this feeling of the poet are - But oh! when comes the icy chill that freezes o'er the heart, When, one by one, the joys we shared, the hopes we held, depart; When friends, like autumn's withered leaves, have fallen by our side, And life, so pleasant once, becomes a desert wild and wide. |

# Lesson 2: Use Those Clues - Make An Inference

| Question No. | Answer | Detailed Explanations |
|---|---|---|
| 1 | C | Answer choice three is correct. The quote indicates that the cabby was not paying attention, lost in thought, or asleep when the policemen called to him. It is meant to explain how the day had been slow, boring and cold, and he was somewhat startled and had a hard time getting his senses together to drive the policeman. |
| 2 | D | Answer choice four is correct. The bear behaved very differently when he went to the zoo. He would not eat and he lost weight. He was a happy bear before going to the zoo. His changed behavior was a clue that he was depressed. |
| 3 | A and B | Julie and Max were best of friends who deeply cared about each other. |
| 4 | B | Answer choice two is the best answer. Because the dog was well fed, unlike the wolf, his master must have cared for the dog. |
| 5 | C | Answer choice three is the correct answer. The wolf is hungry, while the dog is plump (fat) with living a good life free of want. The wolf is always in need of a good meal. |
| 6 | B | Answer choice number one is true, but it is not the best answer because it does not explain fully how the dog lives.<br>Answer choice number two is the best answer because the dog is well fed and does not want or need anything whereas the wolf is hungry and worries about getting food.<br>Answer choice number three is incorrect because the dog is not greedy, he doesn't take from another, he just doesn't have to worry about his needs being met.<br>Answer choice four is not the best answer because the poem does not mention sharing. |
| 7 | A and C | Options A and C are most likely true of the boys. |
| 8 | A | Answer choice one is correct. The captain came back, but he was in a wheelchair. Also, he said he had a leg that was nearly "blown off." These facts explain why he came back home. |
| 9 | B | Answer choice two is correct. The story is told from a third person's point of view. All could be "seen," but we did not know what every one was thinking, so it is not omniscient. |
| 10 | -- | He sought guidance from his grandfather instead of running from the problem, shows that Sam was raised well. |

# Lesson 3: What Is It All About?

| Question No. | Answer | Detailed Explanations |
| --- | --- | --- |
| 1 | B, C and D | Options B, C and D are not the themes of the story. |
| 2 | C and D | The story discusses how open communication helps resolve seemingly difficult problems and how family always comes to one's aid in difficulties. |
| 3 | C | Answer choice three is the best answer. The poem discusses how feeling sorry for oneself is not good because everyone has their problems. And often, they are worse than yours. |
| 4 | C | Answer one is incorrect because the boy was not disobedient. He did as his father asked.<br>Answer two is incorrect because there was no mention of anyone going to Heaven, just a new/different life.<br>Answer three is the best choice because the boy respected and obeyed his father, when he did not want to. However, the end result is not what the father had hoped for. The story tells about acquiring a spirit, but it does not specifically mention dying. |
| 5 | A | Answer one is the best choice. The young man felt he needed to be excused from the fast, but his father would not listen to his son. The father could have still asked his son to remain with his fast, after hearing his son's concerns. But, the father would not even hear what his son had to say.<br>Answer two is incorrect because the strictness of the father was NOT effective to the father's hopes.<br>Answer choice three is not the best answer because the word "always" is used. Any choice that uses "always," or other absolutes are usually not good answer choices.<br>Answer choice four is incorrect because the boy did not take his father for granted, or take advantage of him. This is not a reasonable theme of this story. |

| Question No. | Answer | Detailed Explanations |
|---|---|---|
| 6 | B | Answer choice one is not the best answer. Yes, people should watch out for falling objects, but that is not the point of this poem.<br>Answer choice two is the best. The acorn, although small, had a big impact on this story.<br>Answer choice three is not the best answer because Mother Nature is not questioned in the passage.<br>The fourth answer choice is not the best choice because not EVERY seed becomes a beautiful plant. Some don't grow at all, others sprout into weeds. Try to avoid answer choices that use absolutes such as "always" or "every." |
| 7 | A, B and D | Options A, B and D are not the themes of this selection. |
| 8 | B | Answer choice one is not the best choice. In this answer choice the word "nod" refers to moving ones head. In the story it is about going to sleep/dreaming (nodding off to sleep).<br>Answer choice two is the best selection. The poem describes different places he has to go, alone, while dreaming. Also, he cannot find those places by day (when he is awake), nor can he quite remember the music (what happened in the dreams).<br>Answer choice three might be true, but it is not the best answer. Not everything mentioned in the Land of Nod was exciting.<br>The last answer choice is not the best answer because the poem does not indicate that the person can control where he visits. |

| Question No. | Answer | Detailed Explanations |
|:---:|:---:|:---|
| 9 | C | Answer choice one is not the best answer. Yes, it took extreme force to crack the nut open, but that Devil just happened to be in the nut. Answer choice number two is not the best answer. The young boy did play a trick on the Devil, but it is commonly believed in literature that any way the Devil is controlled is an acceptable act. And, the act of the trick was just part of the story, not the focus of the story.<br><br>Answer choice number three is the best answer because the message from this story, all of the elements, indicate that even though the nut was tiny, something dangerous or bad could still be there. The boy asked for help, but this was not the message this story tries to convey. |
| 10 | B | Answer choice number one is not the best answer. Obviously it is wrong for a parent to want to hurt their children, but in THIS story, there was no indication that anyone was worried about this.<br><br>Answer choice two is the best answer because the family was indeed benefited by the father's actions.<br><br>Answer choice three is not the best answer because this story did not mention protecting the children, only providing food for them.<br><br>Answer choice four is not the best answer because the father is the main character in the story. Without him, there is no story, so he did have influence on the plot. |

# Lesson 4: And The Point Of This Is...?

| Question No. | Answer | Detailed Explanations |
|---|---|---|
| 1 | B | Answer choice two is the correct answer. The bear would not eat, and he was getting too thin. Then the wife came to see him, and he ate again. |
| 2 | B | Answer choice two is the correct answer. The bear and the wife were so close that both of them were not happy/healthy when they were separated. |
| 3 | B | Answer choice two is the best answer. Central idea means center or main idea. The question asks about what is the main point of this story. This portion tells of the pet eating, accidentally, rat poison nearly dying before the vet could get him the antidote shot. |
| 4 | C | Answer choice three is correct. All answer choices apply somewhere in the passage. However, the third answer choice is the best summary of the second paragraph. |
| 5 | -- | No, the title isn't appropriate<br><br>The passage details how "the tryouts for the tennis team were on the same day as his mom's birthday, and he knew his family was planning a huge surprise party for her. He didn't want to hurt his mom's feelings by missing the party, but he also didn't want to miss his one<br>shot at being a champion tennis player just because the tryouts were on his mom's birthday."<br><br>When he took his quandary to his grandfather, he was told- "You know, your mom wants you to be happy," he told Sam. "It would be a great birthday present for her to know you are making your dream come true."<br><br>When he related this to his mom, saying "But Mom, that means I'm going to miss your birthday, I am happy you are so nice about it, but I still feel really bad."- she replied, saying, "Are you kidding? This is the best present I could ask for!" |
| 6 | B, C and D | Options B, C and D are not accurate summarizations of the poem. |

220

LumosLearning.com

| Question No. | Answer | Detailed Explanations |
|---|---|---|
| 7 | D | Answer choice four is the best answer. To summarize something, all the information has to be included (minus small details), so the last answer is the most accurate of what is in the passage. |
| 8 | C | Answer choice three is correct. The paragraph explains how the boy returns, stays silent for a year and then suddenly becomes alert and speaks again. He watches his father making a sword and feels his father is not making it correctly, and this causes him to return to talking and working. |
| 9 | C | Answer choice number three is the correct answer. The paragraph states that the father was offended and he set out to punish the men. He does so by hiding his wisdom from them. |
| 10 | Kweku Tsin | The name of Father Anansi's son was Kweku Tsin. |

# Lesson 5: Key Ideas And Details

| Question No. | Answer | Detailed Explanations |
|---|---|---|
| 1 | A and D | Options A and D accurately describe Verdi's affection for his spinet. |
| 2 | D | The answer choice four is correct. The other choices talk about what skunks eat, but choice four specifically discusses how much they eat. |
| 3 | C | The answer choice three is correct. Choices one and two are not true because the author doesn't need to provide the info in choice one and does provide the info negated in choice two. Choice four is true for the passage, but does not connect with skunks being omnivores. |
| 4 | A | Answer choice one is correct. The other choices explain what the skin does, but none come closer than choice one to explaining WHY it is being developed. |
| 5 | C | Answer choice three is correct. It explains that dogs can smell low blood sugar, so the reader can infer that's what helps diabetic patients. The other choices talk about the training research, and diabetics in general. |
| 6 | A | Answer choice one is correct. The researcher wants to reproduce the sensitivity in a way that will help patients. Dogs already have the sensitivity, so choices two and three are not correct, and choice four, while plausible, doesn't seem very useful. |
| 7 | C | Option C is the correct answer choice as a large number of people can be benefited if a method of reproducing the sensitivity is found. |
| 8 | Rule 3 | Rule 3<br>"You must be in your seat when the bell rings. If you are not, you are tardy and appropriate consequences will be enforced"- explains what happens if a student is late to class. |
| 9 | A | Answer choice one is correct. The other choices talk about the effects and aftermath of his decision. |
| 10 | B | Answer choice two is correct. Booth was an actor, so that likely helped him gain access to the theatre. The other choices do not help answer the question. |

# Lesson 6: Get Right To The Point

| Question No. | Answer | Detailed Explanations |
|---|---|---|
| 1 | B | All answer choices seem to be correct, but the best answer is the second choice. The article does discuss fall weather and trees, but it does not <u>focus</u> on weather. Also, the point is not the life cycle of TREES, but the process of the leaves turning in the fall and dropping from the trees. |
| 2 | B, C and D | Options B, C and D are not the purposes of this excerpt. |
| 3 | -- | How the Olympics Evolved describes that there have been certain developments in the Olympic games specifically. |
| 4 | C | The last answer choice is the best choice. The passage discusses how various parts of the pyramids were possibly constructed. No one is sure exactly how they were built; they only have theories. |
| 5 | B | Answer choice number one is not the best answer because the passage did not discuss the people used to build the pyramids, only the techniques of the actual construction.<br><br>Answer choice number two is the best answer because the passage discusses several beliefs or theories as to how the pyramids were constructed.<br><br>Answer choice number three is not the best answer because carving the boulders or stones is only part of how the pyramids were built. This answer choice is incomplete.<br><br>Answer choice number four is not the best choice because the discussion of architecture is at the beginning of the passage and is referring to how structures are built in modern times. |
| 6 | A | Answer choice one is the best answer. All choices are basically correct, but the first one is the best for the passage. He was from Italy, he did play the spinet every day and probably wore it out sooner than most. But, the point of the passage is to tell the reader that the young boy loved his music and was committed to playing every day. |

| Question No. | Answer | Detailed Explanations |
|---|---|---|
| 7 | A | Answer choice one is the best answer. Lincoln was concerned that the country might stay divided even after the war ended. He was attempting to get people to understand that if the country did not come back together as one nation, all the men who died in the Civil War would have died for nothing. He believes to honor the dead, the country should stay as one. |
| 8 | A | Answer choice one is the best answer. The other answer choices are related to the passage, except for three, but they are not the BEST answers. The best choice indicates that Woo is very good at action scenes and loves to do them. Answer choice three is not at all reasonable for this passage. |
| 9 | B | Answer choice two is the correct answer. Answer choice one is a true statement, but it is not the complete answer for the question. Answer choice three is interesting, and the author sort of hints at this concept in the beginning of the passage, but it is not the point of the passage. The people of Katonah were upset, but they chose to move before someone forced them to move. So, they are not really angry, but more proactive. |
| 10 | B | Answer choice two is the best answer. The article is about strikes and unions but that is not the overall focus of the story. And the article does not really elaborate on the "why" of the strike, only the end and what happened to the men. |

# Lesson 7: One Thing Leads To Another

| Question No. | Answer | Detailed Explanations |
|---|---|---|
| 1 | A | Answer choice one is the correct answer. The cab driver indicates that his son was ill and then died. The story describes him sitting very still and somewhat dazed. |
| 2 | B | Answer choice number two is the correct answer. The cab driver's son died, and due to that he was grief stricken and sad. He was confused and not sure where to go with the policeman. He was sad (lamented) about the death of his child. |
| 3 | C and D | Options C and D describe how Max got busy with football and stopped spending time with Julie. |
| 4 | -- | What Sam's grandfather tells him in the story ""It would be a great birthday present for her to know you are making your dream come true" holds true, and his mother is nothing but excited to have her son go to the tryouts. |
| 5 | C | Answer choice number three is the correct answer. The first line of the story states that no one "except his fool" could play tricks on the king. |
| 6 | B | Answer choice number two is the best answer. The story says "one day an accident befell him." This means Bruno made a mistake, or had something happened to him. In this case, he ate poison intended for rats. |
| 7 | A | Answer choice one is the correct choice. The first man came back to the village with no lump where he previously had one. After some time another man went to the tree. It is a logical conclusion to believe that the second man was attempting to get the same help the first man did. That is the only "real" reason he'd go in to the trees. |
| 8 | B | Answer choice two is the best answer. The little boy is the narrator of the poem, and this innocence of not understanding the shadow completely adds to the mood of this poem. The main character (the boy) adds to the meaning/feeling of the poem because he is young, and everyone can relate to watching and playing with their shadow. |

| Question No. | Answer | Detailed Explanations |
|---|---|---|
| 9 | Because the shadow has been give human-like qualities or is being talked about as a person. | In literature, personification is when something non living is given human-like qualities or is being talked about as a person. |
| 10 | B | Answer two is the best choice. The choice of words, rhythm and rhyme scheme help the poem to be enjoyable to read. Also, this poem is relatable for everyone, as all remember being a child and trying to move in such a way to play with our shadow. |

LumosLearning.com

# Lesson 8: Relationship Between People And Events

| Question No. | Answer | Detailed Explanations |
|---|---|---|
| 1 | A | Answer choice number one is the best answer choice. If the reader substitutes "because" for "due," it is easier to see a relationship. Because indicates a connection of two or more items. |
| 2 | A | Order words indicate the order events occurred. First, second, third, lastly, finally are words that aid the reader in knowing the order events occurred. |
| 3 | B | Answer choice number two. These words are transition words that are used when writing a piece that is cause and effect. |
| 4 | D | The correct answer choice is the fourth answer. The word "as" indicates to the reader that two or more things are occurring at the same time. The sentence says that "As the president slumped, Booth..." |
| 5 | A | The first paragraph states the events in order. After Booth entered the theater, he shoots Lincoln. So, the SECOND thing that occurred was for Booth to shoot Lincoln. |
| 6 | C | Answer choice three is the best answer. The third paragraph tells the reader that the country grieved or mourned the death of Lincoln. This paragraph also says that because of this the people came to train stations to watch his body go by on the train. |
| 7 | D | The bolded sentence explains why Booth shot Lincoln and what the effect of that shooting had on the peace effort. Booth thought that if he killed Lincoln, it would help the south (cause and effect). The cause is still the same, but in reality the true effect was that it created more stress among the participants of the war. |
| 8 | -- | The conspirators were all captured, and Booth was shot while trying to escape from Union soldiers. |

# Lesson 9: When And Where?

| Question No. | Answer | Detailed Explanations |
| --- | --- | --- |
| 1 | little store near the village. | "Hi! Stop Thief!" shouted old Blenkinsopp as he rushed out of his little store near the village. |
| 2 | C | Answer choice three is the correct answer. Snow is not common everywhere, but where it does on a regular basis, it is a winter form of precipitation. |
| 3 | A | Correct answer is the first choice. The other three answers are too general to make a determination of setting. However, the story first states the name of the cab driver, and it is a Russian name. |
| 4 | A | Answer choice one is the best answer. The principal's office is usually a place students go when there is behavior issues. So, if Julie saw Max there she might assume he was in trouble, and that would support her idea that he had changed and was not the same friend she'd had. They likely would not have reconciled. |
| 5 | B | Answer choice two is the correct answer. "Nod" represents sleep (nodding off), so it implies that the person in the poem is dreaming in his sleep. |
| 6 | A, B and D | Options A, B and D are indicative of a local setting. |
| 7 | C | Answer choice number three is the correct answer. Making swords, fairies, and blacksmiths, indicate a time other than present day. People have been carrying Bibles and will continue to carry them. This has no bearing on time or setting. |
| 8 | B | Answer choice two is the best answer. While there are still cities where poor people wash their clothes in a river or pool, the fact that there was a hunter in the area indicates a rural village setting. |
| 9 | C | Answer choice number three is the best answer. The description describes a large (size) room/home and a fire is needed to warm the place (past). Cottage is not mentioned, nor a hotel, and the fire indicates that the time is not in the future. |
| 10 | A | Answer choice one is the best because it indicates that the fireplace has the only source of heat. More modern homes have furnaces. The remaining three answers describe the room and furniture. The first answer choice gives more of an idea about how the remaining part of the home is situated. These other rooms indicate the time frame of the story. Current homes are not designed that way. |

# Lesson 10: Who Or What?

| Question No. | Answer | Detailed Explanations |
|:---:|:---:|:---|
| 1 | B | Answer choice two is the correct answer. The passage states, "But because of the neighborhoods' and our renters' children, poor Bruno, had to be kept chained most of the time." explains why the answer is the correct answer. |
| 2 | B and C | He was starting to feel overwhelmed with all of the things he was supposed to be doing as a student, an athlete, and a friend. |
| 3 | A and D | Options A and D, Max's getting bad grades and being too busy for her led to Julie worrying about him. |
| 4 | Max and Julie | Max and Julie are the two main characters of the story. |
| 5 | A | Answer choice one is the correct answer. The shopkeeper runs out shouting for someone to stop the thief. This tells the reader he left to catch the person who stole his sugar from the store. |
| 6 | B | Answer choice two is the correct answer. The policeman was able to find the "thief" by looking at the line of ants. Ants often are looking for sugar. |
| 7 | D | Answer choice four is the correct answer. Sam let the quandary bother him for a long time. He let it affect his mood and second-guess himself. Had he sought assistance earlier, he could have avoided a lot of stress. |
| 8 | C | Answer choice three is the BEST answer. Choice four is possible, but the third choice best describes Sam in this passage. The first two answer choices are not reasonable for the story. |
| 9 | C | Answer choice three is the best answer. In the beginning of the story he is concerned about the decision he needs to make and how it will affect others. Then, after getting guidance, he is confident and happy that he gets to share his good news with his mom. |
| 10 | D | Answer choice four is the correct answer. The fool's jokes were generally harmless, just fun. The king's joke turned out to be a sad event. So, the king likely had a different view on playing a prank on someone. He might have had a greater appreciation for his fool than he did prior to the fool dying. |

# Lesson 11: Based On A True Story - History And Fiction

| Question No. | Answer | Detailed Explanations |
|---|---|---|
| 1 | A | The first answer choice is the best choice. The first line of the second stanza tells the reader what Revere was planning to do. |
| 2 | B | Answer choice two. The first line of the second paragraph states why Revere was riding. |
| 3 | B | Answer choice two is the best choice. The poem and the passage cover the same historical event. The poem is more entertaining and gives the same information, but leaves out Revere's arrest. |
| 4 | A | Answer choice one is the best choice. Left without a horse is not in the poem, and it would not be because the poem is intended to celebrate the heroics of Revere. |
| 5 | Henry Wadsworth Longfellow | Henry Wadsworth Longfellow is the poet. |
| 6 | Florence Earle Coates | Florence Earle Coates wrote "The Band Of The Titanic". |
| 7 | C | The last stanza of the poem expresses the commitment the band had to helping in any way they could. Answer choice number three is the best answer. |
| 8 | B | Answer choice two is the best choice. The band played on and on trying to boost the spirits of those on the deck of the boat. |
| 9 | C | Answer choice three is the best answer. The poem, in particular, mentions why the band is needed by explaining different situations of chaos. |
| 10 | C | Answer choice three is the correct answer. Both women saw the boat go down, one even mentioned nearly being sucked under by the ship, so they would know what happened at the last minute. |

# Lesson 12: How Is It Built? Analyzing Structure

| Question No. | Answer | Detailed Explanations |
|---|---|---|
| 1 | A | Answer choice one is the best answer. Each paragraph covers a different aspect of the life of the Bushmen. Answer choice two is not at all reasonable. The passage does not narrow down to one aspect. Answer choice three is incorrect because the passage is not organized in the order something happened. Answer four is incorrect too because there is nothing to compare. This is an informative passage. |
| 2 | A | Answer choice one is the best answer to the question. The second answer is part of the passage, but does not address the question asked. The last two answer choices are in the passage, but they are not "sections" that would answer the question. |
| 3 | D | Answer choice four is the correct answer. The title of the book tells the reader the subject of the book. Each chapter title is a <u>place</u> on the <u>farm</u> where <u>specific flowers</u> would grow. Answers one and two are correct, but four is the most correct. Answer three does not make sense for this question. |
| 4 | D | Answer choice four is the correct answer. This section discusses the odor that skunks' spray causes. It also discusses how to alleviate the smell by giving suggestions on what to use to bathe the affected person/animal. None of the remaining three answers discuss removing the smell from a person or animal. |
| 5 | A, B and C | Separate headings in this selection are not meant to relate an interesting fact about skunks; discuss what the whole selection is about or to mention the title of another article about skunks. |
| 6 | A | Answer choice one is the correct answer. The article tells of a tight-rope walker. It chronicles a period of time in the walker's life. It is done so in the order that the events happened, thus the answer is chronological. |
| 7 | B | Answer choice two is the correct answer. There are no true headings for the advertisement (choice one), and choice three does not make sense. How can the person making the advertisement know what everybody else's interests are? The last answer choice is true, but not the best answer for the question. |

| Question No. | Answer | Detailed Explanations |
|---|---|---|
| 8 | A | Answer choice one is the correct answer. The title is at the top of the passage, but sections are labeled with headings to help the reader know what the main topic of the paragraph(s) will be. Graphics are not used, topics are, but the headings are the main way the reader knows the topics. |
| 9 | D | Answer choice four is the correct answer. Humans would dump garbage, and so this is the heading that makes the most sense. |
| 10 | A | Answer choice one is the correct answer. The topic of the article is at the beginning. Each section is about a different tip or concern. This is a sub-topical organization. |

# Lesson 13: Finding Patterns - Comparing And Contrasting

| Question No. | Answer | Detailed Explanations |
|---|---|---|
| 1 | C | Answer choice three is the best answer. The dream predicted what the man should do, and when he did this, his life improved. |
| 2 | A | Answer choice one is the correct answer. The boy was cheerful, strong, and a healthy young man whereas the fairy was a trickster. |
| 3 | B | Answer choice two is the best answer. One woman is decent and good, the other woman only does things to benefit herself. The last answer choice is true, but it is not as good a characterization as the second choice. |
| 4 | A and C | Two themes discussed in the story are greed and the rewards of genuine kindness. |
| 5 | C | Answer choice three is the best answer. All answers might be correct depending on who holds the opinion, but the author's opinion in this poem is that it is not good for siblings to argue. So, the answer choice three is not in agreement with the author's view. |
| 6 | A and D | Options A and D point out the differences between the recipe and a typical one. |
| 7 | A | Answer choice one is the best answer. They have gone different ways to a degree, however they both still are concerned about each other. |
| 8 | C | Answer choice three is the correct answer. This poem says that a bird will give the message of love. Modern valentine cards and poems usually mention hearts and candy. Answers one and two are characteristics of modern valentines. Answer choice four is not applicable to the question. There is a difference. |
| 9 | B | Answer choice two is the best answer. The question asks what the poem and the holiday have in common. Both have fireworks. |
| 10 | A, C and D | The statements that can be inferred by this poem are that the speaker is young and may still be fighting in the war. People have died tragically in the war and the speaker is being sarcastic in the poem about those leaders that make decisions about soldiers and war from the comfort of their homes. |

# Lesson 14: Comparing Media

| Question No. | Answer | Detailed Explanations |
|---|---|---|
| 1 | A | Answer choice one is correct. A time-lapse video of the leaves changing color may be included in a documentary to help someone understand how the leaves change color. Paintings are just representations, not the real thing, animals hibernating are an example given in the text but not helpful, and subtitles wouldn't do much more than the text itself. |
| 2 | C | Answer choice three is correct. A diagram of the process would be most helpful. The other three could be used to make it more entertaining or to add minor details. |
| 3 | B | Answer choice two is correct. While a diagram would be helpful and the picture and photograph would be interesting, letting students see and compare the leaves would be best. |
| 4 | C | Answer choice three is the best answer. Choices one and four are too recent to be useful and answer choice two is not possible because video didn't exist during the original Olympics. |
| 5 | B | Answer choice two is the best answer. Having students play the games will make the passage more interactive and help them understand the different sports it talks about. |
| 6 | B, C and D | It would not make sense to air it rght before the Super Bowl; sometime in the Fall and sometime in the Spring. |
| 7 | A, C and D | It would most likely not be accompanied by the following-<br>Pictures of modern-day construction trucks<br>Relics from Ancient Egypt, and<br>Items from Egyptian kings. |
| 8 | A, B and C | Experts talking about the pyramids; illustrations of the pyramids and of Egyptian kings who got pyramids built are all appropriate to include in the documentary. |
| 9 | C | Answer choice three is correct. Plays are usually fiction, so it would most likely focus on a specific worker or group of workers and tell their story. Choice one is likely but the pyramids wouldn't be the main focus. Choice four could be part, but not the entire thing and choice two does not fit the play genre. |
| 10 | B | Answer choice two is the correct answer. Since plays normally tell stories, this passage could easily inspire a play about Verdi's childhood. A news story is not likely because this passage is from the past, a song would be awkward, and the narrative format doesn't really fit a slideshow. |

# Lesson 15: How It's Made And What It Means

| Question No. | Answer | Detailed Explanations |
|---|---|---|
| 1 | A, B and D | Options A, B and D are indicative of a villanelle. |
| 2 | D | In poetry repetition is used to stress an idea, sound or feeling. The word me is not repeated, so answer choice number four is the best answer. |
| 3 | D | The correct answer is answer choice four. The way this poem is structured in rhyme helps lead the reader from one stanza to the next. This helps with pacing and feeling connected. |
| 4 | C | Answer choice number three is the best answer. When the author states she got the story "bit by bit" from various people, and that it was slightly different each time, she is hinting that she has pieced the story together, and the accuracy is not necessarily the way it actually happened. |
| 5 | B | Answer choice two is the best answer. If the author had explained how she learned of the story, it would help the reader analyze the accuracy of the story and the person telling the story. It would give the story as told more credit. |
| 6 | A | Answer choice number one is the best answer. The prologue is written to rhyme, like a poem. The remaining portion of the passage is written in the format of a play (prose=anything not poetic). |
| 7 | aaba | Rhyming patterns are based on words that rhyme at the end of each line in a stanza. The rhyming pattern in the first stanza is aaba, using the rhyming words at the end of the lines know, though, here, snow. |
| 8 | C | Answer choice three is the best choice. The man in this poem is traveling late at night and he stops for seemingly no reason. A horse that is accustomed to traveling the same paths/roads would realize something was out of the ordinary. His shaking of bells would be an indication of the horse "asking" why they are stopped. |
| 9 | B | The second choice is the correct answer. When analyzing a poem each sound is assigned a letter. Any time that sound appears it is assigned the same letter. When a new sound presents itself, the next letter in the alphabet is assigned. The scheme can be simple, aabb, or very complex, aaba,bbcd etc. |
| 10 | D | Answer choice four is the correct answer. This line indicates that the author hopes to be telling this story a long time from now. |

# Lesson 16: A Matter Of Attitude

| Question No. | Answer | Detailed Explanations |
|---|---|---|
| 1 | B and C | Options B and C- the author aims to create a silly, nonsensical tone. |
| 2 | B | Answer choice two is the best answer. "Thus the man became rich and lived on with his wife and children. And that child, that came to him in his sleep, was an angel sent by the Lord God, whose will it was to aid the poor man, and to reveal secrets which had not been revealed till then." describes a happy, relieved, and JOYFUL feeling.<br>There is no anger, or confusion in this passage's end, nor any seriousness. |
| 3 | C and D | The narrator does not consider them worthy of respect and believes the officers are fat and greedy and don't value the young soldiers. |
| 4 | C | Answer choice three is the best answer. Guzzling and gulping are words that hint at greed. Also, the "best hotel" is annoying to the narrator when young men are at war on the front lines. |
| 5 | A and B | The author's tone toward the woman is one of disgust and repulsion. |
| 6 | A | Answer choice one is the best choice. The author is comparing the sisters to little birds in a nest (metaphor). The author is trying to illustrate how siblings pick on one another by comparing them to birds in a nest who literally peck their siblings. |
| 7 | A | Answer choice one is the correct answer. Jo wants to buy a book, and the author calling her a "bookworm" helps indicate this. |
| 8 | A | Answer choice one is the best answer. The author describes the Martians as organized and thoughtful. So, the tone is one of admiration. |
| 9 | A | Answer choice one is the correct answer. |
| 10 | A | Answer choice one is the best answer. If a person does not have dreams there is no reason to work hard to achieve other things. |

# Lesson 17: Getting Technical

| Question No. | Answer | Detailed Explanations |
|---|---|---|
| 1 | B and C | Options B and C are true of nano hairs according to the article. |
| 2 | Artificial | Prosthetic means artificial. |
| 3 | C | Answer choice three is the best answer. The article describes what has to be recorded and tracked, and it mentions using sensors to do this. |
| 4 | C | Answer choice number three is the best selection. The passage mentions under childhood feet which implies that these are items a child might run across while walking outside. NONE of the other three choices apply to this passage. |
| 5 | B and D | Impure water is unsafe and polluted. |
| 6 | B | Answer choice two is the best. The passage is about workers who did not work in a holdout for more money. When a worker strikes, he/she is trying to get more money by causing the trouble for the employers in hopes they'd give the workers more money. |
| 7 | C | The answer choice three is the best answer. The first line tells the reader what skunks eat, and it mentions eating fruits, veggies and other animals. |
| 8 | C | Answer choice number three is the best answer. The phrase "unable to find live animals to eat," indicates that scavenger means to eat dead animals. |
| 9 | C | Answer choice three is the best answer. The phrase "press the portions outward" explain that "relief" means to not be flat, but to be above the picture. |
| 10 | B | Answer choice two is the best answer. This passage is about counting the votes to elect President McKinley. The process is described and includes the Senate and the House of Representatives. These are parts of the U. S. Government. |

# Lesson 18: What's The Author's Point?

| Question No. | Answer | Detailed Explanations |
|---|---|---|
| 1 | C | Answer choice three is correct. A scientist should present the information without any slant or bias to a specific belief or cause. A journalist might want to tell a story with more exciting aspects to get viewers, a student might not know enough facts and information to be completely accurate, and an activist might have a cause they want focus on, so they might not be as fair at the information as a scientist should be. |
| 2 | B and C | Research and consultation with experts could help verify the selection's claims. |
| 3 | C | Answer choice three is the best answer. It is verifiable. "All accounts" could be interviewed to see if that is really what people believe. The remaining answers involve opinions. Saying someone is too weak, or pretty, or smart is an opinion. What one person believes is too weak is not necessarily what another believes. And no one but Nicholas knows if he is overcome. So, the only reasonable answer is three. |
| 4 | an eyewitness article on the event | An eyewitness article on the event could determine the accuracy of the eighth paragraph's claim. |
| 5 | A | Answer choice one is NOT a fact. It is an opinion that this store is better than any other in the city. That cannot be proven. The other choices are in fact something that could be verified. |
| 6 | D | Answer choice four is the correct answer. A child would need to follow directions in various places. The backyard is not varied enough. Just buying the book will not help prove the bolded portion of the information. Interviewing the author is pointless. Obviously he/she believes it will work, or they would not have included the information in the book. |
| 7 | C | Answer choice three is the correct answer. The word funny is not provable. What is funny to one person is not necessarily funny to another. The remaining three answer choices are facts that can easily be proven by details and information easily obtained. |

| Question No. | Answer | Detailed Explanations |
|---|---|---|
| 8 | B | The article tells the reader where he/she can find more background information on the strike (No.'s 7 & 10); answer choice two is the correct answer. The other answer choices do not make sense. To find information on a specific event, just "other magazines" is not detailed enough to find the necessary information. Newspapers might be a good source, but since the author tells the reader where the information is, looking through old newspapers is not necessary. And an encyclopedia would not have that information recorded yet. The news is too new. |
| 9 | B | Answer choice two is correct. The passage is factual information. Opinions of anyone are not included. |
| 10 | C | Answer choice three is the correct answer. He does not include readers' viewpoints and the other two answers are correct, but the third answer is the most correct. |

# Chapter 4

# Author's Purpose and Craft

## Chapter 4

## Lesson 1: What A Character!

### THE EMPEROR'S NEW CLOTHES
#### by Hans Christian Anderson

Many years ago there was an Emperor, who was so excessively fond of new clothes that he spent all his money on them. He cared nothing about his soldiers, nor for the theatre, nor for driving in the woods except for the sake of showing off his new clothes. He had a costume for every hour in the day, and instead of saying, as one does about any other king or emperor, 'He is in his council chamber,' here one always said, 'The Emperor is in his dressing-room.'

Life was very gay in the great town where he lived; hosts of strangers came to visit it every day and among them one day two swindlers. They gave themselves out as weavers and said that they knew how to weave the most beautiful stuff imaginable. Not only were the colors and patterns unusually fine, but the clothes that were made of the stuff had the peculiar quality of becoming invisible to every person who was not fit for the office he held, or if he was impossibly dull.

Those must be splendid clothes,' thought the Emperor. 'By wearing them, I should be able to discover which men in my kingdom are unfitted for their posts. I shall distinguish the wise men from the fools. Yes, I certainly must order some of that stuff to be woven for me.

He paid the two swindlers a lot of money in advance so that they might begin their work at once.

They did put up two looms and pretended to weave, but they had nothing whatever upon their shuttles. At the outset, they asked for a quantity of the finest silk and the purest gold thread, all of which they put into their own bags while they worked away at the empty looms far into the night. I should like to know how those weavers are getting on with the stuff,' thought the Emperor; but he felt a little queer when he reflected that anyone who was stupid or unfit for his post would not be able to see it. He certainly thought that he need have no fears for himself, but still, he thought he would send somebody else first to see how it was getting on. Everybody in the town knew what wonderful power the stuff possessed, and everyone was anxious to see how stupid his neighbor was.

I will send my faithful old minister to the weavers,' thought the Emperor. 'He will be best able to see how the stuff looks, for he is a clever man, and no one fulfills his duties better than he does!'

So the good old minister went into the room where the two swindlers sat working at the empty loom.

Heaven preserve us!' thought the old minister, opening his eyes very wide. 'Why, I can't see a thing!' But he took care not to say so. Both the swindlers begged him to be good enough to step a little nearer and asked if he did not think it a good pattern and beautiful coloring. They pointed to the empty loom, and the poor old minister stared as hard as he could, but he could not see anything, for of course there was nothing to see. Good heavens!' thought he, 'is it possible that I am a fool. I have never thought so, and nobody must know it. Am I not fit for my post? It will never do to say that I cannot see the stuff.

Well, sir, you don't say anything about the stuff,' said the one who was pretending to weave. Oh, it is beautiful! quite charming!' said the old minister, looking through his spectacles; 'this pattern and these colors! I will certainly tell the Emperor that the stuff pleases me very much.

We are delighted to hear you say so,' said the swindlers, and then they named all the colors and described the peculiar pattern. The old minister paid great attention to what they said, so as to be able to repeat it when he got home to the Emperor.

Then the swindlers went on to demand more money, more silk, and more gold, to be able to proceed with the weaving; but they put it all into their own pockets—not a single strand was ever put into the loom, but they went on as before weaving at the empty loom.

The Emperor soon sent another faithful official to see how the stuff was getting on, and if it would soon be ready. The same thing happened to him as to the minister; he looked and looked, but as there was only the empty loom, he could see nothing at all.

Is not this a beautiful piece of stuff?' said both the swindlers, showing and explaining the beautiful pattern and colors which were not there to be seen.

I know I am not a fool!' thought the man, 'so it must be that I am unfit for my good post! It is very strange, though! However, one must not let it appear!' So he praised the stuff he did not see and assured them of his delight in the beautiful colors and the originality of the design. 'It is absolutely charming!' he said to the Emperor. Everybody in the town was talking about this splendid stuff.

Now the Emperor thought he would like to see it while it was still on the loom. So, accompanied by a number of selected courtiers, among whom were the two faithful officials who had already seen the imaginary stuff, he went to visit the crafty impostors, who were working away as hard as ever they could at the empty loom.

It is magnificent!' said both the honest officials. 'Only see, your Majesty, what a design! What colors!' And they pointed to the empty loom, for they thought no doubt the others could see the stuff.

What!' thought the Emperor; 'I see nothing at all! This is terrible! Am I a fool? Am I not fit to be Emperor? Why, nothing worse could happen to me! Oh, it is beautiful!' said the Emperor. 'It has my highest approval!' and he nodded his satisfaction as he gazed at the empty loom. Nothing would induce him to say that he could not see anything.

The whole suite gazed and gazed, but saw nothing more than all the others. However, they all exclaimed with his Majesty, 'It is very beautiful!' and they advised him to wear a suit made of this wonderful cloth on the occasion of a great procession which was just about to take place. 'It is magnificent! gorgeous! excellent!' went from mouth to mouth; they were all equally delighted with it.

The Emperor gave each of the rogues an order of knighthood to be worn in their buttonholes and the title of 'Gentlemen weavers.'

The swindlers sat up the whole night before the day on which the procession was to take place, burning sixteen candles; so that people might see how anxious they were to get the Emperor's new clothes ready. They pretended to take the stuff off the loom. They cut it out in the air with a huge pair of scissors, and they stitched away with needles without any thread in them. At last, they said: 'Now the Emperor's new clothes are ready! The Emperor, with his grandest courtiers, went to them himself, and both the swindlers raised one arm in the air, as if they were holding something, and said: 'See, these are the trousers, this is the coat, here is the mantle!' and so on. 'It is as light as a spider's web. One might think one had nothing on, but that is the very beauty of it!'

Yes!' said all the courtiers, but they could not see anything, for there was nothing to see.

Will your imperial majesty be graciously pleased to take off your clothes,' said the impostors, 'so that we may put on the new ones, along here before the great mirror?' The Emperor took off all his clothes, and the impostors pretended to give him one article of dress after the other of the new ones which they had pretended to make. They pretended to fasten something round his waist and to tie on something; this was the train, and the Emperor turned round and round in front of the mirror.

How well his majesty looks in the new clothes! How becoming they are!' cried all the people around. 'What a design, and what colors! They are the most gorgeous robes!' The canopy is waiting outside, which is to be carried over your majesty in the procession,' said the master of the ceremonies.

Well, I am quite ready,' said the Emperor. 'Don't the clothes fit well?' and then he turned around again in front of the mirror so that he should seem to be looking at his grand things.

The chamberlains who were to carry the train stooped and pretended to lift it from the ground with both hands, and they walked along with their hands in the air. They dared not let it appear that they could not see anything.

Then the Emperor walked along in the procession under the gorgeous canopy, and everybody in the streets and at the windows exclaimed, 'How beautiful the Emperor's new clothes are! What a splendid train! And they fit to perfection!' Nobody would let it appear that he could see nothing, for then he would not be fit for his post, or else he was a fool. None of the Emperor's clothes had been so successful before. But he has got nothing on,' said a little child.

Oh, listen to the innocent,' said its father; and one person whispered to the other what the child had said. 'He has nothing on; a child says he has nothing on! But he has nothing on!' at last cried all the people. The Emperor writhed, for he knew it was true, but he thought 'the procession must go on now,' so held himself stiffer than ever, and the chamberlains held up the invisible train.

1. **Which excerpt from the text provides the reason the Emperor agreed to buy clothes from the swindlers?**

   Ⓐ Not only were the colors and patterns unusually fine, but the clothes that were made of the stuff had the peculiar quality of becoming invisible to every person who was not fit for the office he held, or if he was impossibly dull.

   Ⓑ Life was very gay in the great town where he lived; hosts of strangers came to visit it every day, and among them one day two swindlers. They gave themselves out as weavers, and said that they knew how to weave the most beautiful stuff imaginable.

   Ⓒ At the outset they asked for a quantity of the finest silk and the purest gold thread, all of which they put into their own bags, while they worked away at the empty looms far into the night.

   Ⓓ 'I know I am not a fool!' thought the man, 'so it must be that I am unfit for my good post! It is very strange, though! However, one must not let it appear!' So he praised the stuff he did not see, and assured them of his delight in the beautiful colors and the originality of the design.

2. **What character trait do the Emperor and his minister share- that they are both insecure about their qualifications or that they both are able to imagine things that are not visible?**

3. **Why does the Emperor continue with the procession after the child reviews the truth?**

## Huckleberry Finn (Excerpt)
## By Mark Twain

*In this excerpt from Chapter Five, Huck's father arrives unexpectedly.*

I HAD shut the door to. Then I turned around and there he was. I used to be scared of him all the time, he beat me so much. I reckoned I was scared now, too; but in a minute I see I was mistaken -- that is, after the first jolt, as you may say, when my breath sort of hitched, he being so unexpected; but right away after I see I warn't scared of him worth bothring about.

He was most fifty, and he looked it. His hair was long and tangled and greasy, and hung down, and you could see his eyes shining through like he was behind vines. It was all black, no gray; so was his long, mixed-up whiskers. There warn't no color in his face, where his face showed; it was white; not like another man's white, but a white to make a body sick, a white to make a body's flesh crawl -- a tree-toad white, a fish-belly white. As for his clothes -- just rags, that was all. He had one ankle resting on t'other knee; the boot on that foot was busted, and two of his toes stuck through, and he worked them now and then. His hat was laying on the floor -- an old black slouch with the top caved in, like a lid.

I stood a-looking at him; he set there a-looking at me, with his chair tilted back a little. I set the candle down. I noticed the window was up; so he had climbed in by the shed. He kept a-looking me all over.

By and by he says:
"Starchy clothes -- very. You think you're a good deal of a big-bug, don't you?"
"Maybe I am, maybe I ain't," I says.

"Don't you give me none o' your lip," says he. "You've put on considerable many frills since I been away. I'll take you down a peg before I get done with you. You're educated, too, they say -- can read and write. You think you're better'n your father, now, don't you, because he can't? I'll take it out of you. Who told you you might meddle with such hifalut'n foolishness, hey? -- who told you you could?"
"The widow. She told me."

"The widow, hey? -- and who told the widow she could put in her shovel about a thing that ain't none of her business?"
"Nobody never told her."

"Well, I'll learn her how to meddle. And looky here -- you drop that school, you hear? I'll learn people to bring up a boy to put on airs over his own father and let on to be better'n what he is. You lemme catch you fooling around that school again, you hear? Your mother couldn't read, and she couldn't write, nuther, before she died. None of the family couldn't before they died. I can't; and here you're a-swelling yourself up like this. I ain't the man to stand it -- you hear? Say, lemme hear you read."

I took up a book and begun something about General Washington and the wars. When I'd read about a half a minute, he fetched the book a whack with his hand and knocked it across the house.

He says:

"It's so. You can do it. I had my doubts when you told me. Now looky here; you stop that putting on frills. I won't have it. I'll lay for you, my smarty; and if I catch you about that school I'll tan you good. First you know you'll get religion, too. I never see such a son.

He took up a little blue and yaller picture of some cows and a boy, and says:
"What's this?"
"It's something they give me for learning my lessons good."

He tore it up, and says:
"I'll give you something better -- I'll give you a cowhide.
He set there mumbling for a minute, and then he says:
"*Ain't* you a sweet-scented dandy, though? A bed; and bedclothes; and a look'n'-glass; and a piece of carpet on the floor -- and your own father got to sleep with the hogs in the tanyard. I never see such a son. I bet I'll take some o' these frills out o' you before I'm done with you. Why, there ain't no end to your airs -- they say you're rich. Hey? -- how's that?"

"They lie -- that's how."
"Looky here -- mind how you talk to me; I'm a-standing about all I can stand now -- so don't gimme no sass. I've been in town two days, and I hain't heard nothing but about you bein' rich. I heard about it away down the river, too. That's why I come. You git me that money to-morrow -- I want it."
"I hain't got no money."

"It's a lie. Judge Thatcher's got it. You git it. I want it."
"I hain't got no money, I tell you. You ask Judge Thatcher; he'll tell you the same."

"All right. I'll ask him; and I'll make him pungle, too, or I'll know the reason why. Say, how much you got in your pocket? I want it."
"I hain't got only a dollar, and I want that to -- "
"It don't make no difference what you want it for -- you just shell it out."

4.  **Why might Huck be afraid of his father? Write in the box below.**

5.  **What does Huck's father want hm to do after he demonstrates his reading ability?**

    Ⓐ He tells Huck he's proud of him and then asks for Huck's money.
    Ⓑ He hits the book out of Huck's hands and flings it across the room, then tells Huck to stop showing off.
    Ⓒ He tells Huck to stop attending school.
    Ⓓ He asks Huck to teach him how to read.

## The Call of the Wild
### Excerpt by Jack London

Buck lived at a big house in the sun-kissed Santa Clara Valley. Judge Miller's place, it was called. It stood back from the road, half-hidden among the trees, through which glimpses could be caught of the wide cool veranda that ran around its four sides. The house was approached by graveled driveways, which wound about through wide-spreading lawns and under the interlacing boughs of tall poplars. At the rear, things were on even a more spacious scale than at the front. There were great stables, where a dozen grooms and boys held forth, rows of vine-clad servants' cottages, an endless and orderly array of out-houses, long grape arbors, green pastures, orchards, and berry patches. Then there was the pumping plant for the artesian well and the big cement tank where Judge Miller's boys took their morning plunge and kept cool in the hot afternoon. And over this great demesne, Buck ruled. Here he was born, and here he had lived the four years of his life. It was true, there were other dogs, There could not but be other dogs on so vast a place, but they did not count. They came and went, resided in the populous kennels, or lived obscurely in the recesses of the house after the fashion of Toots, the Japanese pug, or Ysabel, the Mexican hairless,--strange creatures that rarely put nose out of doors or set foot to the ground. On the other hand, there were the fox terriers, a score of them at least, who yelped fearful promises at Toots and Ysabel looking out of the windows at them and protected by a legion of housemaids armed with brooms and mops. But Buck was neither house-dog nor kennel-dog. The whole realm was his. He plunged into the swimming tank or went hunting with the Judge's sons; he escorted Mollie and Alice, the Judge's daughters, on long twilight or early morning rambles; on wintry nights he lay at the Judge's feet before the roaring library fire; he carried the Judge's grandsons on his back, or rolled them in the grass, and guarded their footsteps through wild adventures down to the fountain in the stable yard, and even beyond, where the paddocks were, and the berry patches. Among the terriers he stalked imperiously, and Toots and Ysabel he utterly ignored, for he was king,--king over all creeping, crawling, flying things of Judge Miller's place, humans included.

6. **Why does Buck "utterly ignore" Toots and Ysabel?**

   Ⓐ Their names are strange.
   Ⓑ The other two dogs don't act the way he feels a dog should behave.
   Ⓒ He's not allowed inside, so he thinks it is odd that they are.
   Ⓓ The other two dogs tease him.

7. **What made Buck proud of being "neither a house-dog or a kennel-dog?"**

   Ⓐ The judge told him so.
   Ⓑ Buck chose that life.
   Ⓒ Buck was part of family events.
   Ⓓ Buck had been with the Miller's longer than other dogs.

8. The quote "...strange creatures that rarely put nose out of doors or set foot to ground..." tells the reader what about Toots and Ysabel?

    Ⓐ Their names are odd, and so are they.
    Ⓑ They are too little to be outside.
    Ⓒ They are "babied" in the house and behave like people.
    Ⓓ There are too many dogs outside already.

9. What is Buck's mood in this excerpt?

    Ⓐ weary and wishful
    Ⓑ relaxed and relieved
    Ⓒ joyful and jaded
    Ⓓ desperate and dejected

10. Based on the excerpts from The Call of the Wild, all of these can describe Buck EXCEPT_____?

    Ⓐ weary and wishful
    Ⓑ relaxed and relieved
    Ⓒ joyful and jaded
    Ⓓ desperate and dejected

# Chapter 4

## Lesson 2: Equal? Alike? Different? Comparing Authors

**PASSAGE A:**

When I was in the fourth grade, no one liked me because my brother was arrested, and that made everyone think that I might do something illegal too. It hurt my feelings to have to sit through school every day and not talk to anyone. When it was time to work in groups, I would have to sit with a group of kids that I knew hated me. Sometimes they would say something mean or move a chair away when it looked like I might sit with them. It was worse during lunch and on the bus when kids would yell things about my brother and ask me if I visited him in prison. After a while, I didn't want to go to school anymore, and I pretended to be sick every day, so I could stay home. Telling my parents and my teachers didn't change anything. After a while, my parents decided to let me change schools. The first year at my new school was bad because I didn't know anyone and was afraid to talk to people because of everything that happened at the old school. After a while, I made a few friends, and I started to feel better about talking to people. Now I have a few friends, and I don't feel like people are bullying me anymore.

**PASSAGE B:**

According to Dr. Norman Anderson, CEO of the American Psychological Association, bullying is any kind of aggressive behavior in which someone intentionally tries to harm or cause discomfort to another person. Bullying can be in the form of physical contact but is just as frequently demonstrated in cruel remarks, intentional exclusion of the victim, or in recent years, cyberbullying, in which the aggressor lashes out to the victim via e-mail, social networking, or text messaging.

There is no single, identifiable cause of bullying. Bullying often occurs as a result of influences from peer groups, family groups, communities, or even the media. It is, therefore, important to engage all of these groups if any anti-bullying effort is to be successful.

For many years, the primary means employed by schools to deal with the student to student bullying has been to punish the aggressor. Research has shown that disciplinary consequences alone will not significantly curb bullying in academic settings. Faculty and administrators must be trained to identify early warning signs that students are either bullies or being bullied, and onlookers, students who are not bullies themselves, but do nothing to inhibit bullying they witness, must be empowered with interpersonal skills training to help them intervene when they witness bullying within their peer groups.

1. **According to the author of Passage B, what strategy would most likely have helped the author of Passage A?**

    Ⓐ  Disciplinary consequences for the bullies
    Ⓑ  Changing schools
    Ⓒ  Training "onlookers" to intervene when they witness bullying
    Ⓓ  Counseling for the bullying victim

2. **What information from Passage B best explains this line from Passage A:**

    *Telling my parents and my teachers didn't change anything.*

    Ⓐ  Faculty and administrators must be trained to identify early warning signs that students are either bullies or being bullied.
    Ⓑ  Bullying often occurs as a result of influences from peer groups, family groups, community, or even the media.
    Ⓒ  Bullying can be in the form of physical contact, but is just as frequently demonstrated in cruel remarks, intentional exclusion of the victim, or in recent years, cyber bullying, in which the aggressor lashes out to the victim via e-mail, social networking, or text messaging.
    Ⓓ  For many years, the primary means employed by schools to deal with student to student bullying has been to punish the aggressor.

3. **Which passage was most likely written by a middle school student?**

    Ⓐ  Passage A
    Ⓑ  Passage B
    Ⓒ  Both passages
    Ⓓ  There is not enough information to determine the authors.

4. **Which passage explains what is meant by bullying?**

    Ⓐ  Passage A
    Ⓑ  Passage B
    Ⓒ  Both passages
    Ⓓ  Neither passage

5. **Which form of bullying described in Passage B was experienced by the author of Passage A? Write in the box below.**

## Success

One should guard against preaching to young people success in the customary form as the main aim in life. The most important motive for work in school and in life is pleasure in work, pleasure in a result, and the knowledge of the value of the result to the community.
- Albert Einstein

The way to learn to do things is to do things. The way to learn a trade is to work at it. Success teaches how to succeed. Begin with the determination to succeed, and the work is half-done already.
- Henry Ford

"What Constitutes Success"
By Bessie Stanley (1905)

He has achieved success who has lived well,
laughed often and loved much;
who has gained the respect of intelligent men
and the love of little children;
who has filled his niche and accomplished his task;
who has left the world better than he found it,
whether by an improved poppy, a perfect poem, or a rescued soul;
who has never lacked appreciation of earth's beauty
or failed to express it;
who has always looked for the best in others
and given them the best he had;
whose life was an inspiration;
whose memory a benediction.

6. **Who wrote "What Constitutes Success"? Write in the box below.**

[ ]

7. **Which of the authors most likely subscribed to what Einstein referred to as "success in the customary form?"**

Ⓐ Albert Einstein
Ⓑ Bessie Stanley
Ⓒ Henry Ford
Ⓓ None of the authors.

Steve Jobs, the CEO of Apple Computer, once said, "Being the richest man in the cemetery doesn't matter to me...Going to bed at night saying I've done something wonderful...that's what matters to me."

8.   **Which of the expressions about success above most closely align with Jobs' idea?**

   Ⓐ  Albert Einstein's
   Ⓑ  Henry Ford's
   Ⓒ  Bessie Stanley's
   Ⓓ  Both B and C.

9.   **Which of the authors above aligns themselves with the desire to succeed through industrial work for the common man?**

   Ⓐ  Albert Einstein
   Ⓑ  Henry Ford
   Ⓒ  Bessie Stanley
   Ⓓ  Both Ford and Einstein

10. **Which of the authors above would most strongly disagree with Ford's interpretation of success?**

   Ⓐ  Albert Einstein
   Ⓑ  Steve Jobs
   Ⓒ  Bessie Stanley
   Ⓓ  None of the above.

## Chapter 4

## Lesson 3: What's The Author's Angle?

### From <u>Guiseppi Verdi</u> by Thomas Trapper

Whenever the organ man came into the village of Roncole, in Italy (where Verdi was born, October 10, 1813), Verdi could not be kept indoors. But he followed the wonderful organ and the wonderful man who played it, all day long, as happy as he could be.

When Giuseppe was seven years old, his father, though only a poor innkeeper, bought him a spinet, a sort of small piano. So faithfully did the little boy practice that the spinet was soon quite worn out and new jacks, or hammers, had to be made for it. This was done by Stephen Cavaletti, who wrote a message on one of the jacks telling that he made them anew and covered them with leather, and fixed the pedal, doing all for nothing, because the little boy, Giuseppe Verdi, showed such willingness to practice and to learn. Thus the good Stephen thought this was pay enough.

1. **Based on these paragraphs, what can you infer is NOT the author's view of Verdi? Select all that apply.**

   Ⓐ He is amazed by Verdi's talent.
   Ⓑ He thinks Verdi started playing an instrument at too young of an age.
   Ⓒ He is jealous of Verdi's talent.
   Ⓓ He is unsure what to make of Verdi's talent.

### <u>The Great Round World and What's Going On In It</u> (magazine article)

The Czar of Russia is quite ill, and everyone feels sorry that he should be sick now when his advice and assistance is so badly needed to settle the worrying Turkish question, which has so troubled Europe.

The young Czar Nicholas, who was crowned with so much pomp and glory at Moscow last August, seems unable to carry on the government of Russia.

Many people say he is too weak to govern, and that there are going to be troubles and revolts in Russia.

The truth of the matter seems to be, that the young Czar is a gentle, kind-hearted man, who will not govern Russia in the stern, cruel way that his forefathers have done, and who is therefore thought to be weak and incapable.

While he is making a part of his people love him for his goodness, by far the larger half, who have, under the old rule, been able to make money and gain great power, are furious against him.

Poor young Nicholas is not only hated by the people who were most friendly to his father, but by the Nihilists, who look upon him as their natural enemy, and, between the two parties, it is said that the Czar goes about in constant fear of his life.

Nicholas never wanted to be a ruler. Those who know him say that he has become grave and sad in the few months since he came to the throne.

It is said that he is of too gentle a disposition to be able to keep his ministers in order and that they quarrel fiercely in his presence, and show very little respect for him.

According to all accounts, his health is giving way under the constant worry, and it is reported that he received a shock a few weeks ago, which so completely upset him, that it brought on his present illness.

He was walking in his gardens, and wishing to speak to one of the men who were at work; he signaled to him to come to him. The gardener, proud of his sovereign's notice, ran towards him at full speed. But a sentry, who had not noticed the Czar's signal, fearing that the man was going to harm the Emperor, fired his gun at him, and he fell dead at the Czar's feet.

Nicholas was terribly overcome by the dreadful mistake.

Some people say that his present illness is due to anxiety about the Czarina, who is also ill, and again others say that the wound which Nicholas received when he was traveling in Japan is the cause.

He was struck by a crazy Japanese, and would have been killed, had not Prince George of Greece, the son of the present King of Greece, who was with him, warded off the blow. As it was, the blow was heavy enough to form a lump on the young man's skull, which has caused him great pain, and which some people declare is troubling him now.

Whatever the cause, the Czar is ill, and in no state to attend to anything but his own affairs. It is a sad pity just at this moment when Europe needs him so badly.

**2. What is the author's view of Czar Nicholas?**

Ⓐ The author does not have much respect for Nicholas.
Ⓑ The author feels sympathy and pity for Nicholas.
Ⓒ The author thinks that Nicholas has no business being a Czar.
Ⓓ The author thinks Russia is worse off now that Czar Nicholas is its ruler.

**Advertisement from <u>The Great Round World and What's Going On In It</u> magazine -- Anonymous author**

School and College Text-Books
AT WHOLESALE PRICES
**At my New Store (FEBRUARY 1ST)**
*3 & 5 West 18th Street, The St. Ann Building*

With the greatly increased facilities, I can now offer to my customers the convenience of an assortment of text books and supplies more complete than any other in any store in this city. Books will be classified according to subject. Teachers and students are invited to call and refer to the shelves when in search of information; every convenience and assistance will be rendered to them.

Reading Charts, miscellaneous Reference Charts, Maps, Globes, Blackboards, and School Supplies at net prices singly or in quantity.

All books removed from old store (more or less damaged by removal) will be closed out at low prices.

*Mail orders promptly attended to*
*All books, etc., subject to approval*
William Beverley Harrison, 3 & 5 West 18th Street
FORMERLY 59 FIFTH AVENUE

3.  **What is the author's point of view in this ad?**

    Ⓐ  His new store is even better than his old store.
    Ⓑ  His store has some of the books teachers and students need.
    Ⓒ  His books are now available by mail order.
    Ⓓ  His store has moved to a new location.

**An Advertisement for SIMPLE LESSONS IN THE STUDY OF NATURE
By I.G. OAKLEY from <u>The Great Round World and What's Going On In It</u>
magazine -- Anonymous author**

This is a handy little book, which many a teacher who is looking for means to offer children genuine nature study may be thankful to get hold of.

Nature lessons, to be entitled to that name, must deal with what can be handled and scrutinized at leisure by the child, pulled apart, and even wasted. This can be done with the objects discussed in this book; they are under the feet of childhood—grass, feathers, a fallen leaf, a budding twig, or twisted shell; these things cannot be far out of the way, even within the stony limits of a city.

Nor are the lessons haphazard dashes at the nearest living thing; on the contrary, they are virtually fundamental, whether with respect to their relation to some of the classified sciences, or with reference to the development of thought and power of expression in the child himself.

The illustrations are few, and scarcely more than figures; it is not meant to be a pretty picture-book, yet is most clearly and beautifully printed and arranged, for its material is to be that out of which pictures are made. It will be found full of suggestions of practical value to teachers who are carrying the miscellaneous work of ungraded schools, and who have the unspeakable privilege of dealing with their pupils untrammeled by cast-iron methods and account-keeping examination records.

Sample copy, 50 Cents, post-paid
WILLIAM BEVERLEY HARISON
3 & 5 W. 18th St. • • • New York City

**4. Which statement about this book would the author of this ad be least likely to agree with?**

Ⓐ The book is educational.
Ⓑ The book offers kids great lessons about nature.
Ⓒ The book is like a children's picture book.
Ⓓ The book features items in nature a child would be likely to find on his or her own.

**Advertisement from <u>The Great Round World and What's Going On In It</u> magazine -- Anonymous author**

*Photographs in relief.*

A new plan in regard to photographs has been invented.
It is to take a photograph, similar to the one that is to be embossed, and, after cutting it in a certain way, press the portions outward so that it shall stand in relief.

An open mask of the same shape as the photograph is then used, and the two photographs are dampened and pressed tightly together until the face and figure stand out from the card, and the picture looks as if it had been carved in wood.
This is a very ingenious invention, but the work is very difficult, and can only be done by people who are regularly trained to do it.

**5. How does the author feel about this new invention? Select those that apply.**

Ⓐ He thinks it will be difficult to work on except by the well trained.
Ⓑ It will cause less people to visit photographers.
Ⓒ He thinks this is an incredible, ingenious invention.
Ⓓ It's too inconvenient and not worth the effort.

## The Great Round World and What's Going On In It
### magazine article -- Anonymous author

The news comes from Hamburg that the strike of the dock laborers is over.
The strikers have been beaten because of their lack of money.
In No. 7 of The Great Round World you will find an account of the strike, and if you will also refer to No. 10, you will see that it was thought that the strikers could not hold out very much longer.

The money the strikers expected to receive from other labor unions to help them was so slow in coming that the men and their families were in want, and no man is likely to stand out for the benefit of others when his own children are suffering from cold and hunger.

The men have gone back to their old employers and asked for work. The pity of it all is, however, that during the strike others have been taken on in their places, and the employers have now no work to give them.

After holding out since the end of October, and refusing the masters' offer to give them $1.10 a day, and let all future troubles be settled by arbitration, the strikers have had to give in without gaining a single point. It is very sad.

**6. Who would the author of this article be most likely to support?**

Ⓐ The business owners of Hamburg
Ⓑ The workers who were on strike
Ⓒ The workers who refused to strike
Ⓓ All of the above

## The Great Round World and What's Going On In It
### magazine article -- Anonymous author

Did you ever see a house move?
If you have not, you have missed a very funny sight.

Imagine driving along a country road, and meeting a three-story house making a journey along the highway to new quarters.

There is a good deal of this to be seen just now at Katonah, New York.

A year or so ago the Croton water-shed water, which is in use in New York City, was found to be impure.

A commission was appointed to go and examine the Croton Water-Shed. This meant that they were to examine the little streams, and brooks, and rivers, and lakes, which supplied the water to our aqueduct, and see what the trouble was.

In consequence of this, all of the houses were ordered to be torn down or moved away, and one small village of shanties was destroyed. Among others, the inhabitants of Katonah were ordered to move, that the banks of the stream might be cleared of dwellings.

Katonah has a railroad depot, and a post office, and thinks a good deal of itself.

When the Water-Shed Commission said that it must move or be destroyed, the residents of Katonah gathered together, and decided that rather than be wiped off the face of the map, it would pick up its houses and move itself.

So a new Katonah was established, about a quarter of a mile away from the old one, and just outside the Water-Shed on which it was forbidden to build, for fear of spoiling the water for New York.

For several months past there has been a procession of houses moving from old Katonah to new.

7.  **What is the author's point of view in this article?**

Ⓐ  The people of Kantonah were silly to move their homes.
Ⓑ  Houses should be moved regardless of the circumstances.
Ⓒ  The Kantonah residents were trying to maintain control by choosing when and where they moved them.
Ⓓ  The Kantonah government should pay to move people's homes.

## Baseball Card Collecting

Looking for a new hobby? Do you like baseball? If you answered "yes" to these two questions, then baseball card collecting might be a fun pastime for you to begin! Ever since candy and gum manufacturers started putting cards with pictures of popular baseball players into the packages in the 1800's to encourage young people to buy their sweets, kids have been collecting baseball cards. Now, more than 200 years later, baseball card collecting has become a popular hobby for children and adults alike.

8.  **Based on this paragraph, which statement describes the author's view of baseball card collecting?**

Ⓐ  The author thinks baseball card collecting is an expensive hobby.
Ⓑ  The author thinks baseball card collecting is a worthwhile hobby.
Ⓒ  The author thinks everyone in the world should become a baseball card collector.
Ⓓ  Baseball card collecting leads people to eat too much candy.

9. **Which statement about the books in this advertisement would the author be least likely to agree with?**

    Ⓐ  The books are educational for children.
    Ⓑ  There are interesting facts and descriptions in these books.
    Ⓒ  Most children would not find these books very useful.
    Ⓓ  Children are likely to be entertained by the information in these books.

## Advertisement from <u>The Great Round World and What's Going On In It</u> magazine -- Anonymous author

Klemm's Practice Relief Maps Advertisement

LIST OF MAPS.

| Small size, 9-1/2 x 11 | {Plain, | 5 | cents | each |
|---|---|---|---|---|
| | {With Waterproofed surface | 10 | cents | each |

Europe, Asia, Africa; North America, South America, East Central States, New England, Middle Atlantic States, South Atlantic States, Palestine, Australia.

| Large size, 10 x 15 | {Plain, | 10 | cents | each |
|---|---|---|---|---|
| | {With Waterproofed surface | 15 | cents | each |

United States, British Isles, Roman Empire, Western Europe, North America, South America, Asia.

(POSTAGE ON SINGLE MAPS, 5 CENTS.)
"I would advise Sunday school teachers to use, in connection with the lessons of 1897, Klemm's Relief Map of the Roman Empire. Every scholar who can draw should have a copy of it. Being blank, it can be beautifully colored: waters, blue; mountains, brown; valleys, green; deserts, yellow; cities marked with pin-holes; and the journeys of Paul can be traced upon it."—Mrs. Wilbur F. Crafts, *President International Union of Primary Sabbath-School Teachers of the United States.*

DESCRIPTION OF THE MAPS.
These maps are made in two forms, both with beautifully executed relief (embossed)—the cheaper ones of plain stiff paper similar to drawing paper (these are to be substituted for and used as outline map blanks), the others covered with a durable waterproof surface, that can be quickly cleaned with a damp sponge, adapted to receive a succession of markings and cleansings. Oceans, lakes, and rivers, as well as land, appear in the same color, white, so as to facilitate the use of the map as a *geographical slate.*
WILLIAM BEVERLEY HARISON
*3 & 5 W. 18th St. • • • New York City*

**10. What strategy does the author of this advertisement use to try to convince readers his point of view is shared by others?**

    Ⓐ He describes the maps in detail.
    Ⓑ He uses a testimonial from someone who uses the maps.
    Ⓒ He lists the costs of the maps at the beginning of the ad.
    Ⓓ He lists all the different types of maps that can be purchased from Klemm's.

# Answer Key and
# Detailed Explanations

## Chapter 4: Author's Purpose and Craft

# Lesson 1: What A Character!

| Question No. | Answer | Detailed Explanations |
|---|---|---|
| 1 | A | Answer choice one is the correct answer. The passage explains that the swindlers (dishonest people) told the Emperor that if a person was wise, and worthy of their job/status, they would be able to see the fabric/costumes. But, the men never intended to make any clothes. No one was willing to admit that they saw no clothes because they did not want to appear to be unworthy. It took a child, who did not know to hide what he saw, to point out the obvious. The remaining three answers describe the swindlers (2 and 3) and what an official thought upon seeing the "clothes." They do not answer the question: <u>why</u> did the Emperor agree to hire the men (swindlers). |
| 2 | they are both insecure about their qualifications | Both the Emperor and the Minister are insecure about their qualifications. |
| 3 | -- | The Emperor continues with the procession after the child reviews the truth because he is too **embarrassed** to admit that he has been **fooled/tricked** and does not want his subjects to **laugh** at him or **find out** about it. He did not want to lose face before his kingdom. |
| 4 | Because his father beat him | The passage states- "I used to be scared of him all the time, he beat me so much" |
| 5 | C | Answer choice three is the correct answer. First, Huck's father slaps the book from Buck's hands, but then he tells him to stay away from the school. Answer choice four is incorrect because he does not ask to learn to read. He seems proud that neither he nor Huck's mom could read or write. Answer choice one is incorrect because Huck's father is NOT proud of him. He does demand Huck give him money, but he is not proud. Answer choice two is partially correct, but not the best answer. Huck's father does hit the book from his hand, but the question asked is what does Huck's father ask/tell him to do. Not what does Huck's dad do. |

| Question No. | Answer | Detailed Explanations |
|---|---|---|
| 6 | B | Answer choice two is the best answer. His attitude towards them is one of shame. They don't come outside at all, and he finds that odd. Answer choice three is incorrect because he is allowed inside (Judge's feet), and answer four is not reasonable. No dogs tease him. |
| 7 | C | Answer choice three is the correct answer. He did not want to be a house dog. He does not respect those dogs who do nothing dog-like. He does not want to be a kennel dog because those dogs are working dogs. He enjoys being part of the family, being around the family, and he is proud of his place. He is trusted with being involved/caring for the family. |
| 8 | C | Answer choice three is correct. Buck feels that it is strange that they rarely put nose out of doors (go outside) or put their feet to the ground (someone holds/carries them all the time). The three remaining answers may be true, but they do not hint at Buck's opinions of the two inside dogs. |
| 9 | B | Answer choice two is the correct answer. After a long, long trip he is relaxing and getting well. He mentions being surprised that the other dogs are not jealous. This indicates being relieved that he does not have to worry about dog fights or any other issues with jealousy. |
| 10 | D | The last answer choice is the answer choice that does NOT describe Buck. He is honorable in his actions (the Jude's), he is persistent (went for long walks and kept others company) and he is grateful (for Thornton and Skeet). Nothing in these passages indicate aggression. |

# Lesson 2: Equal? Alike? Different? Comparing Authors

| Question No. | Answer | Detailed Explanations |
|---|---|---|
| 1 | C | Answer choice number three is the correct selection. If someone had been able to intervene, it would have helped the victim in the first passage. The other three answers are good answers in general, but the third answer best fits the situation of the boy in passage A. |
| 2 | A | Answer choice one is the correct answer. The first passage tells an incident, the second passage is informational. They are both about bullying, but from a different genre. |
| 3 | A | Answer choice one is correct. The first passage tells about a young man who was a victim of bullying. The second passage is informational and contains information, that mostly adults would know. So, the first answer choice is the correct one. |
| 4 | C | Answer choice three is correct. Both passages explain bullying. |
| 5 | Intentional exclusion of the victim | "Intentional exclusion of the victim" is what the author of passage A experienced. |
| 6 | Bessie Stanley | Bessie Stanley |
| 7 | C | Answer choice three is the correct answer. Ford was a creative person, but his ideas were more business minded. So, his ideas were more "customary" or normal. |
| 8 | D | Both Einstein and Stanley wanted a better world. |
| 9 | B | Answer choice number two is the correct answer. Ford was responsible for the assembly line, something that most people could do, and it helped to change the way industry ran in America. But, his ideas and attitudes were more for the regular person, whereas the others were very broad and difficult for many people to grasp. |
| 10 | C | Answer choice three is correct. Stanley gives more of an air of societal success, which in itself is more likely to be criticized. |

# Lesson 3: What's The Author's Angle?

| Question No. | Answer | Detailed Explanations |
|---|---|---|
| 1 | B, C and D | Options B, C and D are not the views of the author on Verdi. |
| 2 | B | Answer choice number two is the best answer. The author describes the Czar's personality and discusses what others thought of him. The author mentions the Czar's gentleness and desire to not be so firm as his father, yet most of the people did not understand this, so he was not well thought of. The author feels the Czar was trying to do well and was misunderstood. |
| 3 | A | Answer choice number one is the best choice. The article describes how the old books will be discounted and that the facilities are "greatly increased." This tells the reader that the author is pleased with his new store. |
| 4 | C | Answer choice three is the best choice. The passage mentions the charts and graphs and then states it is not a pretty picture book. Therefore the author is not to agree with the statement that it is a pretty book. |
| 5 | A and C | He thinks it will be difficult to work on except by the well trained, but it is an ingenious invention. |
| 6 | B | Answer choice number two is the best choice. The author chronicles what the striking workers did and how they felt. Then the author mentions that they worked really hard but were not successful. The author indicates he's sad for the workers' lack of success. |
| 7 | C | Answer choice three is the best answer. The residents knew they were going to have their town destroyed, so they made the decision to move themselves and maintain their town. |
| 8 | B | Answer choice number two is the best. The author explains his opinion of collecting cards. The tone is pleasant and explains how/why one would want to collect cards. |
| 9 | C | Answer choice three is the correct answer. The author states in the first part of the passage that children are curious and want to know things. This indicates that he believes the books listed will be interesting and useful to children. |
| 10 | B | Answer choice two is the correct answer. A testimonial is a technique of advertising where someone who has used the product shares their experiences (positive). This is intended to encourage others to use/buy the product as well. |

# Chapter 5

# Composition

## Lesson 1: Who Are You Talking To?

Within the Great Barrier Reef there are several habitats. Consistent throughout the entire 1,616 mile formation are coral reefs. What we consider a piece of coral is actually a collection of several individual coral polyps. Each coral is actually a number of polyps. Coral polyps are living creatures that encase themselves in hard, protective shells made of calcium carbonate. These shells band together forming colonies. The colonies together are known as reefs. Within the Great Barrier Reef there are millions of coral featuring a multitude of colors and textures. There are more than 400 species of hard and soft corals living in the Reef.

Housed within the reefs is a vastly diverse collection of animal life, many of which are endangered. Within its waters, the Great Barrier Reef provides homes to 5,000 species of mollusks and 125 species of sharks, stingrays, and skates. In addition, there are more than 1,500 species of fish including the colorful clownfish. Thirty species of whales, dolphins, and porpoises live in the Great Barrier Reef including humpback whales which use its warm, shallow waters as breeding grounds before journeying to Hawaii to give birth. Six endangered species of marine turtles also use the area to reproduce. The loggerhead turtle, one of the most highly protected endangered species, lives and breeds in the Great Barrier Reef. Over the last 40 years, the number of these turtles has decreased so rapidly that there are only 3% of the number of creatures alive today. Housed around this extremely diverse collection of animal life are 2,195 species of plants. Above water 215 species of birds live on the Great Barrier Reef.

1.  **If you were asked what the author's purpose in writing this essay is- which three options would you not select?**

    Ⓐ To argue that coral are important to the Great Barrier Reef
    Ⓑ To describe the animal life in the Great Barrier Reef
    Ⓒ To explain how coral are formed
    Ⓓ To show the causes and effects of different life forms living in the Great Barrier Reef

### History of Lawn Bowling

The sport known today as lawn bowling began in England in the 13th century. While lawn bowling has become very popular in England, it was not always so. In the 1200s people in England began playing a game based on the Italian sport "Bocce" which had been brought to the country by Julius Ceasar's followers. They used stones or iron balls to play this game and called it "lawn bowling". Lawn bowling immediately caught on in England and by the 14th century it was extremely popular. In the 1300s the King of England, Edward III banned lawn bowling. Because it was so popular, men stopped practicing archery (shooting a bow and arrow) and started playing lawn bowling. The king was worried that men would not be able to shoot a bow and arrow anymore because they were spending their free time lawn bowling. While this may not seem like a big deal to us today, archery was extremely important back then because it was an important skill for a man to have in war. After Edward III, Richard II, the new King of England continued the ban on lawn bowling. In order to encourage English citizens to stop lawn bowling, the government fined people sums of money if they were found playing the sport in public. The sport eventually came across the Atlantic Ocean to North America. Players in Scotland, although technically under the rule of the King of England, ignored the ban and continued to practice lawn bowling. Though some Americans took up the sport, it became more popular in Canada than the United States. Even today, lawn bowling is very popular in Canada.

2. **Who is most likely the intended audience of this selection?**

   Ⓐ People who want to know more about lawn bowling history
   Ⓑ Professional lawn bowlers
   Ⓒ Historians who study English history
   Ⓓ People who dislike lawn bowling

Every person should play a sport at least once in his life. Sports teach us valuable life skills. A player learns to work with others on a team to achieve a common goal. He also develops the ability to work with people he might not normally get along with. Also, people who play sports have to manage their time carefully since they need to work out, practice, and handle everything else in their lives such as school, work, and family commitments. Finally, sports give a player the chance to release stress in a safe, healthy, and fun way.

3. **What group is this paragraph most likely intended for?**

   Ⓐ People who are involved in sports
   Ⓑ Sports team coaches
   Ⓒ People who have never tried sports
   Ⓓ Middle school teachers

The Battle of the Alamo is often seen as one of or possibly even the most significant events to take place during the Texas Revolution. Prior to March 2, 1836, the area we know as the state of Texas was part of the country of the new country of Mexico. Mexico, which included an area called "Spanish Texas", was formed in 1821 when the Spanish were forced to give up control of the land following the Mexican War for Independence. In order to help bolster their victorious, but sadly crippled army, the Mexican government opened Texas to immigrants from the United States. Settlers wanting to move west to start new lives moved into the area and set up their homes and built towns. Quickly, these new inhabitants became disenchanted with the Mexican government and wanted their own independence. A volunteer army of Texians (white and black immigrants living in Texas) and sympathetic Tejanos (Hispanic Texans wanting independence) was formed. In 1835 a group of these volunteers moved into San Antonio in an attempt to take control over the town from Mexico. After five days of fighting, the Mexican army retreated and the Texians and Tejanos took over the Mexican's base camp, the Alamo.

**4.** **What is mostly likely the intended audience of this paragraph? Select those that apply.**

Ⓐ People who are interested in United States history
Ⓑ People who like studying battles and wars
Ⓒ People who are interested in Texas history
Ⓓ People who know a great deal about Texas history already

What's the first thing you think of when you see a skunk? If you answered "stink" then you're like most people. Many of us connect skunks with their smell. In fact, the name "skunk" comes from the Algonquin Indian word "seganuku" which means "one who squirts". The stinky odor that you smell when skunks are around comes from a liquid that they can spray from two spots near their tails. This "skunk juice" is a mixture of sulfur chemicals. Sulfur is a mineral that smells a lot like rotten eggs which is why skunk spray is so stinky. Watch out if you get any of this juice on you because it is not easy to get off! Skunk spray is very difficult to remove from clothes, skin, and hair. Though lots of pet owners swear that you can get a skunk's smell out of a dog's hair by washing him in tomato juice, the best way to remove the scent is by washing the stinky area with a mixture of hydrogen peroxide, baking soda, and dish-washing soap. This mixture changes the chemicals in the skunk spray so that it no longer stinks.

**5.** **What is the author's purpose in this paragraph?**

Ⓐ To explain why skunks "spray" people
Ⓑ To inform the reader about the cause of a skunk's smell and how to remove it
Ⓒ To persuade the reader to stay away from skunks
Ⓓ To argue that skunks are much more harmful than they appear to be

**6.** **If you were asked to write a letter to your school principal showing him the reasons why the school should have dances that last until midnight, instead of nine o'clock, what would the purpose of this piece of writing be- to inform or to persuade?**

## Essay Assignment

Tell a story about a time in your life when you thought one thing was going to happen, but a completely different thing ended up happening.

**7. What is the author's purpose in completing this writing assignment?**

Ⓐ To inform
Ⓑ To persuade
Ⓒ To entertain
Ⓓ To argue

## Essay Assignment

Write an essay contrasting you and your best friend. Be sure to focus on at least three contrasting ideas in your essay.

**8. What is your purpose in writing this essay?**

Ⓐ To show a cause-effect relationship
Ⓑ To persuade your reader
Ⓒ To show differences
Ⓓ To offer an argument and a counterargument

## Welcome to the 2012-2013 school year!

As your children prepare for another exciting year of learning, there are several important dates you should note in your calendar. On September 8, all students will participate in the back-to-school pep rally. Please help your child select clothing in the school colors and be sure he or she is wearing comfortable shoes.

**9. Who is the intended audience for the passage above?**

Ⓐ Members of the community.
Ⓑ Children enrolled in school.
Ⓒ The school faculty.
Ⓓ Parents of children enrolled in this school.

In 2014 our company will introduce a new wind-powered automobile. Using an innovative technology that transfers energy generated by high-altitude wind-turbines to long-life batteries, the new Breeze sedan will operate entirely on wind-generated battery power, and will not incorporate any components of a fossil-fuel burning engine.

The company understands that your current customers who have driven only fossil-fuel burning vehicles may be apprehensive about purchasing a completely new type of vehicle. The company also recognizes that the shape and styling of the new Breeze sedan may seem unfamiliar to most customers.

To help introduce the new Breeze sedan, the company will be sending to you, and all dealerships, a test model of the new Breeze sedan. This car should be shared among the sales staff at your dealership, and used regularly so that potential customers can become accustomed to seeing the vehicle on the road. In addition, national advertising will begin in the summer of 2013, explaining the features and benefits of the new vehicle.

**10. Who is the intended audience for the passage above?**

   Ⓐ  Drivers of wind-powered automobiles.
   Ⓑ  The sales staff at a car dealership.
   Ⓒ  The general public.
   Ⓓ  The owner of a car dealership

## Chapter 5

## Lesson 2: A Picture Is Worth A Thousand Words

**Summer Safety Tips for your Pets**

Never leave your pets in a parked car.

In the heat of summer there is no safe amount of time to leave your pet in a parked car. Even if you leave the engine running and the air conditioning on, the temperature inside the vehicle can go up very quickly. According to the Humane Society, on an 85 degree day, the temperature in a car with the windows slightly open can go up to 102 degrees in ten minutes or less. In less than an hour, that temperature can go up to 120 degrees or more! Your pet could suffer permanent organ damage or worse from exposure to high temperatures. If you plan to go somewhere where your pet is not allowed inside, leave him home!

Pets feel humidity too.

Unlike humans, animals don't sweat from pores all over their bodies. Animals pant or breathe rapidly to eliminate heat and moisture from their bodies. If there is a lot of moisture in the air, panting is less effective, and the pet could become overheated and have no way to release that heat. A dehumidifier or air conditioner will remove moisture from the air and make your pet's natural cooling mechanism more effective.

Fans don't help animals very much.

When a human stands in front of a fan, the air current rushes over his or her skin and helps evaporate the moisture from sweating. Evaporation helps a human feel cooler. Dogs only sweat from the pads on the bottoms of their feet. Standing in front of a fan doesn't help a dog, since there isn't a large amount of evaporation going on.

Limit exercise on hot days.

Do you feel like running when the temperature is high? Why not? Generally, exercising in extreme heat makes you thirsty and very tired. Too much exercise could lead to heat stroke, a dangerous condition when your body isn't able to cool down. Your pets can suffer the same consequences. When it is extremely hot outside, try to exercise your pet only in the morning or evening when the temperature is cooler and cut down the amount of time your pet spends running around.

1. **What two graphics would add valuable information to this article?**

   Ⓐ A picture of a dog in a car.
   Ⓑ A chart that compares the cuteness of different pets.
   Ⓒ A picture of a fan.
   Ⓓ A picture of someone getting a heat stroke while exercising on a hot day.

Scientists in South Korea have developed a type of artificial skin that will allow robots to feel slight vibrations. This skin, developed by weaving together extremely small nano hairs made of polymer or plastic is more sensitive than human skin. When vibration is applied to this artificial skin, the nano hairs bend against each other to generate an electrical current. Sensors within the skin evaluate the current and using that information to determine the source of the vibration.

Researchers are excited about the potential for this new development. The artificial skin could be used to cover prosthetic limbs to help those who have lost a limb experience more realistic sensations and function more naturally.

2. **What graphic would add important information to this article?**

   Ⓐ A photo of a prosthetic limb.
   Ⓑ An enlarged photo of the nanohairs.
   Ⓒ A photo of a robot covered with the artificial skin.
   Ⓓ A map of South Korea.

### Seed-Grown Easter Lilies Replace Imported Bulbs
### from Popular Mechanics (1921)

As a result of successful experiments conducted at the government farm in Virginia, the Easter Lily has now become a wholly domestic plant, grown from seeds instead of from imported bulbs. Furthermore, the home-grown lilies, reaching full flower 15 months after planting, carry five to 15 blossoms to a stalk, as compared with four to five for the average bulb-grown plants. It is reported that good seeds may be procured by anyone by pollinating the flowers as now obtained.

The importation of lily bulbs is large, some 10,000,000 valued at about $2,000,000 being brought from Japan last year. The experiments have proved that the Easter lily is really a very hardy plant, wintering well in the average temperate climate with the bulbs only 4 inches under ground.

3. **What picture would be MOST appropriate as a graphic for this article? Write in the box below.**

## Longest Commercial Flight in Canada
### Popular Mechanics – May 1921

The longest commercial passenger flight in Canada was accomplished a few weeks ago when an airplane with a pilot, passenger, and mechanic, flew from Winnipeg, Man to The Pas Sask, a distance of 487 miles. The flying time for the trip was six hours and twelve minutes.

The long flight was into the North Country and was made without previous arrangements having been made for landing grounds, gasoline, etc. The landing at Hudson Bay had to be made in a swamp, there being no other place, and great difficulty was experienced.

4. **Which type of graphic would add valuable information to this article?**

   Ⓐ  A photo of the plane.
   Ⓑ  A map showing the route of the flight.
   Ⓒ  A photo of the swamp the plane landed in.
   Ⓓ  A map of Canada.

## Extended Telephone Service for Chinese Province
### Popular Mechanics, September 1921

Telephone extensions, including both local and long-distance service are well under way in the province of Kiangsu, China, according to a late report that part of the world. Long-distance lines between all the important towns of the province are planned. It is figured that telephone connections between Shanghai and Nanking will be completed before the end of the year. Service extensions between Pukow and Nanking are now being actively carried on. The old submarine cable which now connects these two cities and which has only two wires will be replaced by a 26-wire cable.

5. **Which would be the most effective graphic to accompany this article?**

   Ⓐ  A photo of a telephone.
   Ⓑ  A photo of the new cable that will be used.
   Ⓒ  A map of China with the named places highlighted.
   Ⓓ  A graph showing the number of phone lines in each province named.

### Gas Refrigerator for Ice Cream Truck
### Popular Mechanics, November 1929

Ice cream and milk delivery trucks are being equipped with gas-burning refrigerating apparatus as a substitute for salt and ice. The plan is more effective and cleaner and is also said to be cheaper, particularly because the maintenance and service costs are greatly reduced. Successful operation of these refrigeration plants promises more extensive shipment of perishable goods by truck, owners point out.

6.   **What two graphics would be appropriate for this article?**

Ⓐ   A photo of children eating ice cream cones.
Ⓑ   A diagram of the new refrigeration unit described above.
Ⓒ   A sketch of the inside of a refrigerated truck.
Ⓓ   A picture of the owners of the unit.

7.   **Which would be most helpful to a student studying the migration patterns of killer whales?**

Ⓐ   A map of the globe with migration routes outlined.
Ⓑ   A picture of a killer whale.
Ⓒ   A map of the globe with areas where killer whales are found highlighted
Ⓓ   A graph measuring the decline in the killer whale population over the last 50 years.

### The Real Story of Revere's Ride
### From the Paul Revere House official Website

In 1774 and the Spring of 1775 Paul Revere was employed by the Boston Committee of Correspondence and the Massachusetts Committee of Safety as an express rider to carry news, messages, and copies of resolutions as far away as New York and Philadelphia.

On the evening of April 18, 1775, Paul Revere was sent for by Dr. Joseph Warren and instructed to ride to Lexington, Massachusetts, to warn Samuel Adams and John Hancock that British troops were marching to arrest them. After being rowed across the Charles River to Charlestown by two associates, Paul Revere borrowed a horse from his friend Deacon John Larkin. While in Charlestown, he verified that the local "Sons of Liberty" committee had seen his pre-arranged signals. (Two lanterns had been hung briefly in the bell-tower of Christ Church in Boston, indicating that troops would row "by sea" across the Charles River to Cambridge, rather than marching "by land" out Boston Neck. Revere had arranged for these signals the previous weekend, as he was afraid that he might be prevented from leaving Boston).

On the way to Lexington, Revere "alarmed" the country-side, stopping at each house, and arrived in Lexington about midnight. As he approached the house where Adams and Hancock were staying, a sentry asked that he not make so much noise. "Noise!" cried Revere, "You'll have noise enough before long. The regulars are coming out!" After delivering his message, Revere was joined by a second rider, William Dawes, who had been sent on the same errand by a different route. Deciding on their own to continue on to Concord, Massachusetts, where weapons and supplies were hidden, Revere and Dawes were joined by a third rider, Dr. Samuel Prescott. Soon after, all three were arrested by a British patrol. Prescott escaped almost immediately, and Dawes soon after. Revere was held for some time and then released. Left without a horse, Revere returned to Lexington in time to witness part of the battle on the Lexington Green.

8. **Which illustration should be included with this passage?**

   Ⓐ A map of Richard Dawes' ride.
   Ⓑ A picture of the church with the lamps lit.
   Ⓒ A map that included both Revere's and Dawes' rides.
   Ⓓ A picture of Paul Revere.

## The Assassination of President Lincoln
## April 14, 1865

Shortly after 10 p.m. on April 14, 1865, actor John Wilkes Booth entered the presidential box at Ford's Theatre in Washington D.C., and fatally shot President Abraham Lincoln. As Lincoln slumped forward in his seat, Booth leapt onto the stage and escaped through the back door. A doctor in the audience rushed over to examine the paralyzed president. Lincoln was then carried across the street to Petersen's Boarding House, where he died early the next morning.

9. **What graphic would complement this passage?**

   Ⓐ picture of Lincoln
   Ⓑ picture of John Wilkes Booth
   Ⓒ blueprint of the Ford Theatre
   Ⓓ map of Washington D.C.

# The Coconut Crab

The coconut crab is the largest living arthropod in the world. It can be up to 16 inches long and weigh up to nine pounds. The body of the crab is divided into multiple sections. The front section includes ten legs. The legs at the front of the crab have claws. The second set of legs are large and used for walking.

Coconut crabs mate on dry land from May to September. The female lays her eggs and adheres them to the underside of her body. She carries the eggs for a few months until, just before they hatch, she releases them into the ocean. The larvae float in the ocean for a few weeks, then hatch.

The coconut crab eats mostly fleshy fruits. They have also been observed preying on smaller crabs and on the bodies of dead coconut crabs. They have even been observed eating small rats.

Coconut crabs are an endangered species. They are native to Guam and Vanuatu, where hunting restrictions have been put in place so that the crabs are not hunted into extinction.

**10. What graphic would add information to this essay?**

Ⓐ  A diagram of the crab's body
Ⓑ  A map of Guam.
Ⓒ  A photo a coconut crab killing a rat.
Ⓓ  A calendar with the months of crab reproduction highlighted.

## Chapter 5

## Lesson 3: Getting From Here To There - Transitions

A game of lawn bowling begins when one player rolls a metal jack or small white ball called a kitty onto the grass rink. The kitty is the target that the players will try to hit with their lawn bowls or balls. Once the kitty has been thrown and hits the grass, it is lined up with the center of the rink. Now the real fun begins! Players from each team take turns throwing their lawn bowls towards the kitty. Each lawn bowl is a colored, baseball-sized ball made of wood wrapped in leather, pure wood, heavy plastic or metal. _____ each team takes all of their turns, points are given to the team whose bowls are closest to the kitty. The teams keep playing rounds like this until one team earns 21 points. Once your team has 21 points they win the game.

1. **Which of the following transitional words fits best in the blank- Before or After? Write in the box below.**

After

Skunks are nocturnal animals. This means that they sleep during the day and are active when it is dark outside. Skunks cannot see very well, but they have excellent senses of smell and hearing, but they cannot see very well in the daylight. _____ skunks would rather move around during the night. In fact, most skunks are killed when they happen to wander on to roads and are hit by cars. They cannot see where they are and walk into these dangerous areas.

2. **Which of the following transitional words fits best in the blank?**

   Ⓐ Therefore
   Ⓑ Because
   Ⓒ In addition
   Ⓓ Even though

The Venus Fly Trap is one of the only plants on earth that dines on animals (bugs to be exact). Even though it's name makes it sound like a make believe creature from outer space, these insect eating plants really do exist. **Because** Venus Fly Traps are very real, they aren't easy to find. In fact, when scientists that study plants first began telling each other about this different plant, many didn't even believe it existed. This isn't because they live on another planet. It's because they only grow in a small part of the United States. Venus Fly Traps can be found growing in the wild along the coasts of North and South Carolina. They like these areas because they have bogs. These bogs have wet, spongy, and sandy ground that is perfect for growing Venus Fly Traps. They also have lots of sunlight and the moist air that these plants like best. The area where there are the most Venus Fly Traps is the Green Swamp near Wilmington, North Carolina.

3.  **What transition would best replace the bold word in the paragraph- Since or Although? Write in the box below.**

The formation of the Great Barrier Reef began millions of years ago. Volcanic activity created what is known as the Coral Sea Basin and a series of raised islands surrounding the basin. As the sea level changed over time so did life living in the basin and on the islands. Over time coral reefs grew, died, and were buried under sediment from volcanic eruptions. This layer of rich sediment built up over time forming shelves. The earliest individual coral located in the raised area now known as the Great Barrier Reef is thought to have formed a half-million years ago. Around 600,000 years ago complete corals began forming in the area and the origin of the oldest of those still living today dates back 20,000 years. Sea levels in the area continued to rise until approximately 6,000 years ago. **In the past**, the water level evened out creating the ideal conditions for the formation of a fusion of coral and other plant and animal life. The shallow grounds created by years of volcanic activity and sedimentary build up combined with the warm waters and high levels of sunlight provide the perfect environment for the Great Barrier Reef to form and thrive.

4.  **What transition would best replace the bold words in the paragraph?**

    Ⓐ At that time
    Ⓑ After
    Ⓒ When
    Ⓓ In the beginning

The average Venus Fly Trap has a number of long shoots with oval shaped traps at the end of them. Each trap looks like a small set of jaws with a series of long thin trigger hairs on the edges of each side. The colors of the traps can be anywhere from bright green to dark red. The color of the trap depends on the amount of light that the plant receives. The more light a Venus Fly Trap is exposed to, the more red its color becomes. It is quite unusual for a plant to become totally red. _____ to traps, the plant also has long leaves in the Summer and Fall months. It can also grow white flowers to make seeds that fall into the ground and create new plants.

5.  **What transition best fits in the blank space?**

   Ⓐ  Besides
   Ⓑ  When
   Ⓒ  In addition
   Ⓓ  For example

The main thing you need to start a baseball card collection is cards, of course! Baseball cards are usually sold in packs of four or more cards. Large chain stores like Walmart and Target as well as drug stores are the easiest places to find packs of baseball cards. _____you can find cards at special baseball card shops.

6.  **What transition fits best in the blank?**

   Ⓐ  Also
   Ⓑ  Besides
   Ⓒ  Nevertheless
   Ⓓ  But

To make brownies, empty a box of brownie mix into a large bowl. Next, add two lightly beaten eggs, 1/2 cup of vegetable oil, and 1/4 cup of water. Mix the ingredients until all of the dry mix is wet. _____ spoon the brownie batter into a greased pan and bake at 350 degrees for 35 minutes.

7.  **What transition fits best in the blank- first, secondly or finally? Write in the box below.**

Finally

Maria is deathly afraid of speaking in front of large groups of people. _____ she begins speaking, her mouth gets dry, her legs start shaking, and she sweats.

8. **Which transition is the most appropriate?**

   Ⓐ Since
   Ⓑ Then
   Ⓒ When
   Ⓓ Even though

"You can have an ice cream cone _____ you can have a candy bar, " the mom told her three-year old daughter. "You cannot have both."

9. **What transition best fits in the blank?**

   Ⓐ nor
   Ⓑ and
   Ⓒ yet
   Ⓓ or

If the weatherman announces another tornado for our area, _____ tonight's Fall Festival will be canceled.

10. **What transition best completes this sentence?**

   Ⓐ when
   Ⓑ then
   Ⓒ and
   Ⓓ since

## Chapter 5

## Lesson 4: Mixing It Up - More Interesting Sentences

The Highland Games are like the Scottish Olympics. <u>Athletes are skilled at different sports. Athletes compete to earn medals.</u> The sports at the Highland Games are like no other sporting competition in the world.

1. **How can the underlined sentences be combined so that their meaning is preserved?**

   Ⓐ Athletes are skilled at different sports, yet they compete to earn medals.
   Ⓑ Athletes are skilled at different sports, and they compete to earn medals in these sports.
   Ⓒ Athletes are skilled at different sports, so they earn medals.
   Ⓓ Athletes are skilled at different sports, but they compete to earn medals.

<u>The men who participate in the Highland Game sports wear kilts.</u> Kilts are skirts made of plaid material that represents the clan or family that the man comes from. While it might seem unusual to you that a man would be playing sports in a skirt, kilts are one of the Scottish traditions that make up the Highland Games. Each year men and women come to Highland Games competitions to win medals and watch the sports.

2. **What type of sentence is the underlined sentence in this paragraph?**

   Ⓐ simple
   Ⓑ compound
   Ⓒ complex
   Ⓓ compound-complex

Lawn bowling is a game of strategy. <u>Each lawn bowling team wants to earn enough points to win. Its players not only try to get their bowls near the kitty (target), they also try to knock the other team's balls away from the target or off of the bowling Green.</u> When a player sees that a ball from the other team is close to the kitty, he has to carefully plan his throw so that he can move the other ball away from the mark while at the same time getting his bowl as close to it as possible. To be a successful lawn bowler, a player must practice often so that she can develop these complex skills.

3. **How can the underlined sentences be combined so that their meaning is preserved?**

   Ⓐ Because each lawn bowling team wants to earn enough points to win, they not only try to get their bowls near the kitty, they also try to knock the other team's balls away from the target or off of the bowling green.
   Ⓑ Even though each lawn bowling team wants to earn enough points to win, they not only try to get their bowls near the kitty.
   Ⓒ Each lawn bowling team not only tries to get its bowls near the kitty because each the players want to earn enough points to win.
   Ⓓ Each lawn bowling team tries to earn enough points to win.

A game of lawn bowling begins when one player rolls a metal jack or small white ball called a kitty onto the grass rink. The kitty is the target that the players will try to hit with their lawn bowls or balls. <u>Once the kitty has been thrown and hits the grass, it is lined up with the center of the rink.</u> Now the real fun begins! Players from each team take turns throwing their lawn bowls towards the kitty.

4. **What type of sentence is the underlined sentence in this paragraph?**

   Ⓐ simple
   Ⓑ complex
   Ⓒ compound
   Ⓓ complex-compound

<u>Skunks are omnivores. Omnivores eat both plants and animals.</u> Skunks can be found eating nuts, berries, roots, leaves, grasses and even some types of fungi (mushroom-like plants). They also enjoy dining on rodents such as mice and rats, insects, earthworms, frogs, lizards, toads and birds. Sometimes they are unable to find live animals to eat. Skunks become scavengers eating dead animals left behind. Skunks live close to people's homes. Skunks sometimes will even get into trashcans to eat garbage.

5. **How can the underlined sentences be combined so that their meaning is preserved?**

   Ⓐ Skunks are omnivores, but omnivores eat both plants and animals.
   Ⓑ Skunks are omnivores because they eat both plants and animals.
   Ⓒ Omnivores and skunks eat both plants and animals.
   Ⓓ When skunks are omnivores, they eat both plants and animals.

Skunks are omnivores. Omnivores eat both plants and animals. Skunks can be found eating nuts, berries, roots, leaves, grasses and even some types of fungi (mushroom-like plants). They also enjoy dining on rodents such as mice and rats, insects, earthworms, frogs, lizards, toads and birds. <u>Sometimes they are unable to find live animals to eat. Skunks become scavengers eating dead animals left behind.</u> Skunks sometimes will even get into trashcans to eat garbage.

6. **How can the underlined sentences be combined so that their meaning is preserved?**

Ⓐ Sometimes when scavengers are unable to find live animals to eat, skunks eat dead animals left behind.
Ⓑ Skunks are scavengers; sometimes scavengers eat dead animals left behind.
Ⓒ Sometimes when skunks are unable to find live animals to eat, they become scavengers eating dead animals left behind.
Ⓓ Sometimes when skunks are unable to find live animals, then they become scavengers eating dead animals left behind.

Skunks are omnivores. Omnivores eat both plants and animals. Skunks can be found eating nuts, berries, roots, leaves, grasses and even some types of fungi (mushroom-like plants). They also enjoy dining on rodents such as mice and rats, insects, earthworms, frogs, lizards, toads and birds. Sometimes they are unable to find live animals to eat. Skunks become scavengers eating dead animals left behind. <u>Skunks live close to people's homes. Skunks sometimes will even get into trashcans to eat garbage.</u>

7. **How can the underlined sentences be combined so that their meaning is preserved?**

Ⓐ Skunks sometimes live close to people's homes; in addition, they will even get into trashcans to eat garbage.
Ⓑ Skunks sometimes live close to people's homes; therefore, they will even get into trashcans to eat garbage.
Ⓒ Skunks sometimes live close to people's homes; nevertheless, they will even get into trashcans to eat garbage.
Ⓓ Skunks sometimes live close to peoples homes and they even get into trashcans to eat garbage.

(1) It may seem strange that bats have friendships. (2) Scientists have found that bats actually seem to form friendships. (3) A scientist noticed one bat feeding another. (4) He assumed the two bats were related. (5) He found out the shared none of the same genes meaning they couldn't possibly be relatives. (6) The bats appear to take care of those around them even if they are not "family". (6) He concluded that the bonds bats share are like human friendships.

8. **What would be the best way to combine sentences 1 and 2 so that their meaning is preserved?**

   Ⓐ It may seem strange bats have friendships and scientists have found bats actually seem to form friendships.
   Ⓑ When it seems strange bats have friendships, scientists have found they actually form friendships.
   Ⓒ Though it may seem strange, scientists have found bats actually seem to form friendships.
   Ⓓ Although it may seem strange bats have friendships, scientists have found bats actually seem to form friendships.

9. **What would be the best way to combine sentences 3 and 4 so that their meaning is preserved?**

   Ⓐ A scientist noticed one bat feeding another, but he assumed the two bats were related.
   Ⓑ A scientist noticed one bat feeding another, yet he assumed the two bats were related.
   Ⓒ A scientist noticed one bat feeding another, when he assumed the two bats were related.
   Ⓓ A scientist noticed one bat feeding another, so he assumed the two bats were related.

Social networking websites are very popular. Many people who use social networking websites are ages 18 to 25. Sometimes people over the age of 25 use social networking websites.

10. **How can these three sentences be combined into a compound-complex sentence that preserves their meaning?**

   Ⓐ Social networking websites are very popular, many people who use social networking websites are ages 18 to 25, and sometimes people over the age of 25 use social networking websites.
   Ⓑ Social networking websites are very popular, but many people who use social networking websites are ages 18 to 25; therefore, people over the age of 25 use social networking websites.
   Ⓒ Social networking websites are very popular with people ages 18 to 25, although, those over the age of 25 also use these websites.
   Ⓓ Social networking sites are popular with many people, mostly aged 18-25, but sometimes older people

## Chapter 5

## Lesson 5: Taking A Closer Look - Editing

Within the Great Barrier Reef, there are several habitats. Consistent throughout the entire 1,616-mile formation is coral reefs. What we consider a piece of coral are actually a collecshun of a several individual coral polyps. Each coral is actually a number of polyps. Coral polyps are living creatures that encase themselves in hard, protective shells made of calcium carbonate. These shells bands together forming colonies. The colonies together is known as reefs. Within the Great Barrier Reef, there are millions of coral featuring a multitude of colors and textures. There are more than 400 species of hard and soft corals living in the Reef.

1.  **What editing does the author of this paragraph need to do?**

    Ⓐ  correcting subject-verb agreement
    Ⓑ  correcting subject-verb agreement and spelling
    Ⓒ  correcting subject-verb agreement, spelling, and run-on sentences
    Ⓓ  correcting grammar usage and mechanics

### History of Lawn Bowling

The sport known today as lawn bowling began in England in the 13th century, while lawn bowling has become very popular in England, it was not always so. In the 1200s people in England began playing a game based on the Italian sport "Bocce" which had been brought to the country by Julius Ceasar's followers. They used stones or iron balls to play this game and called it "lawn bowling". Lawn bowling immediately caught on in England and by the 14th century it was extremely popular. In the 1300s the King of England, Edward III banned lawn bowling: because it was so popular, men stopped practicing archery (shooting a bow and arrow) and started playing lawn bowling. The king was worried, that men would not be able to shoot a bow, and arrow any more, because they were spending their free time lawn bowling! While this may not seem like a big deal to us today. Archery was extremely important back then because it was an important skill for a man to have in war. After Edward III; Richard II, the new King of England continued the ban on lawn bowling. In order to encourage English citizens to stop lawn bowling. The government fined people sums of money if they were found playing the sport in public. The sport eventually came across the Atlantic Ocean to North America. Players in Scotland, although technically under the rule of the King of England, ignored the ban and continued to practice lawn bowling. Though some Americans took up the sport, it became more popular in Canada than the United States. Even today, lawn bowling is very popular in Canada.

2.  **What does the writer need to edit in this paragraph?**

Ⓐ spelling
Ⓑ verb tenses
Ⓒ punctuation
Ⓓ ending marks

Venus Fly Trap plants are surprisingly small. Each trap is at most one inch long.
Though a plant usually has between four and twenty traps, it rarely gets larger than five inches in diameter.
The reason that the plant and its traps are so small has to do with its diet.
Most insects are small so the traps must be just the right size to catch and eat them.

3.  **What editing does the writer need to do on this paragraph of his essay?**

Ⓐ Correcting spelling mistakes
Ⓑ Correcting punctuation errors
Ⓒ Formatting the sentences into a paragraph
Ⓓ Fixing the word usage in the second sentence

The way that Venus fly trap plants are able to catch insects is remarkable when a plant is hungry it keeps one or more of its traps open it then sends out a sweet smell that insects mistaken for pollen this scent encourages bugs to come near the plant, a Venus Fly Trap is able to "feel" when an object touches it, the trigger hairs are very sensitive and can detect something on the trap, as soon as they feel the object, the hairs bend snapping the trap shut in less than one second. The trap doesn't close all the way instantly though. It stays partly open to allow smaller insects to escape. This is so that the plant doesn't waste its time eating small bugs that won't give it enough nutrients to survive.

4.  **What forms of editing does this writer need to do?**

Ⓐ Correcting spelling errors
Ⓑ Correcting run-on sentences
Ⓒ Correcting run-on sentences and punctuation errors
Ⓓ Correcting run-on sentences, punctuation, and spelling errors

The Highland Games are like the Scottish Olympics. Athletes who are skilled at different sports. Compete to earn medals. The difference is that the sports at the Highland Games are like no other sporting competition in the world. Plus: the men who participate in the sports. Wear kilts! Kilts are skirts made of plaid material, that represents the clan or family that the man comes from. While, it might seem unusual to you that a man would be playing sports in a skirt. Kilts are one of the Scottish traditions that make up the Highland Games. Each year men and women come to Highland Games competitions to win medals and watch the sports.

5.  **What does the writer need to focus on editing in this paragraph?**

    Ⓐ  Correcting fragment sentences
    Ⓑ  Correcting spelling errors
    Ⓒ  Correcting fragment sentences and punctuation errors
    Ⓓ  Correcting fragment sentences and spelling errors

The building that we know as the Alamo wasn't originally intended to be a military headquarters. I'ts beginnings are much more spiritual in nature. In 1724 the Misión San Antonio de Valero, was placed here to support missionaries, in their efforts to convert the Indian inhabitants of the area to Christianity. The mission building was moved from its original site on the San Pedro Creek, several miles to the south of the present location after storms destroyed the existing structure there.

6.  **What needs to be edited in this paragraph?**

    Ⓐ  punctuation
    Ⓑ  spelling
    Ⓒ  sentence structure
    Ⓓ  parallel construction

The caber toss is the event that most people associate the Highland Games with. In this event, each participant takes a turn lifting the caber, a large, solid wooden pole that is often as tall as a telephone pole. Once the competor has picked the caber up, he balances it in his hands and runs forward. He then ejects the pole from his hands atempting to turn it on end. The goal is to turn the caber over in a completely straight line. The participant whose caber toss comes the closest to the twelve o'clock position wins the competshion. Different locations vary the difficulty of the task by changing the length and/or the weight of the caber.

7.  **What needs to be edited in this paragraph?**

    Ⓐ  punctuation
    Ⓑ  spelling
    Ⓒ  sentence structure
    Ⓓ  pronoun-antecedent agreement

While most of the Highland Games events are feats of strength, the dance competitions show the beauty, grace and agility of their participants. In the Scottish country dance competitions teams of two or more dancers demonstrate their skill at social dances that are much like ballroom dances. The real excitement comes from watching the Highland Dancing competitions. To be a part of one of these competitions takes skill and practice. Highland Dancing is a technical and highly skilled art. Many participants study the form for years before competing. One of the most spectacular Highland Dances involves swords which dancers swing and jump over while performing complex dance moves.

**8.  What does not need to be edited in this paragraph? Mark those that apply.**

Ⓐ  punctuation
Ⓑ  spelling
Ⓒ  sentence formation
Ⓓ  the whole paragraph needs reworking

**The building that we know as the Alamo wasnt originally intended to be a military head-quarters.** Its beginnings are much more spiritual in nature. In 1724, the Misión San Antonio de Valero was placed here to support missionaries in their efforts to convert the Indian inhabitants of the area to Christianity. The mission building was moved from its original site on the San Pedro Creek several miles to the south of the present location after storms destroyed the existing structure there. Christian missionaries and their Indian converts used the church for seventy years until the government decided to make the building a non-religious location. The building and land was then given to the Indians to use for their homes and farmland.

**9.  What two punctuation marks are missing from the bold sentence?**

Ⓐ  comma after Alamo
Ⓑ  apostrophe on originally
Ⓒ  colon after Alamo
Ⓓ  quotation marks on Alamo

Skunks are omnivores meaning that they eat both plants and animals. They can be found eating nuts berries roots leaves grasses and even some types of fungi (mushroom-like plants). For animals they enjoy dining on rodents such as mice and rats insects earthworms frogs lizards toads and birds. Sometimes when they are unable to find live animals to eat they become scavengers eating dead animals left behind. When they live close to people's homes skunks sometimes will even get into trash cans eating garbage.

**10. What punctuation mark does the writer need to focus on adding while editing this paragraph?**

Ⓐ  end punctuation (period, question mark, exclamation mark)
Ⓑ  semi-colon
Ⓒ  comma
Ⓓ  colon

## Chapter 5

## Lesson 6: Say What You Mean

Within the Great Barrier Reef there are several habitats. Consistent throughout the entire 1,616 mile formation are coral reefs. What we consider a piece of coral is actually a collection of several individual coral polyps. Each coral is actually a number of polyps. Coral polyps are living creatures that encase themselves in hard, protective shells made of calcium carbonate. These shells band together forming colonies. The colonies together are known as reefs. Within the Great Barrier Reef there are millions of coral featuring a multitude of colors and textures. There are more than 400 species of hard and soft corals living in the Reef.

Housed within the reefs is a vastly diverse collection of animal life, many of which are endangered. Within its waters, the Great Barrier Reef provides homes to 5,000 species of mollusks and 125 species of sharks, stingrays, and skates. In addition, there are more than 1,500 species of fish including the colorful clownfish. Thirty species of whales, dolphins, and porpoises live in the Great Barrier Reef including humpback whales which use its warm, shallow waters as breeding grounds before journeying to Hawaii to give birth. Six endangered species of marine turtles also use the area to reproduce. The loggerhead turtle, one of the most highly protected endangered species, lives and breeds in the Great Barrier Reef. Over the last 40 years, the number of these turtles has decreased so rapidly that there are only 3% of the number of creatures alive today. Housed around this extremely diverse collection of animal life are 2,195 species of plants. Above water 215 species of birds live on the Great Barrier Reef.

1. **Which of these are NOT reasons for the author to use formal language in this essay?**

    Ⓐ because it is an informative essay
    Ⓑ to persuade the reader to visit the Great Barrier Reef
    Ⓒ because she wants to sound intelligent
    Ⓓ so that the spell-check will catch any spelling errors

2. **Why does the writer use specific details in this essay?**

    Ⓐ to draw the reader's attention to the essay
    Ⓑ to help the reader picture the animal life in the Great Barrier Reef
    Ⓒ to show there are many different types of animal life in the Great Barrier Reef
    Ⓓ to make the passage longer

Four men stood on a patch of grass rolling colored balls that were the size of baseballs. One man jumped with joy when the green ball he tossed hit the red ball that the man before him threw. What were these guys doing? They were lawn bowling, of course!

3. **What word in this paragraph would be considered too informal for a school essay?**



## What Do Venus Fly Traps Look Like?

The average Venus Fly Trap has a number of long shoots with oval shaped traps at the end of them. Each trap looks like a small set of jaws with a series of long thin trigger hairs on the edges of each side. The colors of the traps can be anywhere from bright green to dark red. The color of the trap depends on the amount of light that the plant receives. The more light a Venus Fly Trap is exposed to, the more red its color becomes. It is quite unusual for a plant to become totally red. In addition to traps, the plant also has long leaves in the Summer and Fall months. It can also grow white flowers to make seeds that fall into the ground and create new plants.

Venus Fly Trap plants are surprisingly small. Each trap is at most one inch long. Though a plant usually has between four and twenty traps, it rarely gets larger than five inches in diameter. The reason that the plant and its traps are so small has to do with its diet. Most insects are small so the traps must be just the right size to catch and eat them.

4. **Each of the following is a sensory detail used in this essay EXCEPT....**

   Ⓐ the red color of the venus fly trap leaves
   Ⓑ the long, thin trigger hairs on the plant
   Ⓒ the size of the venus fly trap
   Ⓓ the amount of light a venus fly trap gets

Every person should play a sport at least once in his life. Sports teach us valuable life skills. A player learns to work with others on a team to achieve a common goal. He also develops the ability to work with people he might not normally like or whatever. Also, people who play sports have to manage their time carefully since they need to work out, practice, and handle everything else in their lives such as school, work, and family commitments. Finally, sports give a player the chance to release stress in a safe, healthy, and fun way.

5.  **Which detail in this paragraph is not precise enough?**

    Ⓐ  Also, people who play sports have to manage their time carefully since they need to work out, practice, and handle everything else in their lives such as school, work, and family commitments.
    Ⓑ  A player learns to work with others on a team to achieve a common goal.
    Ⓒ  He also develops the ability to work with people he might not normally like or whatever.
    Ⓓ  Finally, sports give a player the chance to release stress in a safe, healthy, and fun way.

Looking for a new hobby? Do you like baseball? If you answered "yes" to these two questions baseball card collecting might be a <u>super fun</u> pastime for you to begin! Ever since candy and gum manufacturers started putting cards with pictures of popular baseball players into the packages in the 1800's to encourage young people to buy their sweets, kids have been collecting baseball cards. Now, more than 200 years later, baseball card collecting has become a popular hobby for children and adults alike.

6.  **Which word states the same idea as the underlined words, but is not slang?**

    Ⓐ  cool
    Ⓑ  neato
    Ⓒ  enjoyable
    Ⓓ  dull

Even though it might seem to people who have been sprayed by skunks that the reason for their stinky smell is to annoy us, there is actually a much more important reason why these animals make and squirt their juice. Skunks use their spray to protect themselves from predators (other animals who are trying to attack them). When the average skunk believes that another animal is about to hurt him he will warn it to get away by doing a few things first. Some types of skunks will also hiss or stand up on their front legs. If the predator does not back away, the skunk shoots a cloud of his smelly juice into the air in front of the other animal so that it will have to walk through it to get to him. Skunks are able to spray their juice up to 15 feet. When the predator comes near the cloud of spray he usually is so bothered by the smell that he leaves the skunk alone. The odor from the spray is so powerful that it even keeps bears from attacking skunks!

7.  **Which sentence in this paragraph needs to be revised because it is not precise enough?**

Ⓐ  Skunks use their spray to protect themselves from predators (other animals who are trying to attack them).

Ⓑ  When the average skunk believes that another animal is about to hurt him he will warn it to get away by doing a few things first.

Ⓒ  If the predator does not back away, the skunk shoots a cloud of his smelly juice into the air in front of the other animal so that it will have to walk through it to get to him.

Ⓓ  Skunks are able to spray their juice up to 15 feet.

Skunks are omnivores meaning that they eat both plants and animals. They can be found eating nuts, berries, roots, leaves, grasses, and even some types of fungi (mushroom-like plants). For animals, they enjoy dining on rodents such as mice and rats, insects, earthworms, frogs, lizards, toads, and birds. Sometimes when they are unable to find live animals to eat they become scavengers eating dead animals left behind. When they live close to people's homes, skunks sometimes will even get into trash cans eating garbage.

8.  **Which word does the writer need to define to help the reader better understand the paragraph?**

Ⓐ  omnivores

Ⓑ  fungi

Ⓒ  scavengers

Ⓓ  rodents

The purpose of the Highland Games competitions was to demonstrate its participants' survival skills. While no one knows for certain, it is thought that the Highland Games originated during the 11th century with King Malcolm III. Looking for a new court messenger, Malcolm staged a race to the top of Craig Choinnich and awarded its winner the position. There are also accounts that clans or family/military groups would gather and participate in events similar to those played in the Highland Games today as a way of training for war. In addition, some races are held in Scotland.

9.  **Which sentence does not include precise language?**

Ⓐ  The purpose of the Highland Games competitions was to demonstrate its participants' survival skills.

Ⓑ  Looking for a new court messenger, Malcolm staged a race to the top of Craig Choinnich and awarded its winner the position.

Ⓒ  There are also accounts that clans or family/military groups would gather and participate in events similar to those played in the Highland Games today as a way of training for war.

Ⓓ  In addition, some races are held in Scotland.

Located off the north eastern coast of Australia is the most <u>wild and crazy</u> and diverse eco-system in the world. The Great Barrier Reef is comprised of more than 3,000 individual coral reefs and is home to a plethora of species of plants and animals.

## 10. Which word states the same idea as the underlined words, but is not slang?

Ⓐ whack
Ⓑ complex
Ⓒ big
Ⓓ cool

## Chapter 5

### Lesson 7: Measure Twice, Cut Once - The Importance Of Planning

**"Bruno the Bear"**
**Excerpt from The Bond of Love**

I will begin with Bruno, my wife's pet sloth bear. I got him for her by accident. Two years ago, we were passing through the cornfields near a small town in Iowa. People were driving away the wild pigs from the fields by shooting at them. Some were shot, and some escaped. We thought that everything was over when suddenly a black sloth bear came out panting in the hot sun.

Now I will not shoot a sloth bear wantedly, but unfortunately for the poor beast, one of my companions did not feel the same way about it and promptly shot the bear on the spot.

As we watched the fallen animal, we were surprised to see that the black fur on its back moved and left the prostrate body. Then we saw it was a baby bear that had been riding on its mother's back when the sudden shot had killed her. The little creature ran around its prostrate parent, making a pitiful noise. I ran up to it to attempt a capture. It scooted into the sugarcane field. Following it with my companions, I was at last able to grab it by the scruff of its neck while it snapped and tried to scratch me with its long, hooked claws.

We put it in one of the large jute-bags we had brought, and when I got back home, I duly presented it to my wife. She was delighted! She at once put a blue colored ribbon around its neck, and after discovering the cub was a 'boy,' she christened it Bruno.

Bruno soon took to drinking milk from a bottle. It was but a step further, and within a very few days, he started eating and drinking everything else. And everything is the right word, for he ate porridge made from any ingredients, vegetables, fruit, nuts, meat (especially pork), curry and rice regardless of condiments and chilies, bread, eggs, chocolates, sweets, pudding, ice-cream, etc., As for drink: milk, tea, coffee, lime juice, aerated water, buttermilk, beer, alcoholic liquor, and, in fact, anything liquid. It all went down with relish.

The bear became very attached to our two dogs and all the children living in and around our farm. He was left quite free in his younger days and spent his time playing, running into the kitchen, and going to sleep in our beds.

One day an accident befell him. I put down poison (barium carbonate) to kill the rats and mice that had got into my library. Bruno entered the library as he often did and ate some of the poison. Paralysis set into the extent that he could not stand on his feet. But he dragged himself on his stumps to my wife, who called me. I guessed what had happened.

Off I rushed him in the car to the vet's residence. A case of poisoning! Tame Bear—barium carbonate— what to do? Out came his medical books, and a feverish reference to index began: "What poison did you say, sir?" he asked, "Barium carbonate," I said.

"Ah yes—B—Ba—Barium Salts—Ah! Barium carbonate! Symptoms— paralysis—treatment—injections of . .. Just a minute, sir. I'll bring my syringe and the medicine." Said the doc. I dashed back to the car. Bruno was still floundering about on his stumps, but clearly, he was weakening rapidly; there was some vomiting, he was breathing heavily, with heaving flanks and gaping mouth. I was really scared and did not know what to do. I was feeling very guilty and was running in and out of the vet's house doing everything the doc asked me.

"Hold him, everybody!" In goes the hypodermic—Bruno squeals — 10 c.c. of the antidote enters his  system without a drop being wasted. Ten minutes later: condition unchanged! Another 10 c.c. Injected! Ten minutes later: breathing less torturous— Bruno can move his arms and legs a little although he cannot stand yet. Thirty minutes later: Bruno gets up and has a great feed! He looks at us disdainfully, as much as to say, 'What's barium carbonate to a big black bear like me?' Bruno was still eating. I was really happy to see him recover.

The months rolled on, and Bruno had grown many times the size he was when he came. He had equaled the big dogs in height and had even outgrown them. But was just as sweet, just as mischievous, just as playful. And he was very fond of us all. Above all, he loved my wife, and she loved him too! And he could do a few tricks, too. At the command, 'Bruno, wrestle,' or 'Bruno, box,' he vigorously tackled anyone who came forward for a rough and tumble. Give him a stick and say 'Bruno, hold the gun,' and he pointed the stick at you. Ask him, 'Bruno, where's baby?' and he immediately produced and cradled affectionately a stump of wood which he had carefully concealed in his straw bed. But because of the neighborhoods' and our renters' children, poor Bruno, had to be kept chained most of the time.

Then my son and I advised my wife and friends advised her, too, to give Bruno to the zoo. He was getting too big to keep at home. After some weeks of such advice, she at last consented. Hastily, and before she could change her mind, a letter was written to the curator of the zoo. Did he want a tame bear for his collection? He replied, "Yes." The zoo sent a cage in a truck, a distance of hundred – eighty – seven miles, and Bruno was packed off. We all missed him greatly, but in a sense, we were relieved. My wife was inconsolable. She wept and fretted. For the first few days, she would not eat a thing. Then she wrote a number of letters to the curator. How was Bruno? Back came the replies, "Well, but fretting; he refuses food too."

After that, friends visiting the zoo were begged to make a point of seeing how Bruno was getting along. They reported that he was well but looked very thin and sad. All the keepers at the zoo said he was fretting. For three months, I managed to restrain my wife from visiting the zoo. Then she said one day, "I must see Bruno. Either you take me by car, or I will go myself by bus or train myself." So I took her by car. Friends had conjectured that the bear would not recognize her. I had thought so too. But while she was yet some yards from his cage, Bruno saw her and recognized her. He howled with happiness. She ran up to him, petted him through the bars, and he stood on his head in delight.

296

LumosLearning.com

For the next three hours, she would not leave that cage. She gave him tea, lemonade, cakes, ice cream, and whatnot. Then 'closing time' came and we had to leave. My wife cried bitterly; Bruno cried bitterly; even the hardened curator and the keepers felt depressed. As for me, I had reconciled myself to what I knew was going to happen next.

"Oh please, sir," she asked the curator, "may I have my Bruno back"? Hesitantly, he answered, "Madam, he belongs to the zoo and is Government property now. I cannot give away Government property. But if my boss, the superintendent, agrees, certainly, you may have him back."

There followed the return journey home and a visit to the superintendent's office. A tearful pleading: "Bruno and I are both fretting for each other. Will you please give him back to me?" He was a kind-hearted man and consented. Not only that, but he wrote to the curator, telling him to lend us a cage for transporting the bear back home.

Back we went to the zoo again, armed with the superintendent's letter. Bruno was driven into a small cage and hoisted on top of the car; the cage was tied securely, and a slow and careful return journey back home was accomplished.

Once home, a squad of workers were engaged for special work around our yard. An island was made for Bruno. It was twenty feet long and fifteen feet wide and was surrounded by a dry moat, six feet wide and seven feet deep. A wooden box that once housed fowls was brought and put on the island for Bruno to sleep in at night. Straw was placed inside to keep him warm, and his 'baby,' the gnarled stump, along with his 'gun,' the piece of bamboo, both of which had been sentimentally preserved since he had been sent away to the zoo, were put back for him to play with. In a few days, the workers hoisted the cage on to the island, and Bruno was released. He was delighted; standing on his hind legs, he pointed his 'gun' and cradled his 'baby.' My wife spent hours sitting on a chair there while he sat on her lap. He was fifteen months old and pretty heavy too!

The way my wife reaches the island and leaves it is interesting. I have tied a rope to the overhanging branch of a maple tree with a loop at its end. Putting one foot in the loop, she kicks off with the other, to bridge the six-foot gap that constitutes the width of the surrounding moat. The return journey back is made the same way.

But who can say now that a sloth bear has no sense of affection, no memory, and no individual characteristics?

1.  Create an outline of the main points you'd want to make for the following essay question on this selection:
    Did the narrator make the right choice in bringing Bruno into his home? Why or why not?
    Be sure to plan your introduction including your thesis statement, your body paragraphs discussing your opinion and details from the story to support it, and your closing paragraph.

2.  Create an outline of the main points you'd want to make for the following essay question on this selection:

    How did the author find Bruno? Explain.

    Be sure to plan your introduction including your thesis statement, your body paragraphs details from the story to support it, and your closing paragraph.

3. **What specific details in the above story tell us that the author was a wealthy man?**

   **Use specific details from the story.**

   **Be sure to plan your introduction including your thesis statement, your body paragraphs discussing your opinion and details from the story to support it, and your closing paragraph.**

## Bushmen

With so much technology around us each day, it is hard to imagine that anyone in the world would live without television, let alone a cell phone or radio. Still, there are a few cultures that maintain an extremely primitive lifestyle, nearly untouched by the modern world. One of those is commonly known as the Bushmen of Kalahari.

The Bushmen, also known as the "Basarwa" or "San" are found throughout southern Africa in regions of the Kalahari Desert. Nomadic hunters and gatherers by nature, they roam the region living in small kinship groups and, relatively isolated from the rest of society, have developed an extremely unique culture not otherwise seen or understood by modern man.

Unlike English, which is built on a complex system of sounds and letters, the Bushmen speak an extremely unique language made exclusively of clicking sounds. The sounds are created with a sucking action from the tongue, and even the click language itself can vary widely from tribe to tribe, making it extremely difficult to communicate with non-Bush people.

In addition to language, the Bushmen have a very different way of living. Similar to Eskimos, groups of Bushmen will live in "kinship" societies. Led by their elders, they travel together, with women in the group gathering food while men hunt for it. Children, on the other hand, have no duties other than playing. In fact, leisure is an extremely important part of the Bushmen society. Dance, music, and humor are essential, with a focus on family rather than technology or development. Because of this, some people associate the Bush culture with a backward kind of living or low status.

Because of the increased speed of advancement and urban development, the Bushmen culture is in danger. Some have already been forced to switch from hunting to farming due to modernization programs in their countries. Others have been forced to move to certain areas of their countries so that modernization can continue to occur there. With so much development, it's clear that though the Bushmen culture is very rich, it is also in danger of extinction. It is unclear how long the Bush culture will continue.

4.  **Create an outline of the main points and details you'd include in an essay on this topic:**

    **Describe a kinship society.**

    **Be sure to plan your introduction including your thesis statement, your body paragraphs including details from the story to support your ideas, and your closing paragraph.**

**Fall leaves**
**From USDA Forrest Service**

We almost always think of trees as being green, but there is one time of year when their leaves turn a myriad orange, red, yellow and brown: the beautiful and chilly days of fall. Those living in the Eastern or Northern United States come to anticipate the change in color starting in September or October every single year. But what causes the leaves to change color, and why?

Just like many animals that hibernate for the winter, trees experience a unique change during the winter months. During summer, for instance, plants use the process of photosynthesis to transform carbon dioxide found in the air into organic compounds like sugars using energy from the sun. During the winter, however, there is less light to go around, and their ability to create food from the photosynthesis process is limited.

What does that have to do with a leaf's color? The substance that allows trees to turn carbon dioxide into food (chlorophyll) is also the cause for the leaf's green sheen. As the photosynthesis process wanes in the colder months due to the lack of sun, so does its greenish hue, allowing other elements present in the leaf to show through. Believe it or not, the yellows and oranges that appear in fall have actually been there all year in the form of nutrients like carotene (also found in carrots). The intense green color of the chlorophyll had simply overshadowed them.

But what about the reds and browns? And what causes the leaves to fall away after they change color?

The bright reds and purples in each leaf come from a strong antioxidant that many trees create on their own because of their protective qualities. The antioxidant helps protect the trees from the sun, lower their freezing levels, and protect them from frost. As winter comes, so does the need for the antioxidant (similar to the way a dog gets more fur during winter to stay warmer).

As for the leaves falling, that is another story. At the base of each leaf, there is a layer of cells that carry food and water from the leaf to the tree during the summer months to keep it fed. In the fall, that layer actually starts to harden, preventing the passage of nutrients. Because of this, the nutrients and waste that previously passed from the leaf into the tree become trapped in the leaf with no fresh water to clean it. Not only does this cause the leaf to turn brown, eventually it causes the cells within it to harden so much that the leaf tears and blows away. Thus the pile of leaves you enjoyed jumping in as a child.

Because each tree, and each leaf, contains a unique amount of nutrients depending on how well-nourished it was over the spring and summer, the way each leaf breaks down during the winter months is also quite different. The result is the unique and complex facet of colors we see in each neighborhood or forest each fall.

5.  **Create an outline of the main points and details you'd include in an essay on this topic:**

    **Describe a kinship society.**

    **Be sure to plan your introduction including your thesis statement, your body paragraphs including details from the story to support your ideas, and your closing paragraph.**

Ever since they were kids, Julie and Max had been best friends. They went to kindergarten together. They went to summer camp together, They hung out together every weekend. But suddenly, things between the two had started to change.

Max had started playing on the football team and didn't have much time for Julie anymore. He was always busy, and he never seemed to make it to study hall, where the two used to swap stories about their favorite (or least favorite) teachers. In class, Julie noticed that Max never seemed to have his homework done on time anymore. She even noticed that he got a 'D' on his last paper. She knew something was going on with him – but what?

At first, Julie decided to play it cool and see how things went. She tried waiting in the hall for Max after class to see if she could ask if he was OK. But days went by, and he never had time to stop. He'd rush right past her in the hall, only to leave her feeling even worse about what was happening between them.

Even though she wasn't sure she could handle the situation herself, Julie didn't want to talk to her parents because she was afraid they would tell her not to hang out with Max anymore. She barely saw him as it was, so she knew it would just make things worse if her parents didn't approve of him. She didn't want to tell Max's parents either because she didn't want him to get in trouble. Still, it seemed like something needed to change.

Julie decided to go to one of her school counselors and let her know she was concerned. When she walked into Mrs. Smith's room, she was surprised to see that Max was already sitting there.
"I'm sorry, I'll come back," Julie said.
"No, stay," said Max. "Maybe you can help."

Julie was surprised to find that Max had visited the counselor's office for the same reason she had: he was starting to feel overwhelmed with all of the things he was supposed to be doing as a student, an athlete and a friend. He needed some guidance on how to determine what truly mattered, and how to divide his time between all of the things that were important to him.

When she realized that Max was still the same old Max (just a little more stressed), Julie was relieved. She was also happy to know that he had come to the conclusion on his own, without her having to talk to someone else about it. She decided it was a sign they were both growing up.

6.  Create an outline and write a response for the following essay topic:
    Compare the ways Julie and Max's relationship had changed

    Be sure to plan your introduction including your thesis statement, your body paragraphs discussing your comparison and details from the story to support it, and your closing paragraph.

The bread-and-butter of the film industry is the action movie. Each summer, audiences can expect to see car chases, gunfights and explosions, and studios can expect to see millions and millions of dollars in return. Though most viewers and critics see these movies as "fluff" entertainment, there is one director that puts as much heart and soul into his "fluff" as any number of talented directors put into their "serious" movies. His name is John Woo. Even though you may not have heard about him, he is widely considered to be the best contemporary director of action films working anywhere.

John Woo, after many years of hard work, has become known as the world's best action film director. His action sequences have become the stuff of legend and are now the basis from which all other action movies are judged. More importantly, along with the bloodshed, Woo has proven that he can create real characters with real emotions that the audience can sympathize with.

He's a bold visual stylist who stages kinetic scene of over- the- top gunplay with fluid camera movements, extremely long takes, and perfectly timed choreography of movement. Woo's on the spot improvising that also delivered one of the most amazing gun blazing sequences when in the middle of the movie a full-blooded gunfight erupts but is played out in balletic slow-motion to Somewhere Over The Rainbow, heard through child's headphones. The song was put in the represent the child's innocence, and also to show how that innocence is being corrupted by the violence around him. Woo gets upset when he hears about violence, and when he is angry and directing he thinks, "lets hit the villain with more bullets, lets beat him up just a little bit more."

Woo considers himself to be an artist, as he does once in a while get emotional while filming one of his movies. This goes to show that he relates his movies well to real life, and has an understanding of what it takes to become a great director.

7.  What specific details in this essay are used to support the thesis that John Woo is an exceptional director?

    Use specific details from the story.

    Be sure to plan your introduction including your thesis statement, your body paragraphs discussing your opinion and details from the story to support it, and your closing paragraph.

8.  Describe a time in your life when you felt proud of yourself. Be sure to use sensory details to help the reader experience the time as you did.

    Create an outline and write a response on the topic which includes the main points and details you'd want to include in it.

    Be sure to plan your introduction including your thesis statement, your body paragraphs in time order, and your closing paragraph.

Today, we have high-tech cranes and other machines to help us create massive skyscrapers and other modern works of architecture. Still, some of the most breathtaking architecture in the world, such as the ancient pyramids of Egypt, were created before those high-tech machines even existed. So how did those ancient civilizations create them?

Believe it or not, though they are one of the most studied and admired relics in history, there is no evidence to tell historians exactly how the Ancient Egyptians built the pyramids. Thus, they have been left to create their own theories as to how Egyptians created such amazing and awe-inspiring works of art.

According to one theory, the Egyptians placed logs under the large stone blocks in order to roll or transport them to the pyramid building location. Large groups of men would work to push or pull them into place (although historians also disagree on whether these men were slaves or skilled artisans). Still more, once the men moved the blocks to the pyramid location, they needed to lift them to ever-increasing heights to reach the top levels of the pyramid as it grew. Without modern cranes, many scientists have been baffled as to how they were able to do it. Some believe they used a ramp system that would allow them to roll the blocks upward around or through the pyramids; others believe they must have used a combination of pulleys and lifts. Still, most agree that once they did, they used a mixture of gravel and limestone to help fill any crevices and hold the mound together.

With such a primitive yet impressive building process, it's obvious that the pyramids must have taken a great deal of time to build. With an estimated 2 million blocks weighing an average of 2.5 million tons each, the Great Pyramid of Giza, for instance, is estimated to have taken some 20 years to build. At 481-feet tall, it held the record of tallest building for 3,800 years – not bad for a building created almost entirely by hand.

Even though scientists don't know exactly how the Egyptians did it, they do know that the method the Egyptians used to build pyramids changed over time. In the early days, the pyramids were made completely of stone, with limestone used to create the main body and higher quality limestone being used for the smooth outer casing. Later on, the pyramids were made mostly of mud brick with a limestone casing. Though they were likely much easier to build, they didn't stand up nearly as well over time, leaving archaeologists with even fewer clues about their creation.

9. Create an outline of the main points and details you'd want to include to answer the following essay question:

Explain, in your own words, what historians theorize about how the pyramids were built.

Be sure to plan your introduction including your thesis statement, your body paragraphs discussing the main ideas and details from the story to support them, and your closing paragraph.

10. Contrast yourself with your best friend. Focus on three ways that the two of you are different. Be sure to give details that help the reader see why you believe you are different in these ways.

Create an essay topic focusing on the three main points and details to support them.

Be sure to plan your introduction including your thesis statement, your body paragraphs discussing the contrast and details to support it, and your closing paragraph.

# Chapter 5

## Lesson 8: Take Another Look - Revising Your Work

Within the Great Barrier Reef there are several habitats. Consistent throughout the entire 1,616 mile formation are coral reefs. What we consider a piece of coral is actually a collection of several individual coral polyps. Each coral is actually a number of polyps. Coral polyps are living creatures that encase themselves in hard, protective shells made of calcium carbonate. These shells band together forming colonies. The colonies together are known as reefs. Within the Great Barrier Reef there are millions of coral featuring a multitude of colors and textures. There are more than 400 species of hard and soft corals living in the Reef.

Housed within the reefs is a vastly diverse collection of animal life, many of which are endangered. Within its waters, the Great Barrier Reef provides homes to 5,000 species of mollusks and 125 species of sharks, stingrays, and skates. In addition, there are more than 1,500 species of fish including the colorful clownfish. Thirty species of whales, dolphins, and porpoises live in the Great Barrier Reef including humpback whales which use its warm, shallow waters as breeding grounds before journeying to Hawaii to give birth. Six endangered species of marine turtles also use the area to reproduce. The loggerhead turtle, one of the most highly protected endangered species, lives and breeds in the Great Barrier Reef. Over the last 40 years, the number of these turtles has decreased so rapidly that there are only 3% of the number of creatures alive today. Housed around this extremely diverse collection of animal life are 2,195 species of plants. Above water 215 species of birds live on the Great Barrier Reef.

1. **If the author wanted to expand this essay, but keep it focused on the same topic, what details should she add?**

    Ⓐ  details about habitats in another coral reef
    Ⓑ  specific details about different animals mentioned in these paragraphs
    Ⓒ  details about animals that used to live in the reef, but are now extinct
    Ⓓ  information about water temperature changes over the course of a year

2. **Which two of the following are reasons for revising an essay?**

    Ⓐ  adding more details to the completed essay
    Ⓑ  deleting irrelevant details from the essay
    Ⓒ  completely re-doing the essay from scratch
    Ⓓ  correcting spelling mistakes in the essay

## History of Lawn Bowling

The sport known today as lawn bowling began in England in the 13th century. While lawn bowling has become very popular in England, it was not always so. In the 1200s people in England began playing a game based on the Italian sport "Bocce" which had been brought to the country by Julius Ceasar's followers. They used stones or iron balls to play this game and called it "lawn bowling". Lawn bowling immediately caught on in England, and by the 14th century, it was extremely popular. In the 1300s the King of England, Edward III, banned lawn bowling. Because it was so popular, men stopped practicing archery (shooting a bow and arrow) and started playing lawn bowling. The king was worried that men would not be able to shoot a bow and arrow anymore because they were spending their free time lawn bowling. While this may not seem like a big deal to us today, archery was extremely important back then because it was an important skill for a man to have in war. After Edward III, Richard II, the new King of England continued the ban on lawn bowling. Players in Scotland, although technically under the rule of the King of England, ignored the ban and continued to practice lawn bowling. In order to encourage English citizens to stop lawn bowling, the government fined people sums of money if they were found playing the sport in public. The sport eventually came across the Atlantic Ocean to North America. Though some Americans took up the sport, it became more popular in Canada than the United States.

3.  **Which sentence in this paragraph seems out of place?**

    (A) In the 1200s people in England began playing a game based on the Italian sport "Bocce" which had been brought to the country by Julius Ceasar's followers.
    (B) In the 1300s the King of England, Edward III banned lawn bowling.
    (C) Players in Scotland, although technically under the rule of the King of England, ignored the ban and continued to practice lawn bowling.
    (D) In order to encourage English citizens to stop lawn bowling, the government fined people sums of money if they were found playing the sport in public.

The way that these plants are able to catch insects is remarkable. When a plant is hungry it keeps one or more of its traps open. It then sends out a sweet smell that insects mistaken for pollen. This scent encourages bugs to come near the plant. A Venus Fly Trap is able to "feel" when an object touches it. The trigger hairs are very sensitive and can detect something on the trap. As soon as they feel the object, the hairs bend snapping the trap shut in less than one second. The trap doesn't close all the way instantly though. It stays partly open to allow smaller insects to escape. This is so that the plant doesn't waste its time eating small bugs that won't give it enough nutrients to survive. Over time the jaws of the trap slowly tighten and the trap seals shut. Venus Fly Traps are remarkably smart. Owls are considered very intelligent, but Venus Fly Traps are smarter than owls are, in my opinion. If the object that became trapped inside the plant isn't an insect, the jaws will reopen in about twelve hours and the trap will "throw" it out. If it does turn out to be an insect, the Venus Fly Traps spends the next twelve days "eating" the insect. Inside the trap juices like the ones our bodies use to digest our food dissolve the insect allowing the plant to absorb the nutrients. The trap remains sealed during this time to keep harmful bacteria out while the bug is being digested. At the end of the twelve days, the trap reopens and "spits out" the exoskeleton (outer shell) of the insect.

**4.  All of the following are true of Venus Fly Traps, EXCEPT...**

Ⓐ  Venus fly traps don't eat small bugs because they don't provide enough nutrients.
Ⓑ  The venus fly trap's jaws close slowly over time.
Ⓒ  Venus fly traps are smarter than owls.
Ⓓ  The venus fly trap "spits out" the unused parts of the insect.


The average Venus Fly Trap has a number of long shoots with oval shaped traps at the end of them. Each trap looks like a small set of jaws with a series of long thin trigger hairs on the edges of each side. The colors of the traps can be anywhere from bright green to dark red. The color of the trap depends on the amount of light that the plant receives. The more light a Venus Fly Trap is exposed to, the more red its color becomes. It is quite unusual for a plant to become totally red. In addition to traps, the plant also has long leaves in the Summer and Fall months. It can also grow white flowers which can help the plant in the future.

**5.  What detail should the writer add to make this paragraph more complete?**

Ⓐ  More information about the color of venus fly traps
Ⓑ  A description of the trigger hairs on the venus fly trap
Ⓒ  The size of the leaves present in the Summer and Fall
Ⓓ  How the white flowers help the venus fly trap


Skunks are also nocturnal animals. This means that they sleep during the day and are active when it is dark outside. Skunks cannot see very well, but they have excellent senses of smell and hearing. It's not surprising that skunks would rather move around during the night knowing that sight is not their best sense. In fact, most skunks are killed when they happen to wander on to roads and are hit by cars.

**6.  Which detail would NOT fit into this paragraph?**

Ⓐ  They cannot see where they are very well and walk into these dangerous areas.
Ⓑ  Skunks tend to do most of their "moving around" while we are asleep.
Ⓒ  Even though skunks can't see cars coming at them, you would think that they could hear cars approaching.
Ⓓ  Skunks are omnivores meaning that they eat both plants and animals.

While Scotland is the birthplace and location where the most Highland Games competitions are held, several of the largest events actually take place in the United States. The biggest Highland Games competition though is held each year in San Francisco, California by the New Caledonian Club. Competitors from around the world travel to play in the San Francisco Highland Games.

7.  **What information should the writer add to expand this paragraph?**

    Ⓐ  details about other Highland Games held in the United States
    Ⓑ  details about Highland Games held in Scotland
    Ⓒ  a comparison of the Highland Games to the Olympics
    Ⓓ  other versions of Highland Games

(1) The Battle of the Alamo is often seen as one of or possibly even the most significant events to take place during the Texas Revolution. (2) Prior to March 2, 1836, the area we know as the state of Texas was part of the country of the new country of Mexico. (3) Mexico, which included an area called "Spanish Texas", was formed in 1821 when the Spanish were forced to give up control of the land following the Mexican War for Independence. (4) In order to help bolster their victorious, but sadly crippled army, the Mexican government opened Texas to immigrants from the United States. (5) Settlers wanting to move west to start new lives moved into the area and set up their homes and built towns. (6) Quickly, these new inhabitants became disenchanted with the Mexican government and wanted their own independence. (7) A volunteer army of Texians (white and black immigrants living in Texas) and sympathetic Tejanos (Hispanic Texans wanting independence) was formed. (8) In 1835 a group of these volunteers moved into San Antonio in an attempt to take control over the town from Mexico. (9)After five days of fighting, the Mexican army retreated and the Texians and Tejanos took over the Mexican's base camp, the Alamo.

8.  **Where does the following sentence best fit into this paragraph?**

    **The Texas Revolution ran from 1823 to 1836.**

    Ⓐ  Before sentence #2
    Ⓑ  Before sentence #6
    Ⓒ  Before sentence #8
    Ⓓ  After sentence #9

(1) To begin, decide what the theme of your party should be.
(2) On the day of the party, decorate and lay out the food.
(3) Everyone loves a great party, but what's the best way to plan one?
(4) Once you have your party location, send out invitations.
(5) Then determine where you'll hold your party.
(6) All that's left is having fun!

**9.  What is the most logical order to place these sentences to form a paragraph?**

Ⓐ  1, 2, 3, 4, 5
Ⓑ  3, 2, 4, 6, 1, 5
Ⓒ  2, 6, 1, 3, 5, 4
Ⓓ  3, 1, 5, 4, 2, 6

**10. If you are writing an essay contrasting dogs and cats as pets, which of the following points would you want to add in your essay?**

Ⓐ  Cats eat much less food than dogs do.
Ⓑ  Cats and dogs are both soft and cuddly.
Ⓒ  Dogs are friendlier than cats.
Ⓓ  Dogs usually operate on their owners' schedules, while cats keep to their own schedules.

## Chapter 5

## Lesson 9: Building Your Foundation

Consistent throughout the entire 1,616 mile Great Barrier Reef formation are coral reefs. What we consider a piece of coral is actually a collection of several individual coral polyps. Each coral is actually a number of polyps. Coral polyps are living creatures that encase themselves in hard, protective shells made of calcium carbonate. These shells band together forming colonies. The colonies together are known as reefs. Fish also live near the reefs. Within the Great Barrier Reef there are millions of coral featuring a multitude of colors and textures. There are more than 400 species of hard and soft corals living in the Reef.

1.  **Which sentences from this paragraph support its topic sentence?**

    Ⓐ  What we consider a piece of coral is actually a collection of several individual coral polyps.
    Ⓑ  Coral polyps are living creatures that encase themselves in hard, protective shells made of calcium carbonate.
    Ⓒ  Fish also live near the reefs.
    Ⓓ  Within the Great Barrier Reef there are millions of coral featuring a multitude of colors and textures.

Within the Great Barrier Reef there are several habitats. Consistent throughout the entire 1,616 mile formation are coral reefs. What we consider a piece of coral is actually a collection of several individual coral polyps. Each coral is actually a number of polyps. Coral polyps are living creatures that encase themselves in hard, protective shells made of calcium carbonate. These shells band together forming colonies. The colonies together are known as reefs. Within the Great Barrier Reef there are millions of coral featuring a multitude of colors and textures. There are more than 400 species of hard and soft corals living in the Reef.

Housed within the reefs is a vastly diverse collection of animal life, many of which are endangered. Within its waters, the Great Barrier Reef provides homes to 5,000 species of mollusks and 125 species of sharks, stingrays, and skates. In addition, there are more than 1,500 species of fish including the colorful clownfish. Thirty species of whales, dolphins, and porpoises live in the Great Barrier Reef including humpback whales which use its warm, shallow waters as breeding grounds before journeying to Hawaii to give birth. Six endangered species of marine turtles also use the area to reproduce. The loggerhead turtle, one of the most highly protected endangered species, lives and breeds in the Great Barrier Reef. Over the last 40 years, the number of these turtles has decreased so rapidly that there are only 3% of the number of creatures alive today. Housed around this extremely diverse collection of animal life are 2,195 species of plants. Above water 215 species of birds live on the Great Barrier Reef.

2. **What would be an appropriate title for this essay?**

   Ⓐ How Coral is Formed
   Ⓑ Life in the Great Barrier Reef
   Ⓒ Coral Reef
   Ⓓ Mammals in the Great Barrier Reef

Following their victory at the Battle of the Alamo, the Mexican army used the site of the Alamo to house injured Mexican soldiers. Though much of the structure had been severely damaged during the battle, Santa Anna wanted to send a clear message that the Texians had been defeated by Mexico. Later that year, he ordered that the church be destroyed before the army left San Antonio. Soldiers tore down the remaining walls reducing the former mission to rubble.

3. **If the writer wanted to make this paragraph into a balanced account of the period after the Battle of the Alamo, what would she want to include?**

   Ⓐ A description of how the Mexican army won the Battle of the Alamo
   Ⓑ Details about how the Texians felt about the Alamo being destroyed
   Ⓒ Details describing how the Mexican army destroyed the Alamo
   Ⓓ Describing how the Alamo became a historical monument.

Skunks are also nocturnal animals. This means that they sleep during the day and are active when it is dark outside. Skunks cannot see very well, but they have excellent senses of smell and hearing. It's not surprising that skunks would rather move around during the night knowing that sight is not their best sense. In fact, most skunks are killed when they happen to wander on to roads and are hit by cars.

4. **Which detail would NOT fit into this paragraph?**

   Ⓐ They cannot see where they are, causing them to walk into dangerous areas.
   Ⓑ Skunks tend to do most of their "moving around" while we are asleep.
   Ⓒ Even though skunks can't see cars coming, you would think that they could hear them.
   Ⓓ Skunks are omnivores meaning that they eat both plants and animals.

(1) Though it may seem strange, scientists have found that bats actually seem to form friendships. (2) A scientist noticed one bat feeding another. (3) He assumed the two bats were related. (4) He found out that they shared none of the same genes meaning they couldn't possibly be relatives. (4) The bats appear to take care of those around them even if they are not "family". (5) Bats feed on other animals drinking their blood. (6) He concluded that the bonds bats share are like human friendships.

5.  **Which sentence in this paragraph should be deleted because it includes information that is not relevant to the main topic of the paragraph?**

    Ⓐ  Sentence #1
    Ⓑ  Sentence #3
    Ⓒ  Sentence #5
    Ⓓ  Sentence #6

6.  **Lee is writing an essay on his favorite season. His thesis is, "Fall is by far the best season of the year." Which of the following details would Lee want to include in his essay because it does not support his thesis statement?**

    Ⓐ  Picking apples with my family is one of the highlights of Fall for me.
    Ⓑ  The cooler weather in the Fall is much more enjoyable than the hot Summer temperatures.
    Ⓒ  In the Fall, I get to wear my favorite sweater that my grandmother in Mexico knit for me.
    Ⓓ  Ski season begins after Fall ends and Winter begins.

Scientists in South Korea have developed a type of artificial skin that will allow robots to feel slight vibrations. This skin, developed by weaving together extremely small nano hairs made of polymer or plastic is more sensitive than human skin. When vibration is applied to this artificial skin, the nano hairs bend against each other to generate an electrical current. Sensors within the skin evaluate the current and using that information to determine the source of the vibration.

Researchers are excited about the potential for this new development. Many people die after suffering serious skin burns. The artificial skin could be used to cover prosthetic limbs to help those who have lost a limb experience more realistic sensations and function more naturally.

7.  **Which sentence is not relevant to this article?**

    Ⓐ  This skin, developed by weaving together extremely small nanohairs made of polymer or plastic is more sensitive than human skin.
    Ⓑ  Sensors within the skin evaluate the current and using that information to determine the source of the vibration.
    Ⓒ  Many people die after suffering serious skin burns.
    Ⓓ  The artificial skin could be used to cover prosthetic limbs to help those who have lost a limb experience more realistic sensations and function more naturally

8.  **Gina is writing an essay about the best pets for people who live in apartments. What facts would be appropriate for her essay?**

    Ⓐ The average large dog requires a lot of room to exercise and enjoys living on farms where there is more land.
    Ⓑ Cats can easily be trained to use a litter box kept in a corner of a room or in a closet.
    Ⓒ Smaller dogs don't need as much exercise as larger dogs.
    Ⓓ Tropical fish make great pets and a ten gallon tank can be kept on a bookcase or on the corner of a desk.

Do you feel like running when the temperature is high? Why not? Generally, exercising in extreme heat makes you thirsty and very tired. Too much exercise could lead to heat stroke, a dangerous condition when your body isn't able to cool down. Your pets can suffer the same consequences. When it is extremely hot outside, try to exercise your pet only in the morning or evening when the temperature is cooler and cut down the amount of time your pet spends running around.

9.  **What technique has this writer used to introduce this essay?**

    Ⓐ A startling fact about heat stroke in pets.
    Ⓑ A quote from an academic source.
    Ⓒ A rhetorical question.
    Ⓓ A thesis statement.

According to a study recently published by a doctoral student at Northwestern University, middle school students who regularly use "texting-language," or shorten words when writing texts or emails, may be forgetting rules of grammar.

Drew Cingel interviewed over 200 seventh and eighth grade students and asked them how frequently they used shortcuts such as typing @ instead of "at," or U instead of "you." After the students completed the interviews, they all took a grammar test. Cingel found that students who reported using texting-language the most scored the lowest on their grammar tests.

The researcher suggests that teachers can help students write appropriately in school settings by assigning writing tasks that are very different from texting tasks. For example, a student who is likely to use texting shortcuts when asked to write a letter may avoid doing so when asked to write a formal essay. This evidence suggests that students may have knowledge of grammar, but not of the different contexts for writing.

10. **What would be an appropriate title for this essay?**

    Ⓐ Frequent Texters May Have Poor Grammar Skills
    Ⓑ Writing In School Can Improve Texting Skills
    Ⓒ Students Should Not Text in School
    Ⓓ Teachers Need To Do More to Help Students With Grammar

## Chapter 5

## Lesson 10: Give Credit Where Credit Is Due

1. **What is missing from the following parenthetical citation?**

   In her book, *Running with Horses*, author Mollie Anderson writes, "I never grow tired of training my horses. They are the joy of my life" (22).

   Ⓐ The page number the quote came from
   Ⓑ The author's last name in parentheses
   Ⓒ The title of the book
   Ⓓ Nothing is missing

2. **What is missing from the following entry in a Works Cited List?**

   Anderson, Mollie. *Running with Horses*. Alabaster Press, 1993.

   Ⓐ The author's name
   Ⓑ The book title
   Ⓒ The publisher
   Ⓓ The publisher's location
   Ⓔ The publication date

3. **What is plagiarism?**

   Ⓐ Not including a Works Cited list with an essay you wrote
   Ⓑ Using someone else's words without giving proper credit to the writer
   Ⓒ Copying someone else's answers during a test
   Ⓓ Forgetting to paraphrase direct quotes

   Halleburn, Sondra. Singing Is For the Birds. Aviery Press. Boston, MA.

4. **What is missing from this works cited entry for a book?**

   Ⓐ The pages the essay references
   Ⓑ The author's middle name
   Ⓒ The book's publication date
   Ⓓ The author's date of birth

5. **If you're using the following book as a resource in an essay, how should you cite it in your list of Works Cited?**

Title: A Glimpse Into the Human Mind
Author: John Doe
Publisher: ABC Publishers
Publisher Location: New York, New York
Date of Publication: 1992
Pages Used: pp. 200-230 and 302-310

Ⓐ <u>A Glimpse Into the Human Mind</u>, John Doe, ABC Publishers, New York, New York, 1992.
Ⓑ <u>A Glimpse Into the Human Mind</u>, John Doe, ABC Publishers, New York, New York, 1992, pp. 200-230 and 302-310.
Ⓒ Doe, John. <u>A Glimpse Into the Human Mind</u>. ABC Publishers: New York, New York, 1992.
Ⓓ Doe, John. <u>A Glimpse Into the Human Mind</u>. ABC Publishers: New York, New York, 1992, 200-230, 302-310.

6. **If you're using the following magazine article as a resource in an essay, how should you cite it in your list of Works Cited?**

Title of Article: "Cats Are A Man's Best Friend"
Title of Magazine: Kitty Kat
Author: Jane Smith
Date of Magazine: September 2003
Pages of Magazine: 122-129

Ⓐ "Cats Are a Man's Best Friend" <u>Kitty Kat</u>. Jane Smith. September 2003. 122-129.
Ⓑ <u>Kitty Kat</u>. "Cats Are a Man's Best Friend" Jane Smith. September 2003. 122-129.
Ⓒ Jane Smith. "Cats Are a Man's Best Friend" <u>Kitty Kat</u>. Jane Smith. September 2003. 122-129.
Ⓓ Smith, Jane. "Cats Are a Man's Best Friend" <u>Kitty Kat</u>. September 2003, 122-129.

7. **What is the proper format for a parenthetical citation?**

Ⓐ (Author's Full Name, Page Number)
Ⓑ (Author's Last Name, Book Title)
Ⓒ (Author's Last Name, Page Number(s))
Ⓓ (Book Title, Page Number(s))

Allen, Skippy. "Peanut Butter King: The Makers of Our Favorite Sandwich Spread" January 2006, 215-217.

8. **What is missing from this works cited entry for a newspaper article?**

    Ⓐ the name of the newspaper article
    Ⓑ the name of the newspaper
    Ⓒ the newspaper's publisher
    Ⓓ the date the student read the article

9. **Which of the following does NOT need to be included in a works cited entry for an Internet site you visited for research?**

    Ⓐ The name of the website
    Ⓑ The website author's name
    Ⓒ The date you visited the website
    Ⓓ The email address of the website's author

10. **What is missing from this citation for an encyclopedia entry?**

    Skyscrapers. (1992) In The New Encyclopedia Britannica (Vol. 22, pp. 1-43). _____: Encyclopedia Britannica

    Ⓐ The city of publication
    Ⓑ The name of the author
    Ⓒ The date the author read the entry
    Ⓓ The name of the publisher

## Chapter 5

## Lesson 11: Beginnings And Endings

### The Great Barrier Reef

Located off the northeastern coast of Australia is the most complex and diverse eco-system in the world. The Great Barrier Reef is comprised of more than 3,000 individual coral reefs and is home to a plethora of species of plants and animals.

1. **How does the author of this essay introduce its topic?**

   Ⓐ by asking a question
   Ⓑ by making a broad statement about reefs
   Ⓒ by painting a brief picture of the Great Barrier Reef
   Ⓓ by telling a short story about the Great Barrier Reef

### The Great Barrier Reef

Located off the northeastern coast of Australia is the most complex and diverse eco-system in the world. The Great Barrier Reef is comprised of more than 3,000 individual coral reefs and is home to a plethora of species of plants and animals.

2. **What mode of writing can you assume the writer will continue in for the rest of this essay, based on its introduction?**

   Ⓐ by asking a question
   Ⓑ by making a broad statement about reefs
   Ⓒ by painting a brief picture of the Great Barrier Reef
   Ⓓ by telling a short story about the Great Barrier Reef

### History of Lawn Bowling

The sport known today as lawn bowling began in England in the 13th century. While lawn bowling has become very popular in England, it was not always so. In the 1200s people in England began playing a game based on the Italian sport "Bocce" which had been brought to the country by Julius Ceasar's followers. They used stones or iron balls to play this game and called it "lawn bowling". Lawn bowling immediately caught on in England and by the 14th century it was extremely popular. In the 1300s the King of England, Edward III banned lawn bowling. Because it was so popular, men stopped practicing archery (shooting a bow and arrow) and started playing lawn bowling. The king was worried that men would not be able to shoot a bow and arrow any more because they were spending their free time lawn bowling. While this may not seem like a big deal to us today, archery was extremely important back then because it was an important skill for a man to have in war. After Edward III, Richard II, the new King of England continued the ban on lawn bowling. In order to encourage English citizens to stop lawn bowling, the government fined people sums of money if they were found playing the sport in public. The sport eventually came across the Atlantic Ocean to North America. Players in Scotland, although technically under the rule of the King of England, ignored the ban and continued to practice lawn bowling. Though some Americans took up the sport, it became more popular in Canada than the United States.

http://www.tradgames.org.uk/games/Bowls.htm

3.  **Which sentence would be the best closing statement for this paragraph?**

    Ⓐ  Even today, lawn bowling is very popular in Canada.
    Ⓑ  Some people think the Scottish actually invented lawn bowling.
    Ⓒ  Many people enjoy lawn bowling.
    Ⓓ  Lawn bowling is a difficult sport to master.

4.  **Which paragraph of an essay should the thesis statement appear in- the introductory paragraph or the conclusion?**



Not far from the huge modern convention center and chic dining and shopping areas along San Antonio's River Walk stands a small stucco structure surrounded by lovely gardens. As you pass by this petite building you might think it's simply an old Spanish church. However, this little building, better known as the Alamo, was the site of one of the bloodiest and most significant battles of the Texas revolution.

5.  **Which of these are not the purposes of the opening sentence in this introductory paragraph?**

    Ⓐ  To introduce the thesis of the essay
    Ⓑ  To offer a counterargument to the author's thesis
    Ⓒ  To catch the reader's attention
    Ⓓ  To ask and answer a question

Not far from the huge modern convention center and chic dining and shopping areas along San Antonio's River Walk stands a small stucco structure surrounded by lovely gardens. **Many people visit this petite building believing it is a holy place because it is an old Spanish church.** However, this little building, better known as the Alamo, was the site of one of the bloodiest and most significant battles of the Texas Revolution.

6.  **What is the purpose of the bold sentence in this introductory paragraph?**

    Ⓐ It is the thesis statement of the essay.
    Ⓑ It tries to catch the reader's attention.
    Ⓒ It offers a counterclaim to the author's thesis.
    Ⓓ It is meant to give a description of the Alamo.

Where would you find a group of men in kilts attempting to turn over timbers as tall as trees and throw stones that heavier than a five-year-old child? The Scottish Highland Games, of course! Held annually in towns all throughout Scotland from May to September, the Highland Games are important celebrations of the nation's rich heritage. Athletes and spectators alike join together to test their strength and agility and preserve a long-standing cultural tradition.

7.  **What strategy does the writer use in this introduction to get the reader focused on her topic?**

    Ⓐ She describes the Highland Games.
    Ⓑ She asks an interesting question about an unusual practice.
    Ⓒ She contrasts the Highland Games with the Olympics.
    Ⓓ She tells a brief anecdote (story) about the Highland Games.

Often when studying a topic, we find that the answers we discover lead to additional questions. Although knowledge leads to understanding on the surface, it also promts us to ask more questions.

8.  **Based on the sentence above, we can assume the essay that will follow will be which kind of writing?**

    Ⓐ Informative
    Ⓑ Narrative
    Ⓒ Expository
    Ⓓ Compare/Contrast

9.  **Which is not a component of an effective introduction?**

    Ⓐ Thesis statement
    Ⓑ Background information on the topic.
    Ⓒ A hook to capture the reader's interest.
    Ⓓ An explanation for why the paper was written.

10. **Which is not a component of an effective conclusion?**

    Ⓐ The words "in conclusion."
    Ⓑ A restatement of the thesis statement
    Ⓒ A call to action for the reader
    Ⓓ A summary of the most important points in the essay

# Answer Key and
# Detailed Explanations

## Chapter 5: Composition

# Lesson 1: Who Are You Talking To?

| Question No. | Answer | Detailed Explanations |
|---|---|---|
| 1 | A, C and D | Options A, C and D are not the purposes of the essay. |
| 2 | A | Answer choice one is the correct answer. The people interested in this passage are interested in how lawn bowling began. |
| 3 | C | Answer choice three is the best answer. Middle school teachers would know the benefits of sports because many students at that age play sports. Sports teams and those already involved in sports don't need this information. They already know it, or they would not be in sports. |
| 4 | B and C | People who like studying battles and wars; and people who are interested in Texas history are most likely the intended audience. |
| 5 | C | Answer choice two is the correct answer. The first line mentions odor and what skunks are mostly associated with. The passage discusses the odor and how to remove it from clothes and animals.<br><br>Answer choice one is related to the passage and answer, but it not the complete answer. Answer choices three and four are not true of the passage. |
| 6 | to persuade | If asked to write a letter to your school principal showing him the reasons why the school should have dances that last until midnight, instead of nine o'clock, the purpose of this piece of writing be to persuade. |
| 7 | C | Answer choice three is the correct answer. The passage would not inform (such as a research paper or an informational article), There is no call to persuade because the prompt did not ask the writer to convince the reader of something. And, by telling a story about something not turning out the way originally thought does not indicate a format to argue/defend a point. |
| 8 | C | Answer choice three is the best answer. By comparing two or more things, the reader would learn how they items are similar or different, or both. This makes the answer choice three the best answer. |
| 9 | D | Answer choice four is the best answer. The first words of the passage say "as your children prepare." This indicates that the parents, or caregivers, are the intended audience. |
| 10 | D | Answer choice four is the correct answer. The passage states that the company is sending "you, and all dealerships" a car. This information would go to the owner because he/she is the person who would typically order and stock vehicles for sale. |

# Lesson 2: A Picture Is Worth A Thousand Words

| Question No. | Answer | Detailed Explanations |
|---|---|---|
| 1 | A and D | Options A and D- a picture of a dog in a car; and a heat stroke effect; would help the article as graphics. |
| 2 | B | Answer choice two is correct. Because the article mentions nanohairs that react like real skin, a picture of that would be beneficial to the reader so they could see how advanced the technology has become. |
| 3 | A picture of an Easter Lily | A picture of an **Easter Lily** bulb is most appropriate for thr article. |
| 4 | B | Answer choice two is the correct answer. The title tells the reader that this is about a long flight, so a map of the flight pattern would be a great addition to help the reader have a better understanding of the flight. |
| 5 | C | Answer choice three is the correct answer. This article describes the expansion of phone service. It would help the reader understand the scope of this project with a map highlighting the important towns. |
| 6 | A and B | A photo of children eating ice cream cones and a diagram of the new refrigeration unit described are appropriate graphics. |
| 7 | A | Answer choice one is the correct answer. If a student needs to learn about patterns of migration, a global map with the paths labeled or highlighted would be necessary. |
| 8 | C | Answer choice three is the best answer. The reader needs to see how the two riders did their task and then met up later. The remaining suggestions are interesting, but won't help the reader understand the actual ride and how it worked. |
| 9 | C | Answer choice three is the best answer. The reader could benefit from seeing how the theater was built and how Booth was able to get to the president and then escape. |
| 10 | A | Answer choice one is the best. A picture of the crab's internal body would help the reader understand what the passage is describing with respect to laying of eggs and other body functions. |

# Lesson 3: Getting From Here To There - Transitions

| Question No. | Answer | Detailed Explanations |
|---|---|---|
| 1 | After | "_____ each team takes all of their turns, points are given to the team whose bowls are closest to the kitty."<br><br>The best word here would be After. |
| 2 | A | Answer choice "therefore" is the correct answer. "So" would be an appropriate word as well, but it is not one of your answer choices. The reader can fill in the blank with his own word that makes sense, and then see what the options are. If the reader's word is not in the list of answer choices, he needs to look for words that mean the same as the chosen word. This will be the correct answer. |
| 3 | Since | **Since** is the best word to replace 'because' here -<br><br>**Because** Venus Fly Traps are very real, they aren't easy to find. |
| 4 | A | Answer choice one is the correct answer. The words in the passage are not consistent with the meaning of the sentence/passage. It goes back in time, and the article is moving forward in time. So, answer choice one is the best answer. |
| 5 | C | Answer choice three, in addition, is the correct answer. The passage is adding a thought/information with that sentence, so it is the only answer choice that makes sense. Even if you weren't sure of the answer, when placing each choice in the blank, the structure of the sentence does not allow for any answer other than choice three. |
| 6 | A | Answer choice one is the best choice. The other three choices are "exception" words; words used to make a counter point. This sentence needs a positive transition. |
| 7 | Finally | Since it is the last step of the recipe, finally is the best word. |
| 8 | C | Answer choice three is the correct answer. This is a time placement word, and it puts the statement about having a dry mouth in the proper place of the passage with respect to sequence of order. |
| 9 | D | Answer choice four is the correct answer. Then the reader reads the entire sentence, the "or" becomes obvious. "Not having both" leaves the only reasonable answer choice as "or." |
| 10 | B | Answer choice two is correct. This is an "If then" sentence. Because the beginning of the sentence states "IF...." the reader knows that a "then" portion is coming. |

# Lesson 4: Mixing It Up - More Interesting Sentences

| Question No. | Answer | Detailed Explanations |
|---|---|---|
| 1 | B | Answer choice two is the best answer. Combining these two sentences into a compound sentence helps the piece flow easier. This will help the reader with comprehension. |
| 2 | C | Answer choice three is the correct answer. The underlined portion is a complex sentence because it has one dependent clause that begins with the relative pronoun 'who'. The dependent clause is - 'who participate in the Highland Game sports'. |
| 3 | A | Answer choice one is the correct answer. By adding "because" this makes the phrase dependent on the next sentence (independent clause). It must have a comma or it becomes a run on. |
| 4 | B | Answer choice two is the correct choice. The dependent clause at the beginning of the sentence (all the words before the comma) added to the dependent clause (actual sentence) makes the sentence a complex sentence. |
| 5 | B | Answer choice two is the correct answer. The two sentences are choppy, and combining them with "because" helps the sentence flow better without being a run on. |
| 6 | C | Answer choice three is the best answer. By adding "when", the first sentence becomes a dependent clause that cannot stand alone. This keeps the passage from being choppy to read. |
| 7 | B | Answer choice two is the correct answer. The last choice is close, but it is a run on. There should be a comma before the and. In the second choice there is a semi-colon with a transition word. A semi-colon is used like a period to connect two sentences that are related in thought. |
| 8 | C | Answer choice three is the best answer. The combination makes the passage's beginning less awkward to read. It creates a dependent clause with a comma, but it does not change the meaning of the two sentences. |
| 9 | D | Answer choice four is the best answer. The two sentences are combined with a comma and a coordinating conjunction (so). The words "yet" and "but" change the meaning of the sentences. "When" is not appropriate for the two sentences and would change the meaning. |
| 10 | C | Answer choice number three is the best answer. It combines the sentences using proper punctuation but does not change the meaning. The other answers are either not correctly punctuated, or change the meaning of the passage. |

# Lesson 5: Taking A Closer Look - Editing

| Question No. | Answer | Detailed Explanations |
|---|---|---|
| 1 | B | Answer choice two is the correct answer. What we consider a piece of coral IS actually a COLLECTION of a several individual coral polyps. A piece of coral is singular, so the verb (is) needs to be singular as well. |
| 2 | C | Answer choice three is the correct answer. The first sentence is a run-on sentence (comma splice) It needs a period or a semi-colon after 13th century. |
| 3 | C | Answer choice three is correct. The sentences need to be placed closer to one another and in a sensible order so that it forms a paragraph. |
| 4 | C | Answer choice three is the best answer. The first line of the paragraph is a string of thoughts that need to be divided into sentences with proper ending marks. |
| 5 | C | Answer choice three is the correct answer. The passage is riddled with punctuation errors and sentence fragments. |
| 6 | A | Answer choice one is the correct answer. The word "i'ts" is not properly punctuated. It is becomes it's when contracted. |
| 7 | B | Answer choice two is the correct answer. The word competitor is misspelled in the first line. |
| 8 | A, B and C | Options A, B and C are the correct answers, since those do not need to be edited in the paragraph. |
| 9 | A and D | Options A and D can be added to the sentence for clarity and better punctuation. |
| 10 | C | Answer choice three is the correct answer. The passage needs commas. There are four general rules of comma usage.<br>1. Compound sentences (combining two complete sentences using a coordination conjunction)<br>2. An appositive (restating the noun)<br>3. Setting off prepositional phrases and dependent clauses<br>4. Listing items.<br>The first sentence has a list of berries and an appositive. |

# Lesson 6: Say What You Mean

| Question No. | Answer | Detailed Explanations |
|---|---|---|
| 1 | B, C and D | The author doesn't use formal language to persuade the reader to visit the Great Barrier Reef; because she wants to sound intelligent; or so that the spell-check will catch any spelling errors. |
| 2 | B | Answer choice two is the best answer. Details are used to describe a scene/setting/character. The more details the better the reader "knows" the story/passage. |
| 3 | guys | The word 'guys' is too informal for a school essay. |
| 4 | D | Answer choice four is the correct answer. Sensory details use the five senses to help the reader "feel" the way the character does or to gain a better understanding of the passage. |
| 5 | C | Answer choice three is the correct answer. The use of "whatever" is not effective writing. This would only be used in VERY casual writing such as a note to a friend. It is not clear or helpful with understanding. |
| 6 | C | Answer choice three is the best answer. The first two are slang words, and the fourth answer does not mean the same thing as "super fun." |
| 7 | B | Answer choice two is the correct answer. The words "a few things" is not clear or precise. The writer would need to name those "few things." |
| 8 | A | Answer choice one is the correct answer. If the reader is not clear on what an omnivore is, then he/she cannot fully understand the remaining part of the passage. |
| 9 | D | Answer choice four is the correct answer. None of that sentence is precise. "Some races" needs to be described. |
| 10 | B | Answer choice two is the correct answer. The other three remaining choices are all slang. Slang is not to be used in writing that is intended for school or professional use. |

# Lesson 7: Measure Twice, Cut Once - The Importance Of Planning

| Question No. | Answer | Detailed Explanations |
|:---:|:---:|---|
| 1 | | The question actually helps the writer set up the outline. It tells you to have an introduction with a thesis (belief statement). And then tells the writer to have body paragraphs with details to support opinions. And, finally the question tells the writer to have a concluding paragraph. <br><br> The writer needs to decide their opinion on the question, and then put the thoughts on the outline in the format suggested. |
| 2 | | The question actually helps the writer set up the outline. It tells you to have an introduction with a thesis (belief statement). And then tells the writer to have body paragraphs with details to support opinions. And, finally the question tells the writer to have a concluding paragraph. <br><br> The writer needs to consider the question, and then put the thoughts on the outline in the format suggested. |
| 3 | | The question actually helps the writer set up the outline. It tells you to have an introduction with a thesis (belief statement). And then tells the writer to have body paragraphs with details to support opinions. And, finally the question tells the writer to have a concluding paragraph. <br><br> The writer needs to decide their opinion/reasons about the topic and the question, and then put the thoughts on the outline in the format suggested and then write essay from outline. Each Roman numeral or capital letter is a new paragraph. |
| 4 | | The question actually helps the writer set up the outline. It tells you to have an introduction with a thesis (belief statement). And then tells the writer to have body paragraphs with details to describe the concept. And, finally the question tells the writer to have a concluding paragraph. <br><br> The writer needs to decide their opinion on the question, and then put the thoughts on the outline in the format suggested. |

| Question No. | Answer | Detailed Explanations |
|---|---|---|
| 5 | | The question actually helps the writer set up the outline. It tells you to have an introduction with a thesis (belief statement). And then tells the writer to have body paragraphs with details to support opinions. And, finally the question tells the writer to have a concluding paragraph.<br><br>The writer needs to decide their opinion/reasons about the topic and the question, and then put the thoughts on the outline in the format suggested and then write essay from outline. Each Roman numeral or capital letter is a new paragraph. |
| 6 | | The question actually helps the writer set up the outline. It tells you to have an introduction with a thesis (belief statement). And then tells the writer to have body paragraphs with details to support opinions. And, finally the question tells the writer to have a concluding paragraph.<br><br>The writer needs to decide their opinion/reasons about the topic and the question, and then put the thoughts on the outline in the format suggested and then write essay from outline. Each Roman numeral or capital letter is a new paragraph. |
| 7 | | The question actually helps the writer set up the outline. It tells you to have an introduction with a thesis (belief statement). And then tells the writer to have body paragraphs with details to support opinions. And, finally the question tells the writer to have a concluding paragraph.<br><br>The writer needs to decide their opinion/reasons about the topic and the question, and then put the thoughts on the outline in the format suggested and then write essay from outline. Each Roman numeral or capital letter is a new paragraph. |

| Question No. | Answer | Detailed Explanations |
|---|---|---|
| 8 | | This essay should have an introductory paragraph stating a general feeling about pride. Then the following paragraphs should discuss the various events when the writer felt proud; using sensory words helps the reader feel what the writer is describing. There should be at least two events, preferably three. Then, the writer should "wrap up" the experiences and how they changed the writer, or taught her something. |
| | | The question actually helps the writer set up the outline. It tells you to have an introduction with a thesis (belief statement). And then tells the writer to have body paragraphs with details to support opinions. And, finally the question tells the writer to have a concluding paragraph. |
| | | The writer needs to decide their opinion/reasons about the topic and the question, and then put the thoughts on the outline in the format suggested and then write essay from outline. Each Roman numeral or capital letter is a new paragraph. |
| 9 | | The question actually helps the writer set up the outline. It tells you to have an introduction with a thesis (belief statement). And then tells the writer to have body paragraphs with details to support opinions/assertions. And, finally the question tells the writer to have a concluding paragraph. A concluding paragraph should restate the thesis. Not in exact words, but restate the sentiment. |
| | | The writer needs to decide their opinion on the question, and then put the thoughts on the outline in the format suggested. |

| Question No. | Answer | Detailed Explanations |
|---|---|---|
| 10 | | This essay asks for a contrast only. Not a compare. So, the writer should start with a general statement about their friend/friendship. The following paragraphs (three because the question asks for three differences) should explain how they are different. The final paragraph should restate how important the friendship is and make a closing statement about accepting differences, for example.

The question actually helps the writer set up the outline. It tells you to have an introduction with a thesis (belief statement). And then tells the writer to have body paragraphs with details to support opinions. And, finally the question tells the writer to have a concluding paragraph.

The writer needs to decide their opinion/reasons about the topic and the question, and then put the thoughts on the outline in the format suggested and then write essay from outline. Each Roman numeral or capital letter is a new paragraph. |

# Lesson 8: Take Another Look - Revising Your Work

| Question No. | Answer | Detailed Explanations |
|---|---|---|
| 1 | B | Answer choice two is the best answer. The first choice is not appropriate because another reef is not needed to answer question. Answer choice three is not appropriate because the article is not about extinct animals. Answer four is not appropriate because although water temperature might be a factor, it is not part of this passage's purpose. |
| 2 | B and D | Options B and D are reasons for revising an essay. |
| 3 | B | Answer choice two is the best answer. This sentence would make more sense after the portion about archery being necessary for survival. |
| 4 | C | Answer choice three is the correct answer. The information about intelligence and the owl is out of place in this passage. There is no more mention of the owl in the passage It is not in place. |
| 5 | D | The fourth answer could be added to complete the essay. The first and second answer choices are possible, but not specific enough. The third answer choice is not on topic, so it is not a reasonable choice. |
| 6 | D | Answer choice four is the correct answer. Whether this statement is true or not, it does not belong in this essay because this portion of the essay is not talking about what the skunks eat. |
| 7 | A | Answer choice one discusses adding information to the passage about other places similar to San Francisco (other areas who like Highland Games). So, answer choice one is the best answer. It would easily relate to the passage. |
| 8 | A | Answer choice one is the correct answer. The information about the span of time of the Texas Revolution shared at this point of the essay helps the reader gain a frame of reference in history. This clarification is valuable when the reader attempts to take notes or follow a timeline. |
| 9 | D | Answer choice four is the correct answer. The first sentence is a hook, and then the other sentences go in order of occurrence. The transition words help the reader know the order. And the final sentence(s) pulls the meaning all together. |
| 10 | A, C and D | Options A, C and D contrast dogs and cats. |

# Lesson 9: Building Your Foundation

| Question No. | Answer | Detailed Explanations |
|---|---|---|
| 1 | A, B and D | Options A, B and D are about corals and support the topic. |
| 2 | B | Answer choice two is the best answer. The other answer choices are limited, and only refer to a small portion of the passage (and reef). The second choice is a broad title that allows the other subjects to be included in that title. |
| 3 | B | Answer choice two is the best answer. The question asks about a "balanced" piece of reading. So, to balance the piece the writer needs to include the Texians feelings and thoughts. |
| 4 | D | Answer choice four is the best answer. The passage discusses skunks and their nighttime activities. The statement about what they eat does not belong in this part of the essay. |
| 5 | C | Answer choice three is the correct answer. The passage discusses the interactions of other bats and their "family" dynamics. Answer choice three discusses diet. |
| 6 | A, B and C | Options A, B and C are about Fall and hence suitable for Lee's essay. |
| 7 | C | Answer choice three is the correct answer. It does NOT belong with the other information because it discusses skin burns and people who do not survive the burns. The other statements are positive about research and helping people have real-like skin after an accident. |
| 8 | B, C and D | Options B, C and D are appropriate for Gina's essay. |
| 9 | C | Answer choice three is the correct answer. A rhetorical question is one that is not expected to be answered. It is often used to hook a reader. |
| 10 | A | Answer choice one is the correct answer. The passage is about texting and the knowledge of grammar. The other choices are either not correct, or they do not fully include the point of the passage. |

# Lesson 10: Give Credit Where Credit Is Due

| Question No. | Answer | Detailed Explanations |
|---|---|---|
| 1 | B | Answer choice two is the correct answer. The numbers in parenthesis is the page number where this information can be found, but the reader must know which source to reference if they need more information. |
| 2 | D | Answer choice four is the correct answer. The location of the publisher is always included in the citation. |
| 3 | B | Answer choice two is correct.<br><br>Plagiarism is defined as using someone else's words, writing or original thoughts without crediting that person. Passing other's work off as your own. |
| 4 | C | Answer choice three is the correct answer. The date of publication should be included in any works cited. Author's name, title of work, publisher's name and location and date published are required. |
| 5 | C | Answer choicer three is the correct answer. There are various styles of citation, which have slight variations. However, if using a large portion of the book, the page numbers do not need to be listed in the works cited page. They will be included in the in-text citations. |
| 6 | D | Answer choice four is correct. The author leads the citation. When doing a works cited page, they are listed alphabetical by author's last name. So, when possible, the author's name goes first in a citation. |
| 7 | C | Answer choice three is the correct answer. When citing a work in the actual text of the essay, the writer should put the author's name and the page(s) being referenced in parenthesis. |
| 8 | B | Answer choice two is the correct answer. The title of the publication is missing. In this instance the newspaper. |
| 9 | D | Answer choice four is the correct answer. The title of the article, author's name of article and of website if possible, the date retrieved and the website itself is necessary. The email of the author is not necessary to cite the source. |
| 10 | A | The city of publication is missing. The volume of the article and the name of the series of encyclopedias is listed with page numbers, but the city of publication is not mentioned and should be. |

# Lesson 11: Beginnings And Endings

| Question No. | Answer | Detailed Explanations |
|---|---|---|
| 1 | C | Answer choice three is the best answer. The first part of the passage briefly describes the great barrier reef and does so with explaining how magnificent the reef is. The remainder of the answers are not true. There is not a story, no question was asked, and the statement was specific about THE reef, not ANY reef. |
| 2 | C | Answer choice three is the correct answer. It is not a story, nor piece that defends or makes a stand. And, there is not persuasion convincing of one to do something. |
| 3 | A | Answer choice one is the correct. Although the question asks the reader to make a decision about "best," the reader must make a decision. The question asks about an ending sentence, so the first choice is a good closing for the passage. |
| 4 | the introductory paragraph | The thesis statement appears in the introductory paragraph. |
| 5 | B, C and D | Options B, C and D are not purposes of the opening sentence in the introductory paragraph. |
| 6 | C | Answer choice three is the best answer. This is intended to let the reader know how the building might look, and it is opposite of what was first described in the convention center area. |
| 7 | B | Answer choice two is the correct answer. The author asks a question to get the reader's attention and hook them into reading the remainder of the passage. |
| 8 | A | Answer choice one is the correct answer. The statement lets the reader know that the initial research is going to lead the reader to other questions and answers. Think of surfing the Internet. You might start in one place and one link leads to another and the reader finds themselves multiple subjects later. |
| 9 | D | Answer choice four is correct. The question asks which one is "NOT" part of an introduction. The remaining answer could all be included in an introduction. |
| 10 | A | Answer choice one is the best answer. While some writers do use this statement, it is not a good phrase to use. A good writer should be able to conclude without using the word. Also, the other three ARE good ways to conclude. |

# Chapter 6

# Inquiry and Research

## Chapter 6

### Lesson 1: Sifting Through The Nonsense - Finding Information

1. **If you are researching information to include in an essay on an event that happened last Tuesday, which resource would NOT give you the most up to date information?**

   Ⓐ A newspaper article
   Ⓑ The Internet
   Ⓒ A magazine article
   Ⓓ A videotaped interview with someone who was at the event

2. **If you have several different books, magazines, and newspapers that you think you might want to use as resources for a research essay, but you're not sure if they'll fit your topic, what would be the best strategy for determining whether or not each resource is appropriate?**

   Ⓐ carefully read each resource
   Ⓑ ask the librarian which resources would be best for your essay
   Ⓒ skim and scan the resources for main ideas
   Ⓓ Google the each source to see if it is usable.

3. **Which is the best note taking strategy for recording information from resources you want to use for a research paper?**

   Ⓐ Write direct quotes and paraphrased information with page numbers of the source (name or number of source) in your notes.
   Ⓑ Write only the main ideas from the resources in your notes.
   Ⓒ Photocopy important pages from the resources.
   Ⓓ Write the title of each source and the overall topic on a note-card.

4. **For which of the following topics would an interview with your school principal NOT be the best resource?**

   Ⓐ Gym vs Tennis- Which is more fun?
   Ⓑ The reasons why the local grocery store went out of business
   Ⓒ The qualities of a good middle school student
   Ⓓ The causes of childhood sicknesses such as the Chicken Pox

## From The Worcester Evening Gazette
## April 20, 1912

New York, April 19- Mrs. John Murray Brown of Acton, Mass, who with her sister, Mrs. Robert C. Cornell and Mrs. E.D. Appleton, was saved, was in the last life-boat to get safely away from the Titanic.

"The band played marching from deck to deck, and as the ship went under I could still hear the music." Mrs. Brown said. "The musicians were up to their knees in water when last I saw them. We offered assistance to Capt. Smith, but he refused."

"Mrs. Astor was in the life-boat with my sister, Mrs. Cornell. I heard Col. Astor tell her he would wait with the men. Our boat was almost dragged down by the suction."

5.  **Which essay topic would this be an appropriate resource for- The Last Minutes of the Titanic or Famous musicians? Write in the box below.**

6.  **For which topic would the local newspaper be a good resource?**

    Ⓐ  real estate trends in your hometown
    Ⓑ  the history of the local government
    Ⓒ  a recent festival in the town square
    Ⓓ  the history of schools in the local town.

The term skyscraper was first used in the 1880s after the first 10 and 20 story buildings began popping up all over the country. Skyscrapers were made possible by several different technological innovations including the elevator, central heating and the telephone.

Skyscrapers also rely on modern building materials. Concrete and steel form the backbone of the modern skyscraper, allowing builder to reach greater heights. Over the past decades many advances have been made in the development of tall buildings. While the first skyscrapers wowed the world at ten or twenty stories, currently the tallest building in the word is over 2,700 feet tall.

7.  **What essay topic would this be an appropriate resource for?**

    Ⓐ  tall buildings in Dubai
    Ⓑ  buildings of the nineteenth century
    Ⓒ  famous buildings in New York
    Ⓓ  the history of skyscrapers

8. **When taking notes on a lecture or other audio material, what are some details you should be sure to capture?**

   Ⓐ Transitions between paragraphs
   Ⓑ Names and dates
   Ⓒ The name of the speaker
   Ⓓ The title of the lecture

The words "dream interpretation" were and still are indeed fraught with unpleasant, unscientific associations. They remind one of all sorts of childish, superstitious notions, which make up the thread and woof of dream books, read by none but the ignorant and the primitive.

The wealth of detail, the infinite care never to let anything pass unexplained, with which he presented to the public the result of his investigations, are impressing more and more serious-minded scientists, but the examination of his evidential data demands arduous work and presupposes an absolutely open mind.

This is why we still encounter men, totally unfamiliar with Freud's writings, men who were not even interested enough in the subject to attempt an interpretation of their dreams or their patients' dreams, deriding Freud's theories and combating them with the help of statements which he never made.

9. **What essay topic would this be an appropriate resource for?**

   Ⓐ Sleep disorders
   Ⓑ Interpreting dreams
   Ⓒ Sigmund Freud's study of dreams
   Ⓓ The history of psychology

One volume of my war-journal completed, and I must confess it is dull reading. I could not help smiling as I read my enthusiastic remarks at the outbreak of war when we visualized battles by the week.

What a contrast between our expectations and the actual facts.

Months of monotony, and I haven't even seen an Englishman yet.

Our battle cruisers have had a little amusement with the coast raids at Scarborough and elsewhere, but we battle-fleet fellows have seen nothing and done nothing.

So I have decided to volunteer for the U-boat service, and my name went in last week, though I am told it may be months before I am taken, as there are about 250 lieutenants already on the waiting list.

But sooner or later I suppose something will come of it. I shall have no cause to complain of inactivity in that Service if I get there.

**10. This excerpt is most likely from what kind of source?**

Ⓐ An encyclopedia
Ⓑ A memoir
Ⓒ A newspaper
Ⓓ A blog

**Article <u>Great Round World and What's Going on in It</u>
magazine--Anonymous author**

The Sanitary Code is a set of rules enacted for the protection of the lives and health of the citizens. These rules relate to all matters that concern our daily life. They prohibit unhealthy businesses being carried on. They require that tenement houses shall be properly built, drained, etc. They prevent the keeping of cows, pigs, or poultry within city limits. They regulate the sale of provisions and prevent unwholesome food being sold in the city.

**Under these rules, all the meat that is dressed for market within the limits of the city is inspected and must be prepared in a certain manner. No one can offer milk for sale without a permit from the Board of Health, and this permit is only granted when the inspectors have assured themselves that the applicants have clean and airy places in which to handle the milk.**

1.  **What is the best paraphrase of the bold sentences in this paragraph?**

    Ⓐ  Cheese and meat need to be inspected before they can be sold in a store.
    Ⓑ  In order to sell milk, a store must be inspected by a health inspector.
    Ⓒ  Foods being sold in stores must be processed in a particular way and those selling the food must have permits from health inspectors.
    Ⓓ  People should be careful buying milk, cheese, and meat from stores without permits from the health inspector.

**Article <u>Great Round World and What's Going on in It</u>
magazine--Anonymous author**

The Sanitary Code is a set of rules enacted for the protection of the lives and health of the citizens. These rules relate to all matters that concern our daily life. They prohibit unhealthy businesses being carried on. They require that tenement houses shall be properly built, drained, etc. They prevent the keeping of cows, pigs, or poultry within city limits. They regulate the sale of provisions and prevent unwholesome food being sold in the city. Under these rules, all the meat that is dressed for market within the limits of the city is inspected, and must be prepared in a certain manner. No one can offer milk for sale without a permit from the Board of Health, and this permit is only granted when the inspectors have assured themselves that the applicants have clean and airy places in which to handle the milk.

2. **If you were writing an essay about how grocery stores can keep chicken safe for their customers, which quote from this paragraph might you want to include in your essay?**

Ⓐ The Sanitary Code is a set of rules enacted for the protection of the lives and health of the citizens.
Ⓑ These rules relate to all matters that concern our daily life.
Ⓒ They prevent the keeping of cows, pigs, or poultry within city limits.
Ⓓ Under these rules, all the meat that is dressed for market within the limits of the city is inspected, and must be prepared in a certain manner.

### Article <u>Harper's for Young People</u> magazine--Anonymous author

The larger varieties of squirrels, which make their nest in trees, are the red squirrel, often found in pine woods, as it is very fond of the cones of pine and fir trees; the gray squirrel, a magnificent fellow, with such a voracious appetite that it is said one squirrel alone will strip a whole nut tree; and the black squirrel, a handsome, glossy creature, which is so hated by its gray brothers that both are never found together in the same nutting grounds. As the gray are the most numerous, at least in this part of the country, they generally succeed in driving away the black members of the family, so that they are not very often seen.

3. **If you were writing an informational essay on common woodland animals of America, which sentence might you want to quote in your essay?**

Ⓐ ...the gray squirrel, a magnificent fellow, with such a voracious appetite that it is said one squirrel alone will strip a whole nut tree.
Ⓑ ...the black squirrel, a handsome, glossy creature, which is so hated by its gray brothers that both are never found together in the same nutting grounds.
Ⓒ As the gray are the most numerous, at least in this part of the country, they generally succeed in driving away the black members of the family, so that they are not very often seen.
Ⓓ The larger varieties of squirrels, which make their nest in trees, are the red squirrel, often found in pine woods, as it is very fond of the cones of pine and fir trees...

### Article <u>Harper's for Young People</u> magazine--Anonymous author

**As all the ground varieties of Christmas trees need to be gathered before ice and snow begin, often weeks before Christmas, care must be taken to keep them from drying. They should be heaped up in some cool, damp place, where they will not freeze, and should be sprinkled plenteously every day.**

The boys make frames in the form of crosses, stars, wreaths, or letters, and the girls find a pretty pastime in tying on the greens. As fast as the designs are finished, they must also be laid away and kept damp until Christmas. Woodland mosses, holly leaves and scarlet berries, and dried everlasting flowers are pretty to mix with the green. Branches of hemlock and young firs for Christmas trees are cut as near Christmas-time as possible. If a room is to be made into a bower of hemlock boughs, they should not be fastened up until the morning of Christmas-eve, as the heated air of the house loosens the flat, tooth-shaped leaves from the branch, and the least movement sends them in clouds to the floor. Any one who has tried to sweep them from the carpet after Christmas will prefer some other variety of green for trimming another year.

4.  **Which is the best paraphrase of the bold sentences in this paragraph?**

    Ⓐ  Christmas trees need to be harvested well before Christmas actually arrives.
    Ⓑ  Because Christmas trees have to be cut before Christmas, it is important to keep them moist by keeping them someplace damp and slightly cold.
    Ⓒ  Christmas trees can easily dry out, so it is important to keep them watered.
    Ⓓ  Christmas trees should be artificial since the have to be cut down so far in advance.

### Article <u>Harper's for Young People</u>
### magazine--Anonymous author

It is very easy to study the habits of the sparrow, for it is so bold and sociable that if a little house is nailed up in a balcony, or by a window where people are constantly sitting, a pair of birds will at once take possession, bring twigs and bits of scattered threads and wool for a nest, and proceed to rear their noisy little family. Chirp, chirp, very loud and impatient, three or four little red open mouths appear at the door of the house, the parent birds come flying with worms and flies, and then for a little while the young ones take a nap and keep quiet, when, they wake up again and renew their clamor for food.

5.  **A brochure about how to attract birds so you can observe them would benefit from which quote from this magazine article?**

    Ⓐ  It is very easy to study the habits of the sparrow.
    Ⓑ  [A sparrow] is so bold and sociable that if a little house is nailed up in a balcony, or by a window where people are constantly sitting
    Ⓒ  Chirp, chirp, very loud and impatient, three or four little red open mouths appear at the door of the house,
    Ⓓ  the parent birds come flying with worms and flies, and then for a little while the young ones take a nap and keep quiet, when, they wake up again and renew their clamor for food.

One volume of my war-journal completed, and I must confess it is dull reading. I could not help smiling as I read my enthusiastic remarks at the outbreak of war when we visualized battles by the week. What a contrast between our expectations and the actual facts.

Months of monotony, and I haven't even seen an Englishman yet.

Our battle cruisers have had a little amusement with the coast raids at Scarborough and elsewhere, but we battle-fleet fellows have seen nothing and done nothing.

So I have decided to volunteer for the U-boat service, and my name went in last week, though I am told it may be months before I am taken, as there are about 250 lieutenants already on the waiting list.

But sooner or later I suppose something will come of it. I shall have no cause to complain of inactivity in that Service if I get there.

**6. What quote from this text would best support why the author joined the U-Boat service?**

Ⓐ Our battle cruisers have had a little amusement with the coast raids at Scarborough and elsewhere, but we battle-fleet fellows have seen nothing, and done nothing.

Ⓑ Months of monotony, and I haven't even seen an Englishman yet.

Ⓒ One volume of my war-journal completed, and I must confess it is dull reading.

Ⓓ I shall have no cause to complain of inactivity in that Service, if I get there.

### From The Worcester Evening Gazette
### April 20, 1912

New York, April 19- Mrs. John Murray Brown of Acton, Mass, who with her sister, Mrs. Robert C. Cornell and Mrs. E.D. Appleton, was saved, was in the last life-boat to get safely away from the Titanic.

"The band played marching from deck to deck, and as the ship went under I could still hear the music." Mrs. Brown said. "The musicians were up to their knees in water when last I saw them. We offered assistance to Capt. Smith, but he refused."

"Mrs. Astor was in the life-boat with my sister, Mrs. Cornell. I heard Col. Astor tell her he would wait with the men. Our boat was almost dragged down by the suction."

7. **What is the best paraphrase of the second paragraph?**

Ⓐ "The band played marching from deck to deck, and as the ship went under I could still hear the music." Mrs. Brown said. "The musicians were up to their knees in water when last I saw them. We offered assistance to Capt. Smith, but he refused."

Ⓑ The band didn't stop playing until all of the men were dead.

Ⓒ Mrs. Brown saw the men in the orchestra continue to play, even though they were up to their knees in water and the boat was clearly sinking.

Ⓓ The Musicians tried to help the captain.

The term skyscraper was first used in the 1880s after the first 10 and 20 story buildings began popping up all over the country. Skyscrapers were made possible by several different technological innovations including the elevator, central heating, and the telephone.

Skyscrapers also rely on modern building materials. Concrete and steel form the backbone of the modern skyscraper, allowing the builder to reach greater heights. Over the past decades, many advances have been made in the development of tall buildings. While the first skyscrapers wowed the world at ten or twenty stories, currently the tallest building in the word is over 2,700 feet tall.

8. **What information would not be too useful for a paper on the tallest skyscrapers? Select three options.**

Ⓐ The term skyscraper was first used in the 1880s after the first 10 and 20 story buildings began popping up all over the country

Ⓑ Skyscrapers were made possible by several different technological innovations including the elevator, central heating and the telephone.

Ⓒ Skyscrapers also rely on modern building materials

Ⓓ While the first skyscrapers wowed the world at ten or twenty stories, currently the tallest building in the word is over 2,700 feet tall.

## Gas Refrigerator for Ice Cream Truck
## Popular Mechanics, November 1929

Ice cream and milk delivery trucks are being equipped with gas-burning refrigerating apparatus as a substitute for salt and ice. The plan is more effective and cleaner and is also said to be cheaper, particularly because the maintenance and service costs are greatly reduced. Successful operation of these refrigeration plants promises more extensive shipment of perishable goods by truck, owners point out.

9.  **What is the most effective paraphrase of the last sentence?**

    (A) The owners of this refrigerated truck claim they will lead to better and farther shipping of goods that spoil easily.
    (B) The owners of this truck want readers to believe refrigeration will help everyone have fresh food.
    (C) If the trucks are successful, the owners will be happy.
    (D) The owners of the refrigerated truck invented the gas-burning refrigerator.

## Extended Telephone Service for Chinese Province
## Popular Mechanics, September 1921

Installation of telephone lines to support advance communication, including both local and long-distance services, are well under way in the province of Kiangsu, China. Long-distance lines between all the important towns of the province are planned. It is figured that telephone connections between Shanghai and Nanking will be completed within a year. Service extensions between Pukow and Nanking are now being actively carried on. The old submarine cable which now connects these two cities and which has only two wires will be replaced by a 26-wire cable.

10. **What quote from this text would be most appropriate for an essay about the first telephones installed in China?**

    (A) Long-distance lines between all the important towns of the province are planned
    (B) The old submarine cable which now connects these two cities and which has only two wires will be replaced by a 26-wire cable.
    (C) It is figured that telephone connections between Shanghai and Nanking will be completed within the year.
    (D) Service extensions between Pukow and Nanking are now being actively carried on.

# Answer Key and
# Detailed Explanations

## Chapter 6: Inquiry and Research

# Lesson 1: Sifting Through The Nonsense - Finding Information

| Question No. | Answer | Detailed Explanations |
|:---:|:---:|:---|
| 1 | A, C and D | Options A, C and D would not be as current in their information as the internet. |
| 2 | C | Answer choice three is the correct answer. Spending time reading each resource option carefully is not feasible. It would take way too long to do this, especially if the topic is something that is controversial and would have large amounts of sources to review. The writer could Google the sources, but this can also take a great deal of time, and possibly take longer than reading each source due to the vastness of the Internet. The librarian is a GREAT source of guidance and help, but she can't have possibly read every document printed on any subject. The best way to evaluate a source's possibe application to the topic is to "skim and scan" the document. Glancing over/through to look for main ideas and topics that relate to the topic the writer is hoping to explore. |
| 3 | A | Answer choice one is the correct answer. There are various computer programs that can aide in keeping track of notes and citation information. These programs are helpful, but not necessary. The writer should number each source and write the information down necessary to cite that source. While reading and taking notes, the writer can keep track of which source noted information is drawn from. This should include page numbers as well.<br><br>Any direct quote must be written EXACTLY as it is in the source with quotation marks. Other information can be paraphrased (main point or ideas written on the reader/writer's own words). |
| 4 | A, B and D | Options A, B and D contain topics for which an interview with your school principal wouldn't be the best resource. |
| 5 | The Last Minutes of the Titanic | This would be an appropriate resource for an essay on The Last Minutes of the Titanic. |

| Question No. | Answer | Detailed Explanations |
|---|---|---|
| 6 | C | Answer choice three is the best answer. The choices that mention "the history of..." might use an article that is archived at the library, depending on exactly what the essay is about. Recent real estate trends COULD be a topic in the paper, but the paper is to report on events around town, not necessarily economic development and business options. So, a town festival would be the topic best covered by the paper. |
| 7 | D | Answer choice four is the best answer. The other remaining choices would be interesting and should be INCLUDED in the essay. These would be good sub-topic headings. But the information given is about the overall history of how skyscrapers came to be. |
| 8 | B | Answer choice two is the best answer. When taking notes from something listened to, names and dates of major events/people are to be noted. Those topics can then be researched at a later date for more detailed information as needed. The title of the lecture and the speaker should also be noted in the event the actual lecture needs to be cited, but the BEST answer is the names and dates of events IN the lecture. |
| 9 | C | Answer choice three is correct. The passage discusses dream interpretation and mentions Freud's work in the field. The other choices are related to the passage, but they do not include Freud, and his thoughts or association with the topic. |
| 10 | B | Answer choice two is the correct answer. The passage is written in first person (uses I) and tells of personal opinions and feelings. A blog might do the same, but unlikely a soldier would have access to the Internet all the time; plus, the details of the passage indicate a war time prior to computers. A newspaper or an encyclopedia would not be written in first person, nor would it include such personal thoughts. |

# Lesson 2: In Your Own Words, Or Not

| Question No. | Answer | Detailed Explanations |
|---|---|---|
| 1 | C | Answer choice three is the correct answer. Choices one and two are also correct, but each leave the information from the other out of explanation. Answer choice four may be true, but the focus is from the buyer's perspective and not the sellers. The passage is intended for the seller's of food. |
| 2 | D | Answer choice four is correct. This answer tells the reader that there are specific rules to ensure the food is safe for consumption. This would meet the needs of the essay being researched/written. |
| 3 | C | Answer choice three is correct. This answer is the best choice because of the portion of the quote "at least in this part of the country." This indicates a specific region, which is asked in the question about the essay. |
| 4 | B | Answer choice two is correct. It includes the main idea of the sentence, but it is written in the words of the person who paraphrased the sentence. It is not a quoted statement. |
| 5 | B | Answer choice two is correct. The brochure would be about how to attract birds, and the information about a bold bird with a tree house on a balcony would be beneficial for the brochure. |
| 6 | A | Answer choice one is the best answer. The person is claiming that others have had some "amusement" (action) in the war, and that his area of service has seen no action. He then says he'll join the u-boat service. |
| 7 | C | Answer choice three is the best choice. This explains what happened (the major points) and in the words of the reader. |
| 8 | A, B and C | Options A, B and C while being about skyscrapers are not too accurate for a paper on the tallest ones. |
| 9 | A | Answer choice one is the correct answer. The last sentence reports the owners' opinions, and this states those thoughts in the reader's own words. |
| 10 | C | Answer choice three is the best answer. The FIRST telephones would be early in their history of telephones. The sentence about connections is the best for an essay about early telephone use and construction. |

# Notes

# Additional Information

## STAAR Redesign FAQs

### What will STAAR Redesign Assessment look like?

The STAAR Redesign assessment will be conducted online, requiring students to successfully complete the test to assess a deeper understanding of the Texas Essential Knowledge and Skills (TEKS).

The STAAR Redesign assessment is designed such that students can complete the 3rd–5th grade assessment in two hours and the 6th–8th grade assessment in three hours. Students can take up to four hours to complete their assessment if needed. The testing time begins after all directions are read to the students. Students may be allowed to take breaks during testing, potentially including breaks for snacks or meals.

### How is this Lumos tedBook aligned to STAAR Redesign Guidelines?

The practice tests provided in the Lumos Program reflect the depth and rigor of the State of Texas Assessment of Academic Readiness, based on the information published by the test administrator. However, the content and format of the assessment that is officially administered to the students could be different compared to these practice tests.

### What Question types are included in the Online STAAR Redesign?

The question types that you will encounter on the STAAR Redesign assessments are:

**In Math:**
Multiple Choice Single Answer
Multiple Choice Multiple Answer
Grid in
Numeric,
Table Questions,
Equation Editor (with explanation)

**In ELA:**
Multiple Choice Single Answer
Multiple Choice Multiple Answer
Short Constructed Response
Extended Constructed Response
Text Entry,
Multi-part

For more information on 2022-23 Assessment year, visit
**www.lumoslearning.com/a/staar-faqs**
OR Scan the **QR Code**

# What is included in this STAAR Redesign Test Practice Book?

The STAAR Redesign Test Practice Book includes practice sections aligned to each TEKS. Students can review questions on each standard, one section at a time, or can choose to study the sections where they need the most practice.

In addition to the practice sections, students will have access to two full-length online practice tests. The Lumos Online StepUp Program provides practice tests that mimic the actual state assessments. Completing these tests will help them master the different areas that are included in the newly-aligned STAAR Redesign assessments.

The results from these tests will help get an insight into the student's strengths and weaknesses in specific content areas. These insights could help students strengthen their skills and improve speed and accuracy while taking the test. Because the STAAR Redesign assessment includes questions covering various TEKS standards, it is necessary for students to regularly practice these questions.

# Why Practice with Repeated Reading Passages?

Throughout the Lumos Learning Practice workbooks, students and educators will notice many passages repeat. This is done intentionally. The goal of these workbooks is to help students practice skills necessary to be successful in class and on standardized tests. One of the most critical components to that success is the ability to read and comprehend passages. To that end, reading fluency must be strengthened. According to Hasbrouck and Tindal (2006), "Helping our students become fluent readers is absolutely critical for proficient and motivated reading" (p. 642). And, Nichols et al. indicate, (2009), "fluency is a gateway to comprehension that enables students to move from being word decoders to passage comprehenders" (p. 11).

Lumos Learning recognizes there is no one-size-fits-all approach to build fluency in readers; however, the repeated reading of passages, where students read the same passages at least two or more times, is one of the most widely recognized strategies to improve fluency (Nichols et al., 2009). Repeated reading allows students the opportunity to read passages with familiar words several times until the passage becomes familiar and they no longer have to decode word by word. As students reread, the decoding barrier falls away allowing for an increase in reading comprehension.

The goal of the Lumos Learning workbooks is to increase student achievement and preparation for any standardized test. Using some passages multiple times in a book offers struggling readers an opportunity to do just that.

References
Hasbrouck, J., and Tindal, G. (2006). Oral reading fluency norms: A valuable assessment tool for reading teachers. Reading Teacher, 59(7), 636644. doi:10.1598/RT.59.7.3.
Nichols, W., Rupley, W., and Rasinski, T. (2009). Fluency in learning to read for meaning: going beyond repeated readings. Literacy Research & Instruction, 48(1). doi:10.1080/19388070802161906.

# Discover Engaging and Relevant Learning Resources

Lumos EdSearch is a safe search engine specifically designed for teachers and students. Using EdSearch, you can easily find thousands of standards-aligned learning resources such as questions, videos, lessons, worksheets and apps. Teachers can use EdSearch to create custom resource kits to perfectly match their lesson objective and assign them to one or more students in their classroom.

To access the EdSearch tool, use the search box after you log into Lumos StepUp or use the link provided below.

| | |
|---|---|
| www.lumoslearning.com/a/edsearchb |  |

**The Lumos Standards Coherence map** provides information about previous level, next level and related standards. It helps educators and students visually explore learning standards. It's an effective tool to help students progress through the learning objectives. Teachers can use this tool to develop their own pacing charts and lesson plans. Educators can also use the coherence map to get deep insights into why a student is struggling in a specific learning objective.

Teachers can access the Coherence maps after logging into the StepUp Teacher Portal or use the link provided below.

| | |
|---|---|
| www.lumoslearning.com/a/coherence-map |  |

# Progress Chart

| Standard | Lesson | Page No. | Practice | | Mastered | Re-practice /Reteach |
|---|---|---|---|---|---|---|
| TEKS | | | Date | Score | | |
| ELAR 7.1 | Speaking & Listening | 10 | | | | |
| ELAR 7.2 | Learning And Using Academic Vocabulary | 11 | | | | |
| ELAR 7.2.A | Consulting Sources | 15 | | | | |
| ELAR 7.2.B | Figuring It Out With Context Clues | 18 | | | | |
| ELAR 7.2.B | Which Fits? Multiple Meaning Words | 22 | | | | |
| ELAR 7.2.C | Review - Roots And Affixes | 25 | | | | |
| ELAR 7.6 | Precise And Concise Language | 28 | | | | |
| ELAR 7.9.D | Give It A Shot - Figures Of Speech | 31 | | | | |
| ELAR 7.9.D | We're Related - Word Relationships | 34 | | | | |
| ELAR 7.10.D.i | Good Sentences Are Built On Agreement | 37 | | | | |
| ELAR 7.10.D.vii | Phrases And Clauses Are Coming To Town | 39 | | | | |
| ELAR 7.10.D.vii | Using Coordinate Adjectives | 42 | | | | |
| ELAR 7.10.D.viii | Managing Modifiers | 44 | | | | |
| ELAR 7.10.D.ix | Spellcheck! | 47 | | | | |
| N/A | Would You Rather Own A Boat Or A Yacht? Denotation And Connotation | 49 | | | | |
| ELAR 7.5.F | Prove It! (with Evidence From The Text) | 70 | | | | |
| ELAR 7.5.F | Use Those Clues - Make An Inference | 77 | | | | |
| ELAR 7.5.G | What Is It All About? | 88 | | | | |
| ELAR 7.5.G | And The Point Of This Is…? | 97 | | | | |
| ELAR 7.5.G | Key Ideas And Details | 108 | | | | |
| ELAR 7.5.G | Get Right To The Point | 113 | | | | |
| ELAR 7.5.H | One Thing Leads To Another | 120 | | | | |
| ELAR 7.6.A | Relationship Between People And Events | 129 | | | | |
| ELAR 7.7.D | When And Where? | 131 | | | | |
| ELAR 7.7.D | Who Or What? | 141 | | | | |
| ELAR 7.8.A | Based On A True Story - History And Fiction | 149 | | | | |

| Standard | Lesson | Page No. | Practice | | Mastered | Re-practice /Reteach |
|---|---|---|---|---|---|---|
| TEKS | | | Date | Score | | |
| ELAR 7.8.D | How Is It Built? Analyzing Structure | 155 | | | | |
| ELAR 7.8.D.iii | Finding Patterns - Comparing And Contrasting | 167 | | | | |
| ELAR 7.8.F | Comparing Media | 176 | | | | |
| ELAR 7.9.B | How It's Made And What It Means | 181 | | | | |
| ELAR 7.9.D | A Matter Of Attitude | 189 | | | | |
| ELAR 7.9.D | Getting Technical | 197 | | | | |
| ELAR 7.9.E | What's The Author's Point? | 203 | | | | |
| ELAR 7.7.B | What A Character! | 241 | | | | |
| ELAR 7.9 | Equal? Alike? Different? Comparing Authors | 249 | | | | |
| ELAR 7.9.A | What's The Author's Angle? | 253 | | | | |
| ELAR 7.10.A | Who Are You Talking To? | 267 | | | | |
| ELAR 7.10.B.i | A Picture Is Worth A Thousand Words | 272 | | | | |
| ELAR 7.10.B.i | Getting From Here To There - Transitions | 278 | | | | |
| ELAR 7.10.B.i | Mixing It Up - More Interesting Sentences | 282 | | | | |
| ELAR 7.10.D | Taking A Closer Look - Editing | 286 | | | | |
| ELAR 7.10.D.vii | Say What You Mean | 290 | | | | |
| ELAR 7.12.B | Measure Twice, Cut Once - The Importance Of Planning | 295 | | | | |
| ELAR 7.12.B | Take Another Look - Revising Your Work | 307 | | | | |
| ELAR 7.12.D | Building Your Foundation | 312 | | | | |
| ELAR 7.12.F | Give Credit Where Credit Is Due | 316 | | | | |
| ELAR 7.12.H.ii | Beginnings And Endings | 319 | | | | |
| ELAR 7.12.D | Sifting Through The Nonsense - Finding Information | 338 | | | | |
| ELAR 7.12.G | In Your Own Words, Or Not | 342 | | | | |

Lumos Learning
Step Up Your Skills

Grade 7

# TEXAS
# Math
## STAAR Practice

Updated for STAAR Redesign

## Updated for 2022-23

((( tedBook )))
ONLINE

## 2 STAAR Practice Tests

## COVERS 25+ SKILLS
Aligned with TEKS Standards

Available
- At Leading book stores
- Online www.LumosLearning.com

Printed in the USA
CPSIA information can be obtained
at www.ICGtesting.com
LVHW060731310823
756592LV00013B/299